Yours truly
J.A. Henshall

BOOK

OF THE

BLACK BASS

COMPRISING ITS COMPLETE

SCIENTIFIC AND LIFE HISTORY

TOGETHER WITH A PRACTICAL TREATISE ON

ANGLING AND FLY FISHING

AND A FULL DESCRIPTION OF

TOOLS, TACKLE AND IMPLEMENTS

BY

JAMES A. HENSHALL, M.D

" I am, Sir, a brother of the Angle." —Izaak Walton

Fully Illustrated

CINCINNATI
ROBERT CLARKE & CO
1881

TO THE

CUVIER CLUB

OF

CINCINNATI, OHIO,

FOR ITS PRAISEWORTHY EFFORTS IN BEHALF OF THE PRESERVATION OF
FISH AND GAME; AND FOR THE GREAT BENEFITS IT HAS BE-
STOWED UPON THE ANGLER, THE SPORTSMAN,
AND THE NATURALIST,

THIS BOOK IS

RESPECTFULLY DEDICATED

BY

THE AUTHOR.

FOREWORD.

For the Bass Angler, Dr. James Alexander Henshall in 1881 first described the perfect fish: "Inch for inch and pound for pound the gamest fish that swims."

To the modern-day bassman, Dr. Henshall was a pioneer. Henshall looked into the future when he penned, "The Black Bass is wholly unknown in the Old World except where recently introduced, and exists, naturally, only in America . . . No doubt the Black Bass is the appointed successor to the Lordly Trout . . . He will eventually become the leading game fish of America is my oft-expressed opinion and firm belief."

Henshall lived to see his prediction come partly true, for in the Foreword of a later writing in 1923 he asserted: "There are now more articles of tackle made for its capture than for all other game fishes combined."

Angling lore described in this BOOK OF THE BLACK BASS will be reverently entertaining to the 20th century Bassmaster. Do not expect to discover a secret bass catching technique long buried in the archives. This is the beginning of America's art of Black Bass angling.

Warm tribute must be expressed to Ray Scott, founder of the Bass Anglers Sportsman Society of America, who in 1968 picked up Henshall's beginning banner and organized a national society of dedicated bass fishermen to give the "Black Bass its proper place among game fishes and to create among anglers, and the public in general, an awareness of the bass fisherman's contributions to American angling, conservation and outdoor recreation."

Scott, like his predecessor Henshall, recognized the Bass Angler as a unique breed. Perhaps it is the unpredictable nature of the bass that accounts for the tremendous interest of fishermen in this country. Despite the fact that the Black Bass hits almost anything that walks, crawls, swims or flies, and can be taken day or night in hot or cold, rain or shine—there are occasions (and often not rare) when the expert Bass Angler with all his sophisticated, modern-day bass tackle and sonar devices cannot smell up his stringer.

Other members of the finny tribe have their particular followers, but none can command such dedicated loyalty as that of Micropterus Salmoides. To the devoted Bass Angler, time, distance and money are only hurdles to be climbed in his compelling curiosity to master the art of Black Bass Angling.

It is for this tremendous group of Bass Anglers that this book was reproduced in its original 463-page form, including every drawing, sketch and illustration. Henshall's book is rarest of all bass fishing chronicles. After a long, diligent search, the Bass Anglers Sportsman Society was able to uncover this American angling treasure.

Dr. James A. Henshall (born, Baltimore, Md., 1836; died, Cincinnati, O., 1925) physician, naturalist, fish culturist and angling writer, is most worthy to be acclaimed the father of Black Bass fishing. His writings, based upon extensive experience as a "brother of the angle" in various parts of the United States and other countries, reflect the gentle, kindly soul of the author and charmingly express his knowledge and appreciation of the denizens of the deep. The fruit of his services with the U.S. Bureau of Fisheries (1896–1917) appeared in the development of several improved methods and devices for the propagation of game fishes, particularly the Black Bass.

Like Henshall, the Bass Anglers Sportsman Society is dedicated to the advancement of the sport. This replica is done with a reverent salute to Dr. Henshall and his devotion, like ours, to the BRAVEST WARRIOR OF THE FINNY TRIBE . . . the BLACK BASS.

Bob Cobb, Executive Editor
BASSMASTER® Magazine

PREFACE.

THIS book owes its origin to a long-cherished desire on the part of the author, to give to the Black Bass its proper place among game fishes, and to create among anglers, and the public generally, an interest in a fish that has never been so fully appreciated as its merits deserve, because of the want of suitable tackle for its capture, on the one hand, and a lack of information regarding its habits and economic value on the other.

THE BOOK OF THE BLACK BASS is of an entirely practical nature, both as regards its subject-matter and its illustrations. It has been written more with a view to instruct, than to amuse or entertain the reader; he will, therefore, look in vain, between its covers, for those rhetorical flights, poetic descriptions or entertaining accounts and pleasing illustrations of the pleasures and vicissitudes of angling, which are usually found in works of this character. Nor is it to be regarded, on the other hand, as a book of a purely scientific nature — far from it — for the author has written as an angler rather than as a naturalist. With these apologies, I trust the reader will not be disappointed in its perusal.

Some of its chapters are based on articles heretofore contributed by the author to *Forest and Stream*, the *Chicago Field*, and other journals, which have since been re-written, enlarged and elaborated.

The full-page illustrations of the two species of Black Bass were drawn from life by Dr. E. R. Copeland, and are faithful representations in every particular. It was the original intention of the author to have had these illustrations lithographed in colors; but the fact that the species vary so greatly in coloration in different sections, rendered this inexpedient, and the design was abandoned.

In the technical portion of the book the author has availed himself of all published information on the subject of the *Micropteri*, for which he has given due credit in the proper places. But I desire particularly to express my profound obligation to Prof. Theo. Gill, for permission to use his valuable writings, and likewise to him, Profs. Spencer F. Baird and G. Brown Goode, for information freely given, and for excerpts from rare books in the library of the Smithsonian Institution. I also tender my sincere thanks and grateful acknowledgments to Prof. David S. Jordan, for his uniform kindness, encouragement and advice, for the loan of books, and for the cordial, kindly and courteous interest he has manifested in me and my book.

I am aware that the change made in the scientific names of the Black Bass species, will be looked upon by many, at first, as unwise and injudicious; but, under the circumstances, I could not have done otherwise than to restore the names rightfully belonging to them, inasmuch as by so doing it clears up the former confusion attending the nomenclature of the species, and renders plain the causes of the same. Moreover, as the names *Micropterus* for the genus, and *dolomieu* and *salmoides* for the species, are the first ever bestowed, in each instance, their adoption will be not only an act of justice, but of expediency, for as we can not go back of them, it sets the matter at rest, forever.

JAMES A. HENSHALL.

CINCINNATI, JULY, 1881.

TABLE OF CONTENTS.

PART FIRST.

TERMINOLOGY, MORPHOLOGY, AND PHYSIOLOGY.

PART SECOND.

TOOLS, TACKLE AND IMPLEMENTS.

PART THIRD.

ANGLING AND FLY-FISHING.

PART FIRST.

TERMINOLOGY, MORPHOLOGY
AND
PHYSIOLOGY.

BOOK OF THE BLACK BASS.

CHAPTER I.

SCIENTIFIC HISTORY OF THE BLACK BASS.

(MICROPTERUS.)

"For my name and memory, I leave it to men's charitable speeches, to
foreign nations, and to the next ages."—BACON.

THE scientific history of the Black Bass is a most unsatisfactory one. This is owing to a train of accidental circumstances, and to the neglect of thorough investigation
of its earliest history, as recorded by Lacépède, the re-
nowned French naturalist, in his great work, "Histoire
Naturelle des Poissons."*

It will be well, perhaps, before entering upon the minu-
tiæ of the subject, to present a brief synopsis of the scien-

---

* "The great work on the natural history of fish, by the Count Lacépède, was the next publication after that of Bloch upon general Ichthyology. . . . It is not, like others in different branches of Zoology, a
servile copy of the Linnæan divisions, but numerous others are defined
for the first time: and when we look back to what systematic ichthyology
was before, and what it became by the labors of Lacépède, no one can
in fairness deny but that a great and important advance in this science
had been effected. No naturalist can hope to achieve more than this,
however great may be his abilities; and we do not, therefore, understand
upon what ground so much censure has recently been cast upon the
works of this distinguished Frenchman by some of his own country-
men."—SWAINSON, Nat. Hist. and Class. of Fishes, I., 58, 1838.

tific history of the Black Bass, as heretofore understood and accepted in this country, from its first description by Lacépède down to the present time.

This representative American fish was first brought to the light of science in a foreign land, and under the most unfavorable auspices. Its scientific birth was, like Macduff's, untimely ; it was, unhappily, born a monstrosity ; its baptismal names were, consequently, incongruous, and its sponsors were, most unfortunately, foreign naturalists.

It has been, heretofore, considered by American naturalists that the first scientific description of a Black Bass was that published by Lacépède, about the year 1800, in the work just referred to. This description was founded upon a drawing of a Black Bass, and accompanying manuscript notes sent to him by M. Bosc, from the vicinity of Charleston, South Carolina, with the local name of "trout," or "trout-perch." This figure, and its accompanying description, were said to be so uncertain and inaccurate, that it has been considered very doubtful which species of Black Bass was intended to be represented. However, Lacépède named it *Labrus salmoides* (*Labre salmoïde*)—the "trout-like" *Labrus* (*wrasse*)—in accordance with its general appearance and vernacular name.

It has been held by American ichthyologists that it was after this, in 1801-2, that Lacépède received his first example of a Black Bass. This was a fine adult specimen of the small-mouthed species, but, unfortunately, it was an abnormal specimen, with a deformed dorsal fin, the last rays having been bitten off and torn loose from the others when the fish was young. In conformity with this accidental peculiarity, Lacépède named it *Micropterus dolomieu*—Dolomieu's "small-fin"—he supposing that the little fin was a permanent and distinctive feature, and of generic value; he accordingly created the new genus *Micropterus*, and named the type in honor of his friend Dolomieu.

In 1817, Rafinesque,* another French naturalist, then living in America, procured specimens of the small-mouthed Bass in the region of Lake Champlain, which he named *Bodianus achigan*, from the Canadian vulgar name of *l'achigan*. He either failed to recognize, or repudiated, Lacépède's former descriptions of *Labrus salmoides* and *Micropterus dolomieu*. During the next few years, from 1818 to 1820, while fishing in the Ohio River and its tributaries, in Kentucky, Rafinesque took and described specimens of the small-mouthed Black Bass, at different stages of its growth, as *Calliurus punctulatus, Lepomis trifasciata, Lepomis flexuolaris, Lepomis salmonea, Lepomis notata*, and *Etheostoma calliura*, and specimens of the large-mouthed Bass he described as *Lepomis pallida*.

In 1822, Le Sueur, also a French naturalist, while in this country described and named specimens, of various ages, of the small-mouthed Black Bass, as *Cichla variabilis*, (this name was never published by Le Sueur, but specimens sent by him and thus labeled, are still preserved in the Museum D'Historie Naturelle at Paris,) *Cichla fasciata*,

---

* "If I have dwelt too long upon this subject, I hope the benevolent and candid reader will excuse me; it has originated in my desire to do adequate, though tardy, justice to one whose whole life has been devoted to science, and who has been singularly unfortunate in his worldly concerns; who, notwithstanding his eccentricities, has a kind and benevolent heart; and whose labors have never been appreciated as I think they deserve. But for this, M. Rafinesque would not, in advancing life, have to contend with pecuniary difficulties, from which a small pension from the Ameriican Government, proverbially generous to her scientific sons, would set him free."—SWAINSON, *Nat. Hist. and Class. of Fishes*, I., 62, 1838.

Cichla ohiensis and *Cichla minima,* and the large-mouthed
Bass from Florida as *Cichla floridana,* thus dissenting from,
or entirely ignoring, Rafinesque.

In 1828, the great Cuvier and his coadjutor, Valenciennes, received from Lake Huron a specimen of the large-
mouthed Black Bass, and which, as in the case of the first
small-mouthed Bass sent to France, was an abnormal or
monstrous specimen, having likewise a deformed dorsal fin.
In this instance, the last three or four rays of the spinous
dorsal fin were torn off, thus leaving, apparently, two separate and distinct dorsal fins, the first composed of six
spines, and the second of two spines and twelve or thirteen
soft rays.   This specimen was sent to them under the local
name of "Black Bass," or "Black Perch;" and not sus-
pecting the mutilation of the specimen, they named it
Huro nigricans — the "Black Huron."

In the following year, 1829, Cuvier and Valenciennes
obtained two specimens (the largest of which, at least, was
a large-mouthed Bass) from New York, under the name
of "Growler," and four specimens of the small-mouthed
Bass from the Wabash River, in Indiana, all of which
they identified with Lacépède's *Labrus salmoides,* and Le
Sueur's *Cichla variabilis,* and which they named *Grystes
salmoides;* subsequently Cuvier and Valenciennes announced
that Lacépède's *Micropterus dolomieu* was also identical
with their *Grystes salmoides.*

In 1842, Dr. DeKay, in his "Fishes of New York," after
reproducing Cuvier and Valenciennes' figures and descriptions of *Huro nigricans* and *Grystes salmoides,* described
specimens of the small-mouthed Black Bass under two additional names: *Centrarchus fasciatus* and *Centrarchus obscurus,* claiming the latter as a new species.

In the same year, Dr. Kirtland adopted *Centrarchus fasciatus* as synonymous with Le Sueur's and Rafinesque's numerous descriptions of the small-mouthed species.

In 1850, Prof. Agassiz recognized the generic identity of the former descriptions of the Black Bass by Le Sueur, Cuvier and Valenciennes, and DeKay, and retained the name *Grystes* for the same.

In 1854, Prof. Agassiz obtained specimens of the large-mouthed Bass from the Tennessee River, near Huntsville, Ala., which he named, provisionally, *Grystes nobilis.* In the same year, Messrs. Baird and Girard described specimens of the same species from Texas, as *Grystes nuecensis.*

In 1857, Dr. Garlick described the small-mouthed Black Bass as *Grystes nigricans,* and the large-mouthed species as *Grystes megastoma.*

In 1858, Girard described the large-mouthed Bass as *Dioplites nuecensis.*

In 1860, Prof. Theo. Gill restored Rafinesque's earliest name for the small-mouthed form of the Black Bass, calling it *Lepomis achigan;* which, however, he changed in 1866 to *Micropterus achigan;* and still later, in 1873, he adopted Lacépède's name, *Micropterus salmoides,* for the same species.

In 1866, Prof. Gill named the large-mouthed Bass, *Micropterus nigricans,* which name was also adopted by Prof. E. D. Cope about the same time.

In 1874, when, apparently, the oldest generic and specific names had been restored ; after Prof. Gill's masterly review of the species in the previous year (when the tangled web had been, seemingly, straightened), when dry land was thought to have been reached at last;—then came the French naturalists, again.   MM. Vaillant and Bocourt, of Paris, instead of profiting by the experience of their predecessors in this matter, tried to show that we had four species of Black Bass, where but two really existed, and this in spite of the fact that the Gallic misnomer of the type species still existed as a terrible warning to them, of the folly of indulging their national love of novelty where so grave a matter as science was concerned. They proposed the title *Dioplites variabilis* for the small-mouthed form, and *Dioplites treculii, Dioplites nuecensis* and *Dioplites salmoides*, for the large-mouthed form, under several unimportant varietal, or individual, differences.

In 1876, Professor G. Brown Goode restored Le Sueur's name, and called the large-mouthed Black Bass *Micropterus floridanus*.

In 1877, Professor David S. Jordan restored the still older name of Rafinesque for this species, and with the full concurrence of Professor Theo. Gill, designated it *Micropterus pallidus*.

In 1878, Professor Jordan divided the small-mouthed species into two geographical varieties, distinguishing the Northern form as *M. salmoides* var. *achigan*, and the Southern form as *M. salmoides* var. *salmoides*.

Finally, MM. Vaillant and Bocourt (Miss. Sci. au Mexique : ined.) adopted the generic title *Micropterus*, but recognized four provisional species: *M. dolomieu* and *M. variabilis* for the small-mouthed form and *M. salmoides* and *M. nuecensis* for the large-mouthed form, under certain, evidently, unimportant variations. As they have not yet published these names, they may conclude to suppress or change some or all of them.

Thus, it will be seen that, from the first, the nomenclature of the Black Bass species had been involved in great doubt, uncertainty, and confusion; and while much of the complexity had been, apparently, dissipated, there still existed among ichthyologists some difference of opinion as to the proper differentiation of the species. Even the generally accepted nomenclature of the past few years—unfortunately and unavoidably established, as it was, on an insecure basis—was liable, at any time, to fall to the ground, while the said differences among the authorities existed.

It was the earnest hope of the writer, however, that the generic and specific names and distinctions as proposed by Professors Gill and Jordan would be found correct, and their position prove impregnable; and that, in good time, all naturalists, to avoid further confusion, would finally agree to accept and adopt the same, and so set the vexed question at rest forever; for these eminent ichthyologists had really investigated the matter more thoroughly and intelligently, and had had larger opportunities and greater facilities for doing so than all other ichthyologists combined. They labored faithfully and well, with strict fairness, and, with the light afforded them, in perfect accordance with the established principles of nomenclature, and had, at least, placed the *anglers* of America under a lasting debt of gratitude.

But these very differences among the authorities showed that the end was not yet; that the problem had not been solved; that there was still something hidden that should be brought to the light; some flaw in the chain that would eventually destroy it; some stone in the foundation that would yet crumble and work the destruction of the superimposing pile.

And, now, with much hesitation, and I hope with be-

coming modesty (for I do not wish to be thought presump-
tuous), and with feelings akin to regret—much like that of
tearing down an old homestead endeared by many tender
associations and fond remembrances, to make room for a
more substantial structure—but at the same time feeling
that I am doing an act that is simply right and just, I
feel constrained to make a radical change in the nomenclature of the Black Bass as it is at present understood
in America.

But in order to arrive at a clear understanding of the
subject, I propose, in the first place, to present to the
angler, as well as to the student of ichthyology, all that is
really worth knowing of the scientific literature of the
Black Bass; in doing which it becomes a matter of necessity, as well as of choice, to draw liberally upon the
writings of Professors Gill and Jordan.

The following disquisitional résumé is from Professor
Gill's admirable monograph, entitled, "On the Species of
the Genus Micropterus (Lac.) or Grystes (Auct.),"* and is
the most able, concise and original paper ever written upon
the subject; and, so far as it goes, presents the whole
matter clearly and succinctly, and according to the views
of most of our best naturalists.

The nomenclature of the species has become involved in much
doubt, and, if we may judge from the literature and the distinctions
insisted on by Prof. Agassiz and others,† at least four or five species

---

* On the Species of the Genus Micropterus (Lac.) or Grystes (Auct.).
By Theodore Gill, of Washington, D. C.   < Proceedings of the American
Association for the Advancement of Science, XXII, 1873, pp. B. 55–72.

---

† In the nominal (1) "*Grystes fasciatus* Agass.," it is said, "the *scales are* a
little *smaller*, but of the same form as in (2) *G. salmoides;* the radiating striæ
are perhaps less marked. They cover the opercular apparatus and the *cheeks*,

are supposed to exist in our waters; but it is evident from a perusal of the descriptions that the distinctions hitherto made are of very doubtful value.

Having been requested by the United States Commissioner of Fish and Fisheries (Prof. S. F. Baird) to determine the number of species represented in the fresh waters of the United States, and the earliest names respectively assigned to them; all the specimens in the collections of the Smithsonian Institution were examined, as well as a large series from many other localities kindly transmitted for that purpose by the Museum of Comparative Zoology (Prof. Agassiz, Director).   Study and comparison of those specimens clearly demon-

---

but at this latter place *their* [*the scales'*] *smaller size is quite remarkable;* this latter character is very striking when we compare both species."—Agass., Lake Superior, p. 296.—The italicized portion (not italicized in original) indicates that the *G. salmoides* Agass. was a large-mouthed form. (3) "*Huro nigricans* Cuv. is another species of the lower Canadian lakes, which occurs also in Lake Champlain . . . . I shall, therefore, call it in future *Grystes nigricans* . . . . Dr. DeKay describes it as *Centrarchus fasciatus*, although he copies also Cuvier's description and figure of *Huro nigricans*, but without perceiving their identity." Agass., Lake Superior, p. 297.—*Huro nigricans* Cuv. and Val. and *Centrarchus fasciatus* DeKay are unquestionably distinct, the former being the large-mouthed species, and the latter the small-mouthed one. It is probable, however (thus giving him the benefit of the doubt), that Prof. Agassiz based his idea of the species on the large-mouthed form.

"The species of this group [*Grystes* Cuv.] are indeed very difficult to characterize. They differ chiefly in the relative size of their scales, the presence or absence of teeth on the tongue, ... etc. There are, besides, marked differences between the young and adults. These circumstances render it impossible to characterize any one species without comparative descriptions and figures. (4) The species from Huntsville [Ala.] . . . differs equally from [*G. fasciatus* Agass. and *G. "salmoneus"* Agass.]. I call this species provisionally *Grystes nobilis* Agass."—Am. Jour. Sci. and Arts (2), xvii, p. 297, 298, 1854.

Prof. Agassiz thus recognized four species (besides indeterminate ones), viz :—

1. *G. fasciatus* Agass. = *M. salmoides.*
2. *G. salmoides* Agass. (not Cuv. and Val. nor *G. salmoneus* Agass., 1854) = *M. nigricans.*
3. *G. nigricans* Agass. = *M. nigricans?*
4. *G. nobilis* Agass. = *M. nigricans.*

Judging by the comparisons, Prof. Agassiz had in view, in 1854, in the "*G. salmoneus,*" the true *M. salmoides.*

Baird and Girard added to these species, also, in 1854, (5) their *G. nuecensis* = (*M. nigricans*).

strated that two perfectly distinct types of the genus were represented in most of the waters of the cismontane (east of the Rocky
Mountain) slope of the United States, except those of the New
England States and the Atlantic seaboard of the Middle States. In
limitation of this general statement it need only at present be remarked that but one of those types, the small-mouthed, appears to
have been an original inhabitant of the hydrographic basin of the
Ohio River.

In order to obtain as clear and unprejudiced ideas as possible
respecting the species, the specimens from all the localities were in
the first place examined without reference to their names but only
with the view to ascertain their relations to each other. This examination confirmed the previous experience of the author for a
more limited range, and led to the combination of all into the two
groups just referred to: between these many differences existed,
but none were discovered which permitted further definite sub-
division. The differences thus ascertained may be tabulated as
follows:

CONTRASTED DIFFERENTIAL CHARACTERISTICS.

SMALL-MOUTHED.	LARGE-MOUTHED.
Scales of trunk	
Small (*e. g. lat. line*, 72–75; between lateral line, and back, 11 rows).	Moderate (*e. g. lat. line*, 65–70; between lateral line and back, 7½ or 8 rows).
Scales on nape and breast	
Much smaller than those of sides.	Scarcely (on nape), or not much (on breast) smaller than those of sides.
Scales of cheeks	
Minute (*e. g.*, between orbit and preoperculum, about 17 rows in an oblique line and about 9 in a horizontal one).	Moderately small (*e. g.*, between orbit and preoperculum, about 10 rows in an oblique line and about 5–6 in a horizontal one).

Scales of interoperculum uniserial

Covering only about half the width of the bone.

Covering the entire width of the bone.

Scales of preopercular limb

None.

Developed in an imperfect row (*e. g.*, 3–5 in number).

Scales on dorsal

Developed as a deep sheath (involving last spine) of small scales differentiated from those on the back, and with series advancing high up the membrane behind each ray (except last two or three).

Developed as a low (obsolete) shallow sheath, and with series ascending comparatively little on membrane behind the rays (none behind the last five or six).

Scales on anal

Ascending high behind each ray.

None (or very few).

Mouth

Moderate.

Large.

Supramaxillary

Ending considerably in front of hinder margin of orbit (about under hinder border of pupil).

Extending considerably behind the posterior margin of orbit.

Rays

Dorsal, articulated, 13.
Anal III, 10–11.
Pectoral, 1·16–1·17.

Dorsal, articulated, 12 (I. 11).
Anal III, 10.
Pectoral, 1·14 (1·13).

Dorsal fin in front of soft portion

Little depressed, the ninth spine being only about a half shorter than the longest (3, 4, 5) and a fourth shorter than the tenth.

Much depressed, the ninth spine being only about a fourth as long as the longest and half as long as the tenth.

Thus numerous and well marked are the differences between the two groups; within the limits of neither of these groups were found differences in the slightest degree comparable with them, or that suggested the differentiation of the forms into distinctly marked subordinate types: in other words, no differences were found of specific value, and, although a renewed examination may possibly result in the discovery of some, their value must be very slight in comparison with those distinguishing the two groups indicated: these groups may therefore be considered as specific. The question now arises, What are the names to which they are respectively entitled? In order to ascertain this, it is advisible to enter quite fully into the very complicated history of the genus. Bearing strictly in mind the differential features of the two species, we may now proceed to an analysis of the successive descriptions of forms of the genus and endeavor to refer them to their respective types.

The first scientific allusions to any species of the genus are found in the great work on fishes by Comte de Lacépède.*

In 1800, in the third volume (pp. 716, 717), Lacépède introduced into his system, under the name *Labrus salmoïdes*, a species based on a description and figure sent him by Bosc from South Carolina, which, according to Cuvier and Valenciennes, relate to the small-mouthed type.

In 1801, in the fourth volume (p. 325), Lacépède described, as a new generic type, named *Micropterus Dolomieu*,† a fish concerning which no particulars were given as to habitat or station, and which could not have been positively identified from the description: the original specimen having been preserved, however, Cuvier and Valenciennes ascertained that it belonged to the genus *Grystes*, and was,

---

* LACÉPÈDE (Bernard Germain Étienne de la Ville-sur-Illon, Comte de). Histoire Naturelle des Poissons, . . . Paris, . . . [1798-1803, 4to, 5 v].

† " 121e genre. Les Microptères.

" Un ou plusieurs aiguillons, et point de dentelure aux opercules; un barbillon, ou point de barbillon aux mâchoires; deux nageoires dorsales; la seconde très-basse, très-courte, et comprenant au plus cinq rayons.

" Espèce. Le Microptère Dolomieu.

" *Caractères.* Dix rayons aiguillonnés et sept rayons articulés à la première nageoire du dos; quatre rayons à la seconde; deux rayons aiguillonnés et onze rayons articulés à la nageoire de l'anus; la caudale en croissant; un ou deux aiguillons à la seconde pièce de chaque opercule." [Br. 5; p. 16; v. i, 5; c. 17].

in fact, identical with the species described by Lacépède from the notes and figures of Bosc as *Labrus salmoides*.

In 1817, C. S. Rafinesque* described a form of the same genus under the name *Bodianus achigan* which evidently belonged to the small-mouthed type : while most of the characters noted are common to all the species (or erroneous), the number of rays (D. IX I, 14 † ; A. III, 11 ‡) and the absence of scales on the preoperculum (gill covers " all scaly except the second ") indicate the pertinence of the species to the group in question : the number of rays (15) attributed to the pectoral does not confirm this identification, but the number (admitting even the accuracy—very doubtful—in the case of the very careless observer) is within the range of variation of the type. The exact locality from which Rafinesque derived his types was not specified, but they were probably observed by him at Lake Champlain, where he had shortly before collected (See Am. Month. Mag. and Crit. Rev., ii. p. 202, Jan., 1818).

In 1820, the same naturalist described, in his way, various specimens which appear, almost without doubt, to be referrible to the same type. These descriptions appeared originally in the "Western Review and Miscellaneous Magazine," published at Lexington, Kentucky, and were reprinted (from the same types) for the "Ichthyologia Ohiensis." ¿ No less than six generic and subgeneric names appear to have been based primarily on a species of this type and as many as seven nominal species, viz.:

---

*RAFINESQUE-SCHMALTZ (Constantine Samuel). Museum of Natural Sciences. By C. S. Rafinesque, Esq. First Decade of New North American Fishes. < The American Monthly Magazine and Critical Review. Vol. ii, New York, . . . 1817 (pp. 120, 121).

† " The dorsal depressed in the middle and with twenty-five rays, whereof ten are spinescent." It is assumed that the last or double branched ray is counted as two.

‡ " Anal fin with fifteen rays whereof three are spinescent and short." The last ray was also in this case probably counted as two.

¿ Ichthyologia Ohiensis, or Natural History of the Fishes inhabiting the River Ohio and its tributary streams. . . . Lexington, Kentucky ; printed for the author by W. G. Hunt. (Price one dollar.) 1820. (Pp. 26-36). Reprinted (with separate pagination and adjustment for form) from the Western Review and Miscellaneous Magazine, Lexington, Ky. Vols. i, ii and iii (Dec. 1819 to Nov., 1820).

GENERA AND SUBGENERA.

1. Calliurus (n. g.).
2. Lepomis (n. g.).
    Aplites (n. s. g.).
    Nemocampsis (n. s. g. prov.).
    Dioplites (n. s. g.).
3. [Etheostoma].
    Aplesion (n. s. g.).

SPECIES.

1. Calliurus punctulatus.
2. Lepomis pallida (s. g. Aplites).
3. Lepomis trifasciata (s. g. Aplites).
4. Lepomis flexuolaris (s. g. Aplites, or n. s. g. Nemocampsis).
5. Lepomis salmonea (s. g. Dioplites).
6. Lepomis notata (s. g. Dioplites).
7. Etheostoma calliura (s. g. Aplesion).

Of these, it need here only be in general remarked that the differential characters employed result (1) partly from erroneous observation, and (2) partly from erroneous assumptions: that is, because the author had not signalized certain characters in specimens previously examined, but which were noticed in others examined later, he assumed that they did not exist in the former, and therefore the two differed. Inasmuch, however, (1) as all the descriptions cited, best (and decidedly so) agree with species of the genus *Micropterus*, and (2) as, in those respects in which they differ, they equally deviate from all known forms in the waters from which they were obtained, and (3) as it is in the highest degree improbable that forms better agreeing with them have been overlooked, the names in question are all relegated to the synonymy of *Micropterus*. Within that genus in almost every case some specification (chiefly as to the number of rays) indicates that the several descriptions were based on individuals of the small-mouthed type. This probability is greatly enhanced by the fact that (so far as known or recorded) the small-mouthed species was the only one known from the localities where Rafinesque observed.

The description of *Calliurus punctulatus*, however, it has been thought by Prof. Agassiz, was based on a form of the sunfish type with large mouth. But such could not have been the case, as is quite evident from the armature of the operculum ("opercule with an *acute* and membranaceous appendage, before which stands a flat *spine*"), the contour of the dorsal ("*depressed* in the middle"), and above all the number of the rays of that fin ("dorsal fin yellow with *twenty-four* rays, of which ten are spiny"); in all these respects (as well as others), the description is inapplicable to a Pomotid and only applicable to a *Micropterus*.

A couple of years later (in 1822), a much more reliable naturalist [*] published descriptions of five supposed new species of the genus Cichla of Bloch (as supposed to have been adopted by Cuvier). All except one `(*C. ænea = Ambloplites rupestris*) really belong to the genus *Micropterus*, and all the northern forms (*C. fasciata, C. ohiensis, C. minima*), as is evident from the allusions to the number of rays, squamation, or size of mouth, belong to the small-mouthed type, while the description of the Floridian species (*C. floridana*) is as applicable to the same as to the large-mouthed type. The descriptions are not sufficiently contrasted, and are too general and therefore vague; nor, on comparison with specimens, are the differences suggested by the mention of characters in one case and their neglect in another apparent. As no reference was made to the forms of the same type previously described, although the author was doubtless acquainted with Rafinesque's memoir, it is presumable that the neglect was intentional (and doubtless provoked by the character of that author's work) and not without strong suspicion that the species named had already, perhaps, received designations, but with unrecognizable descriptions.

In the great "Histoire Naturelle des Poissons,"[†] Cuvier and Valenciennes described the two species of the genus, but, deceived by the state of their specimens—in one case at least (*Huro nigricans*),

---

[*] LE SUEUR (Charles A. . .). Descriptions of the [*sic*] five new species of the genus Cichla of Cuvier. By C. A. Le Sueur. Read June 11, 1822. <Journal of the Academy of Natural Sciences of Philadelphia. Vol. ii, Part i. Philadelphia, ... 1821. [Pp. 214-221].

[†] CUVIER (Georges Chrétien Leopold Dagobert *baron*) and Achille VALENCIENNES. Histoire Naturelle des Poissons, ... Paris, ... 1828-1849. [t. ii, 1828, pp. 124-126 ; t. iii, 1829, pp. 54-58].

completely failed to recognize the relations of the two.   (1) In 1828 (tome second, pp. 124–126) they described the large-mouthed species as a new generic type (under the name *Huro nigricans*), but, misled by an injury to the spinous portion of the dorsal fin (and apparently the loss of the seventh spine), they ranked it in their group of Percoids with two dorsal fins, attributing to it a first dorsal with six spines, and a second with two spines in front (instead of ten dorsal spines).   (2) In the following year (1829) and volume (tome troisième, pp. 54–58), they described the small-mouthed species, identifying it with the *Labrus salmoides* of Lacépède, and forming for it (and at the same time associating with it an Australian fish) the genus Grystes: this was referred to the section of Percoids with a single dorsal fin and placed after *Centropristes* and before *Rhypticus*.   The descriptions of both species (after making allowance for the error induced by the state of the dorsal in *Huro*) were quite good, and especially in the case of *Grystes salmoides*, much better than any subsequently published, and they can consequently be identified without difficulty.

Subsequently, Dr. DeKay, in his "Zoology of New York," * reproduced the figures and (in a modifièd form) the descriptions of the two species from Cuvier and Valenciennes' work; but, failing to identify them, redescribed and refigured one of them (*Grystes salmoides*) under two names (*Centrarchus fasciatus*=*Cichla fasciata* Les., and *Centrarchus obscurus* DeKay, n. sp.).   Of course all were adopted by Dr. Storer in his " Synopsis of the Fishes of North America."†   In those works, therefore, the species stand under three generic and four specific names.

In 1850, Prof. Agassiz, in his " Lake Superior,"‡ decidedly advanced

---

* DEKAY (James E. . .). Zoology of New York, or the New York Fauna; comprising detailed descriptions of all the animals hitherto observed within the State of New York, with brief notices of those occasionally found near its borders, and accompanied by appropriate illustrations. By James E. DeKay. Part IV. Fishes.—Albany ; printed by W. & A. White & J. Visscher. 1842. [4to, xiv [1, errata], 415 pp.; atlas, 1 p. 1., 79 p. 1].

† STORER (David Humphreys). A Synopsis of the Fishes of North America. <Memoirs of the American Academy of Arts and Sciences.   New series. Vol. ii., (Cambridge, 1846), pp. 253–550.

——A synopsis of the Fishes of North America. . . . Cambridge: Metcalf and Company, printers to the University. 1846. [4to, 1 p. 1. (= title), 298 pp.]

* ‡ AGASSIZ (Louis).   Lake Superior; its Physical Character; Vegetation

beyond his predecessors, (1) recognizing, for the first time, the generic identity of the forms described by LeSueur, Cuvier and Valenciennes, and DeKay, (2) retaining for the genus thus enlarged the name Grystes, and (3) recognizing two species as inhabitants of the north; he was, however, less fortunate in his appreciation of their specific relations, (1) his *Grystes fasciatus* being the small-mouthed form, (2) his "*Grystes salmoneus*" (as is evident from the contrasted characters noticed in his comparison of *G. fasciatus* with it) being the large-mouthed southern form, and (3) his *Grystes nigricans* being differentiated without statement of reasons and the *Centrarchus fasciatus* of DeKay identified with it.

At a later period (1854), Prof. Agassiz distinguished specimens of the genus obtained from Huntsville,* Alabama, as *Grystes nobilis*, which evidently belongs to the large-mouthed type; the brief notice is only comparative, contrasted with the small-mouthed type, and contains no specific peculiarities.

In the same year and month (March,. 1854), Messrs. Baird and Girard† described specimens of the same type from the "Rio Frio and Rio Nueces, Texas," under the name *Grystes nuecensis*. This form was subsequently described in greater detail and illustrated by Dr. Charles Girard, in the Report on the Mexican boundary Survey.

In 1857, Dr. Theodatus Garlick,‡ of Cleveland, Ohio, in a treatise on the propagation of fish, described and published rough woodcut figures of the two forms of the genus: (1) the small-mouthed species under the name "*Grystes nigricans*; or black bass;" (2) the other, as a new species, designated "*Grystes megastoma*; or large-mouth

---

and Animals, compared with those of other and similar regions. . . . Boston; 1850. (p. 295.)

  * AGASSIZ (Louis). Notice of a collection of Fishes from the southern bend of the Tennessee River, Alabama. . . <The American Journal of Science and Arts, second series. Vol. xvii. . . . 1854. [pp. 297-308; 353-365=Grystes, pp. 297, 298].

  † BAIRD (Spencer Fullerton) and Charles GIRARD. Descriptions of new species of Fishes collected in Texas, New Mexico, and Sonora, by Mr. John H. Clark, on the U. S. and Mexican Boundary Survey, and in Texas by Capt. Stewart Van Vliet, U. S. A. . . .<Proceedings of the Academy of Natural Sciences of Philadelphia. Vol. vii, 1854, 1855. [pp. 24-29; Grystes, p. 25].

  ‡ GARLICK (Theodatus). A treatise on the Artificial Propagation of certain kinds of Fish, with the descriptions of such kinds as are the most suitable for pisciculture. . . . Cleveland, Tho. Brown, publisher, Ohio Farmer office, 1857. [12mo, 142 pp. Grystes, pp. 105-110.]

black bass."* The species are quite well distinguished by the size of the mouth and the comparative size of the scales: his *Grystes nigricans* is, however, not the true *Grystes nigricans* (*Huro nigricans*, Cuv. & Val.), as that name really belongs to his *Grystes megastoma*.

In 1859, Dr. Günther† described specimens of the small-mouthed species under the name *Grystes salmoides*, and first restricted the genus to that species (having removed the Australian species as the type of a new genus—*Oligorus*). Having overlooked the rectifications by Prof. Agassiz, he continued the errors of his predecessors, admitting as nominal species (1) *Huro nigricans*, (2) *Centrarchus fasciatus*, and (3) *Centrarchus obscurus*, and also the same species as doubtful forms (in foot-notes) of *Grystes*, i. e., *G. nuecensis* and *G. fasciatus*.

For the present, the notices and descriptions of the several forms of the genus by other authors may be passed over in silence, as they do not involve any questions of nomenclature. It may be added, however, (1) that the author had long recognized the existence and differences of the two species of the genus, one under the name *Micropterus achigan*, the other as *Micropterus nigricans*, and (2) that Prof. Cope, under the names *Micropterus fasciatus* (which he attributed to the present author through some misapprehension) and *Micropterus nigricans* has signalized the same species from widely distant regions (*e. g.*, Michigan, Virginia, North Carolina), and has evidently understood their relations.

Analysis of all the published descriptions and comparison with the fishes themselves, led to the following conclusions:

SECTION 1.—MORPHOLOGICAL.

After an examination and comparison with each other of specimens from the great lakes (Champlain to Michigan), the states of New York, Pennsylvania, Ohio, Michigan, Illinois, Iowa, Kentucky, Missouri, Tennessee, Alabama, Texas, Wisconsin, West Virginia, Virginia, North

---

* "This fish has been identified with the common black bass (*Grystes fasciatus*), but is by no means the same fish, differing in many respects, both in its habits and physical structure, and has not been described in any work on American fishes, so far as I can learn " (*op. cit.* p. 108).

† GÜNTHER (Albert). Catalogue of the Acanthopterygian Fishes in the Collection of the British Museum, . . . Vol. i, . . . London, . . . 1859 [pp. 252–255].

and South Carolina, and Georgia, no differences could be found much, if any greater, than such as could be detected among numerous individuals from any given locality. There are differences resulting from age and condition ; the fins may be (slightly) more or less developed, and the colors may be more or less intense, but no deviations have been found, from the ordinary standard, of such a character as at all to compare, for example, with the differences between the large-mouthed and small-mouthed forms, or to indicate that there are any specific differences among the small-mouthed or large-mouthed forms. The natural course, then, appears to be to recognize only the two forms whose differences are so obvious as species, and—at least till differences may be detected, of which none have yet been found— to consider all the other forms, and from all localities, however distant they may be, as representatives or varieties of those species.

SECTION 2.—NOMENCLATURE.

A critical analysis of the numerous notices and descriptions of the forms of the genus indicates that the differences between the respective species have been very imperfectly apprehended, and mostly confined to the size of the mouth and in vague terms to the size (comparatively large or small) of the scales: most of the other differences signalized are either non-existent or individual and dependent on the condition of the specimens. The charge of vagueness and insufficiency of diagnosis is especially applicable to the first descriptions of species of the genus; guided, however, by a knowledge of the geographical distribution of the genus and hints furnished by the radial formulas, etc., it may be safely concluded, (1) that most of the names referred to in the historical introduction may be relegated to the synonymy of the small-mouthed species; (2) that the first name applied to that species was *Labrus salmoides ;* (3) that only the names *Huro nigricans,* (and most of its derivatives), *Grystes megastoma, Grystes nobilis,* and *Dioplites nuecensis* belong to the large-mouthed species; (4) that the name *nigricans* is therefore the first specific term applicable to it; (5) that the name *Micropterus* was the first applied to the genus; and (6) that therefore, if we only take into consideration the priority of the names (irrespective of the applicability or erroneousness of the description), and combine the first specific names applied to the respective species with the first generic name given to a representative of the genus, the two species should be designated as (*a*) *Micropterus salmoides*, the small-mouthed black bass, and (*b*) *Micropterus nigricans*,[*] the large-mouthed black bass.

In 1873, Professor Gill traced back the large-mouthed Black Bass only to *Huro nigricans* Cuv. & Val., and named it *Micropterus nigricans* (C. & V.) Gill, as shown in the foregoing review.

But in 1874, Professor G. Brown Goode, while collecting in Florida, found this species exceedingly abundant, and the only species of the Black Bass represented in that State; consequently, in 1876, he restored the name bestowed on this species, from the same locality, by Le Sueur, in 1822 (*Cichla floridana*), and in accordance with the law of priority, called it *Micropterus floridanus* (Le Sueur) Goode.

In the following year (1877), however, Professor Jordan found that the same species was very numerous in the tributaries of the Ohio River, in Kentucky, where Rafinesque fished in 1818–20, and after a thorough investigation, he and Prof. Gill identified this species as *Lepomis pallida* Raf.; whereupon, in obedience to the same law of precedence, they gave to it its present name, *Micropterus pallidus* (Raf.) Gill and Jordan; which, by the way, is as appropriate as all other synonyms are incongruous, and which might be expected from its having been the name by which the species was designated by a naturalist who took his specimens, alive and kicking, from nature's book.†

---

* Profs. Gill and Jordan subsequently substituted *Micropterus pallidus* for *Micropterus nigricans*, for reasons which will appear later in this chapter.— J. A. H.

---

† "In further justification of the opinions here advanced, it may be

In order to make it perfectly clear why this change of name was considered necessary, I can not do better than to reproduce the following characteristic communication from the pen of Prof. David S. Jordan to the anglers of America:—*

Since the publication of the name *Micropterus pallidus* (Raf.), Gill and Jordan, as a substitute for *Micropterus nigricans* for the scientific name of the large-mouthed Black Bass, I have received numerous congratulations, verbal and written, from brother fishermen on the appropriateness of the name "selected," and I presume that my colleague in this matter, Professor Gill, has had a similar experience. Lately, a correspondent of FOREST AND STREAM suggests that the name *Micropterus salmoides* be likewise "stamped out" to make room for some more appropriate appellation. It seems timely, therefore, that we should "rise and explain."

The name *Micropterus pallidus* is not a name of our own selection, but a name which by the laws of scientific nomenclature we are bound to use. By the operation of these laws every genus must bear the oldest (generic) name bestowed on any of its members, unless this name has been previously used for something else, or is glaringly false (not simply irrelevant or inappropriate), or is otherwise ineligible; every species must bear the first (specific) name

---

proper for me to state that I had the pleasure of M. Rafinesque's society, during the three years of my official residence in Sicily, from 1807 to 1810, and again in 1812, when we were both at Palermo, prosecuting our botanical and ichthyological researches together. . . . M. Rafinesque, unfortunately, was unable to publish more than a synopsis of his ichthyological discoveries; and his figures, being very slight, are often not calculated to clear up those doubts which the brevity of his descriptions sometimes creates; nevertheless, to one who examines the species on the spot, in a *fresh* state, there are few which may not be identified. M. Cuvier often asserts that all M. Rafinesque's species were described from preserved specimens; but this is an error—they were all taken from the life."—SWAINSON, *Nat. Hist. and Class. of Fishes*, I, 62, 1838.

* Scientific Names of the Black Bass. By David S. Jordan, M. D. < FOREST AND STREAM, XI, 1878, p. 340.

imposed upon it (unless, as before, it be for one reason or another ineligible), and the proper name of any species must be made by combining the above-mentioned specific and generic names.

This is the law on the subject, and, as elsewhere, the law is usually, though not always, simply right. We accept many meaningless or even objectionable names to avoid the confusion attendant upon arbitrary changes. Were it not for these rules science would ever suffer, as it has much suffered in the past, from the efforts of the improvers of nomenclature—men who invent new names for old objects for the purpose of seeing their own personal designations: Smith, Jones, Brehm, Reichenow, or what not, after them. In the words of "a right Sagamann," John Cassin: "There is not, evidently, any other course consistent with justice and the plainest principles of right and morality, and, in fact, no alternative, unless, indeed, an operator is disposed to set himself up for the first of all history, as is said of an early Chinese emperor. The latter course, in a degree, singular as it may appear, is not entirely unknown to naturalists, especially to those who regard science as a milch cow rather than as a transcendent goddess, a distinction in classification first made by the great poet Schiller."

Now, as to the names of our species of bass, I take it for granted that the reader knows (a) what a Black Bass is and what it is not (b); that there are two species of Black Bass, the large-mouthed and the small-mouthed, the latter being with most anglers the Black Bass *par excellence*, the other the off horse, and (c) what the difference between them is. In any event you will find it all written in Professor Gill's most excellent paper, "On the Species of the Genus *Micropterus*," in the "Proceedings of the American Association for the Advancement of Science in 1873."

The earliest published notice of a Black Bass with a scientific name was of one of the small-mouthed kind, sent to Lacépède from South Carolina. This specimen bore with it the name of "trout," after the abominable, contemptible, pernicious and otherwise detestable custom of our erring Southern brethren of calling a Black Bass in the river, or a weak fish in the sea, a "trout." Now, we may presume that the great French naturalist was puzzled by this name, and put on his spectacles to see what in the world could be "trout-like" about such a fish, with its coarse scales and spinous fins. To him it looked more like a wrasse or cunner, *Labrus*, than a trout; but no matter, it must resemble a trout somehow or the Americans would not call it so. So he put it down in his great work as *Labrus salmoides*, the trout-like *Labrus*, to the everlasting injury of the fish. The name is not only senseless, but bad Latin, the proper form of the word being *Salmonoides*.

Lacépède had another specimen of the Black Bass, without label, and from an unknown locality. This one had the last rays of the dorsal broken and torn loose from the rest, and was otherwise in a forlorn condition. This specimen he considered as a genus distinct from the other, and he gave it the name of *Micropterus dolomieu*— "Dolomieu's small-fin." Dolomieu was a friend of Lacépède, who had had about as much to do with the fish as George Washington or Victor Hugo. No one could tell, either from figure or description, what this *Micropterus dolomieu* was; but Cuvier, thirty years later, found the original type and pronounced it a Black Bass, in poor condition, and declared that "the genus and species of *Micropterus* ought to disappear from the catalogue of fishes."

Then the versatile and eccentric Professor Rafinesque appeared upon the scene, and in rapid succession gave the small-mouthed Black Bass names enough for a whole family. First he called it *Bodianus achigan*, being told that the Canadian voyageurs knew the fish as *l'achigan*. Then afterward specimens of different sizes appeared as *Calliurus punctulatus*, *Lepomis trifasciata*, *Lepomis flexuolaris*, *Lepomis salmonea*, *Lepomis notata*, and *Etheostoma calliura*. Soon after Le Sueur, with a lofty scorn for Rafinesque and his doings, named specimens of different sizes, *Cichla fasciata*, *Cichla ohiensis*, and *Cichla minima*. Lastly, DeKay, in 1842, called it *Centrarchus obscurus*, and we hope this may be the last.

Now, the name *salmoides*, being the oldest, is, of course, the one to be adopted. But suppose we "stamp it out." Is *Micropterus dolomieu* any better? Out with it! *Micropterus achigan?* Just as bad. I fear that the "stamping out" process would have to be continued too long. You may spell it *salmonoides* if you like, but you can not get rid of it.

Now for the large-mouthed Bass. The oldest description we find is that of a young specimen from the Ohio by Rafinesque, in 1820, as *Lepomis pallida*. The description is poor enough, and not

altogether correct, but the name is a happy inspiration, as good as
salmoides is bad.   Soon after (1822) Le Sueur described the same fish
from Florida as *Cichla floridana*, a name which would be well enough
if it were confined to the streams of the orange groves, but it seems
rather narrow in view of the fact that the fish is found in Mexico
and Manitoba, and every-where between.

Next, a specimen came to Cuvier and Valenciennes, under the
title of "Black Bass of Lake Huron." To their eyes the fish was
black enough, but not a Bass (*i. e. Labrax*), and they called it *Huro
nigricans*, the "Black Huron," making a new genus for it because
their specimen had but six dorsal spines, the last four having been
broken off, leaving two dorsal fins. The colored figure which they
published remained a standing puzzle for some time.

In Dr. Kirtland's private copy of his own fishes of Ohio he had
carefully drawn off and colored a copy of Cuvier's figure of his Black
Huron, and had all his life sought for such a fish in the lakes and
never found it. About a year before his death, Dr. Kirtland asked
me if I had ever seen that fish or could tell him what it was, and I
had the pleasure of informing him that it was a demoralized Black
Bass. Next, in 1854, Professor Agassiz, thinking that this fish in the
Tennessee River could not be the same as in Lake Huron, called it
Grystes nobilis, a good name enough, but 34 years too late. In the
same year, specimens from Texas were named *Grystes nuecensis* by
Baird and Girard, but the fish is found in other streams than the
Rio Nueces. Then a meaty and excellent name, *Grystes megastoma*,
was given by Dr. Garlick in 1857, which closes the American synonymy, but the disease has broken out in France again, and Messrs.
Vaillant and Bocourt, of Paris, who ought to know better, have again
described it as *Dioplites treculii* and *Dioplites variabilis*. The poorest
business a French naturalist can engage in is that of describing new
species of American fishes. A good share of our cumbersome and
confusing synonymy is due to Gallic assistance.

Now, in 1873, Prof. Gill, in his masterly review of these species,
followed the thread back only to *Huro nigricans* in 1828, and so
called the big-mouthed Black Bass, as he was bound to do, *Micropterus nigricans*. The names *floridanus* and *pallidus* were presumed by
him to refer to the other species, for the reason that he had never
seen a big-mouthed Black Bass, either from the Ohio River or from

Florida. In 1876, Prof. Goode had collected it in Florida, and so felt bound to restore Le Sueur's name and to call it *Micropterus flor-idanus*. In 1877, I called Professor Gill's attention to the fact that there were big-mouthed as well as small-mouthed Black Bass in the streams where Rafinesque fished, and he agreed with me at once that the *Lepomis pallida* of Rafinesque was the big-mouth, which is why the big-mouthed Black Bass, Oswego Bass, Grass Bass, and Bayou Bass is *Micropterus pallidus* (Rafinesque) Gill and Jordan, at present date, and such may it ever remain.

Now, as to the name of the genus itself, the difficulty is just as great. The name *Micropterus* is unquestionably the oldest. But (*a*) we are perhaps not absolutely certain that the original *Micropterus dolomieu* was a Black Bass at all; (*b*) it was described as distinct under the erroneous impression that it had a little adipose fin behind the dorsal, and (*c*) the name (small fin) refers to this imaginary peculiarity, and is therefore incorrect.

On the other hand, the Black Bass really has smaller fins than any of its relatives, and the name has therefore a certain appropriateness. I think, with Professor Gill, that it should be retained, although Professor Cope and others, as good authority as we are, are inclined to demur.

Next comes *Calliurus* (beautiful tail), not a bad name, for the young Bass have the tail ornamented with black, white, and yellow, but not a very good name. Then comes *Lepomis* (scaly opercles), previously applied to the sunfishes, and therefore not usable for a Bass. Then come Rafinesque's *Aplites*, *Nemocampsis*, *Dioplites*, and *Aplesion*, unworthy of any attention, although, for some reason, *Dioplites* has kept up a sort of life, while the other three have wholly died.

Next come the name *Huro* for the large-mouthed, and *Grystes* for the small-mouthed. Of course the two do not belong to separate genera. The name *Grystes* was given as a translation of the name Growler, under which name the Black Bass was sent to the museum at Paris. Thus our two species are often called in foreign books the Black Huron (*Huro nigricans*), and the Salmon-formed Growler (*Grystes salmoides*). The name *Grystes* is a graceful one, and has been used more frequently than any other, but there are seven names ahead of it on the record, and first come first served and synonymy take the hindmost.

The names *Labrus, Bodianus, Cichla,* and *Centrarchus* belong to wholly different fishes, and were given by different authors through mistakes as to the relationship of the Black Bass.

I trust that this hasty and rather rambling account will be of some service to the numerous class of my fishing brethren who like to be right in their use of names, and who want to know, you know, but who, like Wilhelm Tell, can not "lange prüfen oder wählen."

In the summer of 1877, while investigating the fish fauna of the Alleghany region of South Carolina, Georgia, and Tennessee, Professor Jordan became impressed with the fact that the small-mouthed Black Bass of the Southern States differed constantly in some features from the Northern form of the same species ; consequently, he separated the species into two varieties, designating the Northern form as *Micropterus salmoides* var. *achigan,* and the Southern form as *Micropterus salmoides* var. *salmoides.* His views and arguments are detailed in the following extract :—*

The small-mouthed Black Bass or "Trout" of the Southern streams (*i. e.*, Savanah, Altamaha, Chattahoochee, Alabama) differs so constantly from Northern representatives of the same species that the two forms may be taken as geographical varieties of one species, and it is probably worth while to distinguish each by name. The *Labrus salmoides* of Lacépède was collected by Bosc, near Charleston, S. C. It was therefore, presumably, the Southern variety which should be designated as var. *salmoides.* The oldest name known to apply to the Northern form is that of *Bodianus achigan* Rafinesque. The Northern form may therefore be designated as *Micropterus salmoides* var. *achigan,* whenever it is deemed desirable to call attention to these variations.

The body is appreciably longer and slenderer in var. *salmoides* than in var. *achigan,* the head being about 3¼ in length instead of

* Contributions to N. A. Ichthyology, No. 3, p. 30. <Bulletin U. S. National Museum, XII, 1878.

about 2¾. The anal rays in *salmoides* are usually 10 instead of 11;
the dorsal formula X, I, 12, instead of X, I, 13. The scales are larger
in *salmoides*, there being about 70 in the lateral line instead of 77.
The coloration of *salmoides* is uniformly unlike that of *achigan*. The
lower part of the sides is marked by pretty regular lines of dark
olive-green spots along the series of scales. The lower fins are usually more or less red, and the black, yellow, and white coloration of
the caudal fin, so conspicuous in young specimens of the Northern
form—in the Western States, at least—is not noticeable in the Southern variety.

And now, if we could feel perfectly confident and reasonably sure that the premises adopted by our American
naturalists were correct, to wit: that *Labrus salmoides* Lacépède, was the *first* scientific description of the *small-
mouthed* Bass, we could then leave this subject here, with
the firm conviction that this matter was settled for all time,
and could thus feel assured of the ultimate and universal
adoption and perpetuity of the American nomenclature of
the Black Bass, viz: *Micropterus salmoides* (Lacépède)
Gill, for the small-mouthed species, and *Micropterus pallidus*
(Rafinesque) Gill & Jordan, for the large-mouthed species.
In this event, I say, we could rest content; for, although
the generic appellation, and the specific title of the small-
mouthed Black Bass, as proposed, are misnomers (the
generic name is not very inappropriate, inasmuch as the
fins are really smaller than in other centrarchids, though
not in the sense intended by Lacépède; and the specific
name, though not in any degree descriptive, was conferred
by reason of its being called " Trout " in its native waters),
they are the only names that could rightly be bestowed,
under the circumstances, and we could well afford to sub-
mit gracefully to what could not be bettered, or helped.

But now come our Gallic friends, MM. Vaillant and

Bocourt, "once more unto the breach," to tell us what
they know about the Black Bass. In their work (Mission Scientifique au Mexique: ined.), they propose once
more to split up our genus *Micropterus*, this time into
four species, viz:—

M. variabilis (Le S.) V. & B. (=*M. salmoides* var. *achigan* Jordan.)
M. dolomieu (Lac.) V. & B. (=*M. salmoides* var. *salmoides* Jordan.)
M. salmoides (Lac.) V. & B. (=*M. pallidus* (Raf.) Gill & Jordan.)
M. nuecensis (G'rd) V. & B. (=*M. pallidus*, with lingual teeth.)

Dr. Vaillant, however, has only proposed these species
provisionally, and acknowledges that upon examining a
considerable number of specimens these specific distinctions
shade into each other:

"Au premier abord, on reconnaît sans peine plusieurs types, en
ayant égardaux proportions du corps, au nombre des écailles et a
diverses autres particularités, mais si on examine un certain nombre
d'individus, les différences s'attenuent par des transitions graduelles."*

Perhaps Dr. Vaillant's views can not be better expressed
than by the annexed analytical table ("*tableau dichotomique*") of provisional species as defined by him, and
which explains itself:

| Rows of scales above and below the lateral line. | 7 to 8 15 to 20 | 60 to 70 scales along the lateral line. | With lingual teeth – – – *M. nuecensis* G'rd. Without lingual teeth – – *M. salmoides* Lac. |
| | 9 to 11 25 to 30 | Lateral line: | 69 to 75 scales – – – – – – *M. variabilis* Le S. 80 to 86 scales – – – – – – *M. dolomieu* Lac. |

It will be observed that Dr. Vaillant proposes the title

---

* Mission Scientifique au Mexique, Zool. IV: ined.

Micropterus salmoides for the large-mouthed Bass; and as
we call the small-mouthed Bass by the same name, it
would produce endless confusion were this state of things
to continue. If the Black Bass of Europe were always to
be confined to a few preserved specimens and plaster casts
in the museums, it would not matter so much; but as this
desirable game fish has been already introduced into English waters, and will no doubt, in time, be transplanted
into those of the Continent, it would seem to be a matter
of some interest to obtain a correct, uniform, and universal
nomenclature of the species.   Even at the present day,
Dr. Günther, the great English authority, in a work recently issued (Introduction to the Study of Fishes, 1880),
nails *Grystes* and *Huro* to the mast-head as valid
genera.

It will be noticed that Dr. Vaillant adopts the northern and southern varieties of the small-mouthed Bass as
provisional species, and likewise separates the large-
mouthed Bass into two species, one being distinguished
by teeth on the tongue, the other by their absence.   I have
often noticed this peculiarity of the presence or absence of
lingual teeth in the large-mouthed species in fish from
various waters, (and am not sure but I have observed it
in the small-mouthed species occasionally), but I have
always considered it as developed, possibly, by the character of the food in certain localities, or merely a phase
of individual variation.   Prof. Jordan takes this same
view of it, as the following extract will show: *

---

* Notes on a Collection of Fishes from East Florida, obtained by Dr.
J. A. Henshall. By David S. Jordan, M.D. <Proceedings of United
States National Museum, III, 1880, pp. 17–22.

12. MICROPTERUS PALLIDUS (*Raf.*) *Gill & Jordan.*

Dr. Léon Vaillant (Mission Scientifique au Mexique: ined.) divides this species provisionally into two, adopting the name "*Micropterus salmoides*" for the ordinary form, and that of *Micropterus nuecensis* (Baird & Girard) for the south-western form (Texas and Mexico). According to him the two are externally identical, but *M. nuecensis* is distinguished by the presence of a small patch of teeth on the tongue, the tongue being entirely smooth in the ordinary form.

I have examined a number of specimens in regard to this point.

I find lingual teeth in the following specimens:

(1.) Two specimens, one large, one small, from the Falls of the Ohio.

(2.) One small specimen from a tributary of White River at Bloomington, Ind.

(3.) One specimen (in the museum at Paris) from Texas.

I find them absent in the following:

(1.) Several specimens in Henshall's collection from Indian River, [Fla.].

(2.) Specimen from Neuse River.

(3.) Specimens from White River at Indianapolis.

(4.) Specimens from Lake Erie.

The presence of these teeth evidently does not depend on age, and apparently not on sex. It may be a specific feature, but I am inclined at present to think it only a feature of individual variation. I have not seen such teeth in the small-mouthed Black Bass.

In 1878, Professor Jordan, while in Europe, gave great attention to the investigation of the Black Bass from the Paris standpoint. He examined, with the greatest care, Lacépède's original type specimen, and the specimens of Cuvier and Valenciennes, which are still preserved in the Museum of Natural History at Paris. He was determined to get to the bottom of the matter, if possible, and to this end consulted freely, and compared notes, with the

French ichthyologists, who aided him in every possible way.

Professor Jordan afterwards published the result of his researches, which forms one of the most valuable papers yet added to the literature of the Black Bass, and which I take great pleasure in reproducing here : *

In a recent visit to Europe the writer has had the privilege of examining the original types of certain species of American fishes described by Dr. Albert Günther from specimens in the British Museum, and by Cuvier, Valenciennes, and others from examples in the Museum at Paris. Notes on some of these, the proper identification of which may affect our nomenclature, are here presented.

1. MICROPTERUS DOLOMIEU *Lacépède.*

Lacépède, Histoire Naturelle des Poissons iv, 324.

The original type of this species is a large specimen, still in good condition. Its peculiarity, which led to its separation from "*Labrus*" by Lacépède, is that the last rays of the dorsal are detached from the others, and somewhat distorted, the result of some accident to the fish while young. The injury to the specimen is therefore not a museum mutilation, as I had heretofore understood, but a healed wound. This specimen belongs to the southern variety of the small-mouthed Black Bass, recognized by me (Bull. U. S. Nat. Mus., xii, 1878, p. 30) as *Micropterus salmoides* var. *salmoides*. Prof. Vaillant recognizes this form provisionally (MSS. Mission Scientifique au Mexique) as a distinct species (*Micropterus dolomieu* Lac.) from the northern form, but the differences seem to me to have no more than varietal value.

As shown below, there is little doubt that the specific name *dolomieu* is the first ever distinctly applied to our small-mouthed Black

---

* Notes on Certain Typical Specimens of American Fishes in the British Museum and in the Museum D'Histoire Naturelle at Paris. By David S. Jordan, M. D. < Proceedings of United States National Museum, II, 1879, pp. 218-226.

4

Bass, as the name *Micropterus* is its earliest generic appellation. Unless we adopt the earlier *salmoides*, its name should, therefore, be *Micropterus dolomieu.*

On the other hand, it is true that the name *Micropterus dolomieu* was applied to a deformed specimen, which was considered as a distinct genus and species solely on account of its deformity.

It is an established rule of nomenclature (Dall, Rept. Comm. Zoöl. Nomenc., 48) that "a name should be rejected . . . when it expresses an attribute or character positively false in the majority or the whole of the group in question, as in cases (among others) when a name has been founded on a monstrous, abnormal, immature, artificial or mutilated specimen."

The name *Micropterus* was founded on a monstrous specimen; in the sense intended by its author it expresses a false character, although the species really have smaller fins than are found in related genera. In the opinion of some writers it should be set aside and the next name in order (*Calliurus* Raf.) should be adopted in its stead. The species might then stand as *Calliurus dolomieu.* The specific name "*dolomieu*" is also open to objection, as it is a French noun having neither a Latin nor a genitive form, but being an unmodified name of a person. This hardly seems to me a reason for rejecting the name, although, if retained, it should receive a genitive form, as *dolomii* or *dolomiei.*

The question of the adoption of the name *Micropterus* is still an open one. The weight of authority is, however, at present in favor of its retention, and the writer sees no sufficient reason for setting it aside.

2. Grystes salmoides *Cuvier & Valenciennes.*

Labrus salmoides Lacépède, Hist. Nat. des Poiss. III, 716.
Grystes salmoides Cuv. & Val., Hist. Nat. des Poiss. III, 54, pl. 46.

It seems rather a thankless task to reopen the question of the proper nomenclature of the Black Bass, but it is evident that we have not yet reached the bottom. The name *Micropterus salmoides* is now generally adopted in America as the proper name of the small-mouthed Black Bass, not only among naturalists but among anglers and sportsmen as well. In the Museum at Paris, however, the same name is fully adopted for the large-mouthed Black Bass. Let us inquire into the history of the use of the name *salmoides*.

In 1800, the name *Labrus salmoides* was given by Lacépède to a fish inhabiting the waters of Carolina, and known to Americans as "Trout." This fish was known to Lacépède only through a drawing and manuscript description by Bosc. Both species of Black Bass occur in Carolina, the large-mouth most abundantly. Neither drawing nor description is exact enough to enable us to tell with certainty, or even with reasonable probability, which species was meant by Bosc and Lacépède. It is unlikely that Bosc discriminated between them at all, both being alike "Trout" to the Carolina fishermen. In the figure the mouth is drawn large, and if we *must* choose, the large-mouth is best represented.

The specific name *salmoides* next appears in the great work of Cuvier and Valenciennes (III, p. 54) as *Grystes salmoides*. The description here given is for the most part applicable to both species; the small size of the scales ("il y en a quatre-vingt-dix sur une ligne longitudinale et trente-six ou quarante sur une verticale." *) and the naked preoperculum render it evident that at least that part of the description was taken from a small-mouth, while the accompanying figure more resembles the large-mouth.

We are, however, not here left in doubt. The original material of the French naturalists is still preserved in the museum. It consists of the following specimens as described by Cuvier and Valenciennes:

1. "Nous avons reçu, par M. Milbert, un individu de huit à neuf pouces et un de six à sept. C'est ce dernier qui a six rayons à la membrane des ouies et quatorze rayons mouse à la dorsale."

From one of these specimens the figure in the Histoire Naturelle des Poissons (pl. 46) was taken.† This specimen is unquestionably a large-mouthed Black Bass.

2. "Plus tard, M. Lesueur nous en a envoyé de la rivière Wabash un individu long de seize pouces, et trois autres qui n'en ont guère que cinq. Les jeunes sont d'un vert plus pale, et ont sur chaque flanc vingt-cinq à trente lignes longitudinales et parallèles brunes, qui paraissent s'effacer avec l'age."

---

*The very small precaudal scales are doubtless here included.
†*Fide* Vaillant.

These specimens are still preserved, bearing the MSS. name of *Cichla variabilis* Le Sueur, and belong to the small-mouthed species. This name, which, so far as I know, was never published by Le Sueur, is thus noticed by Cuvier and Valenciennes:

"M. Lesueur, croyant l'espèce nouvelle, en a publié une description dans le Journal des sciences à Philadelphie, sous le nom de *cichla variabilis;* mais nous avons tout lieu de croire que c'est ce poisson qui est représenté et décrit par M. de Lacépède (t. iv, p. 716 et 717, et. pl. 5, fig. 2), sous le nom de *labre salmoïde,* d'après des notes et une figure fournies par M. Bosc qui le nommait *perca trutte.* La figure en est un peu rude, mais la description s'accorde avec ce que nous avons vu, sauf quelques détails, qui tiennent peut-être moins au poisson même qu'à la manière dont il a été observé."

Later (vol. v, p. v), the type of *Micropterus dolomieu* was reexamined and fully identified by Cuvier as a *Grystes salmoides.*

It is thus evident that Cuvier and Valenciennes completely confounded the two species under the name *Grystes salmoides,* and that the uncertain *salmoides* of Lacépède became in their hands a complex species. We may perhaps say that their *salmoides* must be the fish *described* by them, and that the figure is to be taken into consideration only when other evidence is wanting. M. Vaillant, however, maintains that the large-mouthed species should be considered as the *salmoides* of Cuvier and Valenciennes, inasmuch as one of that species served as the type of their published figure.

The next writers who use the name *salmoides* (De Kay, Storer, etc.), have merely copied or echoed the description of Cuvier and Valenciennes, and have in no way given precision to the name.

Later Agassiz uses the name "*salmoneus*" (slip of the pen for *salmoides*"?) apparently referring to the large-mouthed species.

The description given by Dr. Günther of *Grystes salmoides* in the Catalogue of the Fishes of the British Museum, I, 252, adds nothing to the precision of our knowledge of the species, the characters given being either taken from Cuvier and Valenciennes, or else common to both species.

Next a description is given of *Grystes salmoides* by Holbrook (Ich. S. Car., p. 28, pl. 4, f. 2), accompanied by an excellent figure, which leaves no possible doubt of the species intended. This is the large-mouthed Bass.

Omitting papers of lesser importance, we come finally to the very able discussion of these questions by Professor Gill (Proc. Am. Ass. Adv. Sci., 1873, p. 55–72), in which the whole subject is exhaustively treated, and the name *Micropterus salmoides* is definitely adopted for the small-mouthed Black Bass. This arrangement has been followed by most recent ichthyologists. In an important paper just now passing through the press (Mission Scientifique au Mexique), however, Messrs. Vaillant and Bocourt have adopted the name *Micropterus salmoides* for the large-mouthed species, for the reasons indicated above.

This question resolves itself into two. Is the specific name *salmoides* available for either species? and if so, for which?

Between the publication of the works of Lacépède and Cuvier both species had been more than once described under different names by Rafinesque and Le Sueur. Of these names, *Lepomis pallida* Raf. for the large-mouthed Black Bass, *Micropterus dolomieu* Lac. for the southern, and *Bodianus achigan* Raf. for the northern variety of the small-mouth have priority over the others. All these, therefore, antedate any precise definition of the name *salmoides*.

The question as to whether a specific name, at first loosely applied and afterwards precisely fixed, shall claim priority from its first use or not, has been differently answered by different writers, and has perhaps never been settled by general usage. I suppose that the amount of doubt or confusion arising from its use or rejection enters with most writers as an element. The name *salmoides*, left unsettled by Lacépède, has been generally received by writers, in consequence of the supposed precision given to it by Cuvier. We have seen, however, that both species were included by Cuvier under one name, and that we must look farther for real restriction of the species. The first distinct use of the name *salmoides* for any particular species is by Holbrook, for the large-mouthed form. On the basis of the first unquestionable restriction, the name, if used at all, must be applied to that species. Forty years previous to this restriction, however, the specific name *pallidus* was conferred on the same fish by Rafinesque.

In the writings of nearly all the older naturalists, as well as in many of the later ones, we find descriptions of species which are really generic in their value, and which, as our knowledge of species becomes greater, can not be disposed of with certainty or even with any high degree of probability, for absolute certainty rarely accompanies any identification.

In the absence or impossibility of any general rule regarding such cases, the following supposed examples will illustrate what seems to the present writer a fair method of treating them.

Let us suppose that the genus *Micropterus* contains two well-marked species; that to one of these the name *salmoides* was early applied; that next the names *dolomiei* and *pallidus* were applied to the two respectively, and that *subsequently* the name *salmoides* was restricted to the one called *pallidus*.

Now if (1) the original *salmoides* were definitely a complex species, distinctly including both, we may hold its author to be a "conservative" writer, and that the subsequent restriction, like the restriction of a genus, is a change of view or the elimination of an error. In this case, the name *salmoides* should be retained, dating its priority from its original use, and applying to the species *pallidus*.

If (2) the original *salmoides* be not complex, but simply uncertain, the probabilities being undeniably in favor of its identity with *pallidus* rather than with *dolomiei*, it should be adopted instead of *pallidus*. Absolute certainty of identification can not be expected of many names older than the present generation, and each writer must judge for himself of the degrees of probability. If we may express it numerically, a probability of 75 per cent. should perhaps be sufficient, and this probability should be unquestionable—that is, not merely subjective and varying with the mental differences of the different writers.

If (3) the original *salmoides* be evidently a *Micropterus*, but hopelessly uncertain as to the species intended, it should claim priority from its first use for a definite species of *Micropterus*. If the name *pallidus* intervene between its first use and its final precise use, *salmoides* should become a synonym of *pallidus*, and should not be available for the other species. This rule is followed more or less consistently by most writers, and it seems to me a fair one. The revival of hopelessly uncertain ancient specific names in place of well-defined modern ones is productive only of confusion, and is open to gross abuse. The revival even of well-defined but forgotten names is confusing enough, and it has been strongly objected to by many writers.

If (4) the name *salmoides*, left hopelessly uncertain by its author, should have been definitely used for some species to which it might not improbably have referred *before* the use of the name *pallidus* for the same species, it should be retained, dating its acceptance from its second use, and the name *pallidus* should be considered as a synonym of *salmoides*.

If (5) the name *salmoides* should have been adopted by the second author supposed in (4) for some species not a *Micropterus*, or for some species which could not reasonably be identical with the original *salmoides*, the identification should be taken as an erroneous one, and should not be considered in our nomenclature.

The actual state of the name *salmoides* is that supposed under (3) above. I do not consider the name *salmoides* as rightfully entitled to priority over either *pallidus* or *dolomiei* as the specific name of a species of Black Bass. If it must be used, however, I think it wisest to retain it, with Professor Gill, for the small-mouthed species. For this purpose, we must consider the *salmoides* of Lacépède as complex, including both species. The case would then be that supposed by (1) above. We must hold further that Cuvier and Valenciennes restricted the name to the *small-mouthed* form. No possible settlement of the case can be free from question or objection. I propose to adopt the following view of the case, proposed by Dr. Gill (in *lit.*), to whom I have submitted the evidence above given.

Dr. Gill remarks :

" I think we can retain our old names (*i. e.*, *Micropterus salmoides* and *Micropterus pallidus*) on the following grounds:

"(1) Let us admit that *Labrus salmoides* Lac. *may be* the small-mouthed.

"(2) The name *salmoides*, it may be considered, was re-established by Cuvier and Valenciennes for the largest specimen (the small-mouthed, according to your observations). The description was evidently based on that, as appears from the number of scales, the absence of any on the preopercular limb ('le limbe de son préopercule [etc.] en manquent'), and the form of the dorsal. Even if it is certain that the figure was taken from a large-mouthed specimen, this would not affect the question, inasmuch as we must accept the description when that is definitive, and such is the case here.

"(3) It may be held that the name is further specialized by Cuvier

and Valenciennes by its use to supersede the name of Le Sueur
(p. 55), and as a substitute for M. Dolomieu (vol. v, p. 5).

"(4) The majority of the C. & V.'s specimens belonged to the
small-mouthed Bass.

"(5) The figure was based on a large-mouth simply through acci-
dence of size and condition, not selected on account of exhibition
of characters. In the same way, we might maintain that the type
of *Pomotis vulgaris* C. & V. (although the description plainly points
to *Eupomotis aureus*) was *Lepomis pallidus* [rather *auritus*], for the
figure apparently represents such."

3. MICROPTERUS VARIABILIS *Vaillant & Bocourt.*

Cichla variabilis Le Sueur, MSS.
Micropterus variabilis Vaillant & Bocourt, MSS., Mission Scientifique au
　　Mexique.

This is the ordinary Northern small-mouthed Black Bass, *Micropterus achigan*, or var. *achigan* of authors, *Micropterus salmoides achigan*
of the present writer.

The conclusions of Professor Gill at the close of the
paper just quoted, are based, apparently, on his faith in
Cuvier and Valenciennes, superinduced, perhaps, by a
reluctance to re-open the question, and a desire to retain
our present nomenclature of the Black Bass species,
for the sake of peace and harmony. If Dr. Gill's
conclusions could be sustained, and our nomenclature of
the species become universally adopted, no one would be
more gratified than the writer; but we can not expect
peace or security until the matter is definitely, positively,
and indisputably settled, or, at least, so far as this can be
done, *consistently*, with the facts.

After a careful reading of the foregoing review, it would
seem that the estimate of the Black Bass species, as entertained by Dr. Vaillant, should have great weight, and
meet with profound consideration; and it might be ques-

tioned whether *Micropterus dolomieu* for the small-mouthed
Bass, and *Micropterus salmoides* for the large-mouthed Bass,
are not more in accordance with the evidence set forth in
Professor Jordan's clear and exhaustive paper, than our
own view of the matter, based, as the latter is, upon the
conflicting testimony of Cuvier and Valenciennes, who
embraced every thing known of the Black Bass, in their
day, in their *Grystes salmoides*, except *Huro nigricans;* and
had it not been for the gap in its dorsal fin, the inference
is, they would have included that also.   I do not make
this statement unguardedly, or disrespectfully; for while I
venerate the name of Cuvier, I am convinced that he failed
to discriminate between the two species of Black Bass.*

I incline to the belief that Professor Jordan, with his
usual acumen, is disposed to take some such view as this,
for he says:—

" As shown below, there is little doubt that the specific
name *dolomieu,* is the first ever distinctly applied to our
small-mouthed Black Bass, as the name *Micropterus* is its
earliest generic appellation.   Unless we adopt the earlier
salmoides, its name should, therefore, be *Micropterus
dolomieu.*"

But why adopt *salmoides* for the small-mouthed Black
Bass at all?   It is only synonymous with *dolomieu* on the
authority of Cuvier and Valenciennes.   Does not the

---

* "We are again obliged to advert to the partial and often the superficial examination with which nearly allied species have too often been
regarded by the authors of the *Hist. Nat. des Poissons;* an imperfection
which we can only account for by nearly all their descriptions having
been made from preserved specimens; and by supposing that these
eminent writers, not unfrequently, have been absolutely overwhelmed
with their materials."—SWAINSON, *Nat. Hist. and Class. of Fishes,* II, 407,
1839.

weight of evidence favor the adoption of *salmoides* for the
large-mouthed Black Bass ? We certainly must take this
view of it if we set aside Cuvier and Valenciennes' description of *Grystes salmoides*, whether we retain their
figure (which was taken from a large-mouthed Bass) or
not, and we would be justified in excluding their description, for, as Professor Jordan truly says :—

"It is thus evident that Cuvier and Valenciennes completely confounded the two species under the name *Grystes
salmoides*, and that the uncertain *salmoides* of Lacépède
became in their hands a complex species."

Now, if we discard both the description and figure of
Cuvier and Valenciennes' *Grystes salmoides*, we have left
(ignoring for the time both Rafinesque and Le Sueur)
only Lacépède's *Labrus salmoides* and *Micropterus dolomieu*.

Then, let us take Bosc's figure of *Labrus salmoides*, first.
Of this, Professor Jordan says :—

"In the figure the mouth is drawn large, and if we
must choose, the large-mouth is best represented."

Now, if we conclude from this that *Labrus salmoides* is
the large-mouthed Black Bass, then the small-mouthed
Black Bass claims its birthright of *Micropterus dolomieu*,
which unquestionably belongs to it.

This, in short, seems to be the view of Dr. Vaillant,
and it seems to me to be the correct one, though he takes
the *figure* of *Grystes salmoides* as additional evidence.

There is but one contingency that could prove the
right of the small-mouthed Bass to the name *Micropterus
dolomieu* in a stronger, or absolute manner, and it would
be stronger, because incontrovertible, namely: the *priority*
of Lacépède's description of *Micropterus dolomieu* to his
description of *Labrus salmoides*.

Now, the writer proposes to show that this is the *actual* state of the case, and that Lacépède really described and named *Micropterus dolomieu*, from the specimen which is still preserved in the Museum D'Histoire Naturelle at Paris (and which Professor Jordan examined and declared to be a small-mouthed Black Bass), *before* he described and named *Labrus salmoides* from M. Bosc's drawing and description of the Carolina "Trout."

After reading Professor Jordan's paper, so often referred to here, and from my personal knowledge of the Carolina Black Bass or "Trout," I became convinced, in my own mind, that the name *Micropterus dolomieu* should be restored to the small-mouthed Bass, and that the name *Labrus salmoides* should be restricted to the large-mouthed Bass ; and entertaining these heretical views, I scanned closely the literature relating to the early history of the species.

In collating the bibliography of the Black Bass for the present work, I discovered an apparent discrepancy, which, if it really existed, had an important and significant bearing on the proper nomenclature of the species. I noticed that most American authors, in referring to Lacépède's description of *Labrus salmoides*, gave the reference as " Lacépède, Hist. Nat. des Poiss. Vol. III, p. 716, 1800 ? ", and that of *Micropterus dolomieu* as " Lacépède, Hist. Nat. des Poiss. Vol. IV, p. 325, 1800 ? "; thus, of course, giving the priority to *Labrus salmoides*, as we have always understood and accepted it.

On the other hand, I noticed that Cuvier and Valenciennes* gave the reference to *Labrus salmoides* in Lacépède's work as " Vol. IV. p. 716, 717," and that of

* Cuv. & Val. Hist. Nat. des Poiss. Vol. III, p. 55, 1829, and Vol. V, p. v, 1830.

Micropterus dolomieu as "Vol. IV. p. 325." I noticed
further that all references to the figure of Lacépède's *Micropterus dolomieu* were given as " Vol. IV, pl. 3, fig.
3," and that of *Labrus salmoides* as "Vol. IV, pl. 5, fig. 2."
I was at once struck with this discrepancy, for if Cuvier
and Valenciennes' reference of *Labrus salmoides* Lacépède
(Vol. IV. p. 716, 717) was correct, it would give the priority of description to *Micropterus dolomieu* Lacépède
(Vol. IV. p. 325). The numerical sequence of the plates
also gave it priority.

While revising this chapter of the present book for the
press, I learned from Professor Jordan that he had just
received from France, a copy of Lacépède's *original* edition
of his great work. I at once wrote to him to ascertain
which reference to *Labrus salmoides* was the correct one.
His characteristic reply was:—

"In answering your questions I have struck a mare's
nest; *M. dolomieu*, Vol. IV, 325, 1802; *L. salmoides*, Vol.
IV, 716, 1802; the latter being in a supplement, which, in
some of the reprints, is restored to its proper place in the
genus *Labrus* in Vol. III. From this you will see that
dolomieu has priority over *salmoides*. I still believe that
salmoides was intended for the large-mouthed Bass, but
don't know that I can prove it."

Thus, after the lapse of four-fifths of a century, the
small-mouthed Black Bass has recovered the name to which
it is clearly entitled, *Micropterus dolomieu;* truth and
justice have prevailed; Lacépède and his illustrious friend
Dolomieu have been vindicated.

And now let us inquire as to *Labrus salmoides*.* This,

---

* " Certain it is, however, that Lacépède's *Ichthyology* will always be a

as we know, was the name applied by Lacépède to Bosc's drawing and description of the Carolina "Trout."

It has never been definitely settled which species of Black Bass was best represented by the drawing or its description; but I think this vagueness existed more in the imagination than in realty, and that "the wish was father to that thought;" or, in other words, that we were willfully blind in deference to authority; for, as Cuvier had identified it with his *Grystes salmoides* (which we have supposed to be the small-mouthed Bass, inasmuch as he included, also, *Cichla variabilis* Le Sueur, and *Micropterus dolomieu* as synonyms), *Labrus salmoides* must, therefore, either be pronounced a small-mouthed Bass, or be invested with sufficient ambiguity to admit of its becoming synonymous with *Grystes salmoides*.

On the other hand, Dr. Vaillant, as we have seen, maintains that Cuvier and Valenciennes' *Grystes salmoides* is the large-mouthed Bass, and therefore truly synonymous with *Labrus salmoides*, he claiming the latter to be the large-mouthed Black Bass. Viewed in either light, *Grystes salmoides* Cuv. and Val. is a *crux criticorum*; but fortunately it is not essential to us now.

Let us take Lacépède's figure and description of *Labrus salmoides*, just as they are, on their own merits, without any reference to Cuvier's valuation of them; and to render

standard authority, even for his supposed errors; and it will be found by those who have occasion to consult them, that he is by no means chargeable with several that have been of late attributed to him. The figures, on the other hand, although well engraved, are, in general, very deficient in accuracy; the major part being either copies, or drawn by artists who were totally ignorant of the scientific details of their subject."—SWAINSON, *Nat. Hist. and Class. of Fishes*, I, 59, 1838.

the matter plain, I have reproduced, at the close of this chapter, *fac-simile* representations of Lacépède's plates of both *Labrus salmoides* and *Micropterus dolomieu*, with his descriptions, from the original edition of his " Histoire Naturelle des Poissons."

In the first place, as Professor Jordan says of the figure of *Labrus salmoides :* " if we *must* choose, the large-mouth is best represented." This is reasonably correct, for no one could mistake this figure for a small-mouthed Black Bass. Then, Lacépède's description says the opening of the mouth is *very large* ("l'ouverture de la bouche fort large "). The radial formula of the dorsal fin is given as nine spinous rays and thirteen soft rays (" neuf rayons aiguillonés et treize rayons articulés à la nageoire du dos "). This number of dorsal spines will hold good in seventy-five per cent. of cases, in the large-mouthed Bass of the South ; sometimes there will be found but eight. The rest of the description will apply to either species Then, again, Lacépède, on the authority of M. Bosc, says the species is *very abundant* in the rivers of Carolina, where they are called " Trout," and are caught with the hook baited with a minnow (" On trouve un très-grande nombre d'indivdus de cette espèce dans toutes les rivières de la Caroline ; on leur donne le nom de *traut* ou *truite*. On les prend à l'hameçon ; on les attire par le moyen de morceaux de *cyprin* ").

Now, if we had not been trying to reconcile *Labrus salmoides* with the small-mouthed Bass, contrary to the evidence of our own senses, so as to accord with Cuvier's creation of the complex *Grystes salmoides*—becoming blind to the points of difference and enlarging upon the vagueness and inaccuracy of the drawing and its description—we might have discovered that this figure had, as Lacépède says, a *"very large mouth;"* and that while the large-mouthed Black Bass, or *"Trout"* is *"very abundant"* in Carolina waters, the small-mouthed Black Bass is apparently unknown, at least in the vicinity of Charleston, where Bosc collected.

As an angler, I have fished for the Black Bass in all the South Atlantic States, from Maryland to Florida; and while I have found the large-mouthed Bass *"very abundant"* in all parts of North Carolina, South Carolina, and Georgia, I never took a single small-mouthed Bass in either of these latter states within a hundred miles of the coast. I have taken it in the hill-country of each of these states, about the head-waters of the rivers flowing into the Atlantic, but I doubt very much if it is found anywhere in the lowland region of that section of country.

Professor E. D. Cope, who fished the streams of North Carolina, in the autumn of 1869, from the Cumberland Mountains to the sea, found the large-mouthed Bass, "abundant in all the rivers of the state," but failed to find the small-mouthed Bass, except in the Alleghany region of the extreme western part of the state; and says that it is "apparently not found east of the great Water-shed."*

If the small-mouthed Black Bass inhabits the Atlantic slopes of North Carolina, South Carolina, or Georgia, Dr. Holbrook would have known it; for there has been no ichthyologist before or since his time, who understood the structure and habits of the "Carolina Trout" so well, or caught more of them. The best description, and the best

---

* A Partial Synopsis of the Fresh Water Fishes of North Carolina. By E. D. Cope, A.M. <Pro. Am. Phil. Soc., p. 450, 1870.

figure of the large-mouthed Bass (Trout) ever published, is found in his work (Ichthyology of South Carolina).

In order to show that he clearly understood the relations of the Black Bass species, I will quote as follows:—" The Trout has, however, its representatives both in the North and West, with which it is closely allied: as *Grystes Nigricans* (*Huro nigricans*) of Cuvier and Valenciennes, and *Grystes fasciatus* (*Cychla fasciata*) of Le Sueur, both of which have been referred by Agassiz to the genus Grystes."* Dr. Holbrook knew that the southern Trout (large-mouthed Black Bass) was neither *Huro nigricans* (with its two distinct dorsal fins), nor *Cichla fasciata* (the small-mouthed Bass). He called the "Trout" *Grystes salmoides* LACÉPÈDE, for he knew that Lacépède's *Labrus salmoides*, or Bosc's *Perca trutta* could be nothing else but the "Carolina Trout" (large-mouthed Black Bass); and, moreover, he distinctly repudiated Cuvier and Valenciennes' complex *Grystes salmoides*.

Professor Agassiz clearly recognized the complex character of Cuvier's *Grystes salmoides*, saying he "probably mistook specimens of our *Grystes fasciatus* for the southern species."† Professor Agassiz regarded *Grystes salmoides* as the proper name for the southern large-mouthed Black Bass (Trout), and in comparing with it *Grystes fasciatus* Agassiz, says: "The mouth is less opened and the shorter labials do not reach a vertical line drawn across the hinder margin of the orbits, whilst they exceed such a line in *G. salmoides*." ‡

---

* Ichthyology of South Carolina. By John Edwards Holbrook, M.D. 25, 1855.

† Agassiz, Lake Superior, p. 295, 1850.

‡ Agassiz, Lake Superior, p. 295, 1850.

And yet we have deceived ourselves, with all this evidence staring us in the face, with the flimsy delusion that Bosc's drawing of the "Carolina Trout" was a small-mouthed Bass, simply because Cuvier pronounced it synonymous with *Cichla variabilis* Le Sueur and *Micropterus dolomieu* Lacépède.

Presuming that I have proved the names *Micropterus dolomieu* for the small-mouthed Black Bass, and *Micropterus salmoides* for the large-mouthed Black Bass to be rightly bestowed, and the names by which the two species should hereafter be designated, perhaps it will be well to refer to some objections heretofore raised to the generic appellation *Micropterus*, and the specific titles *salmoides* and *dolomieu*, on the score of irrelevancy. I can do no better than to refer the reader to Professor Jordan's paper on this subject, on page 31. I might add, however, that *priority*, like charity, covers a multitude of sins.*

Micropterus (little-fin) is really less objectionable than any of the names yet proposed for the genus, for it has, comparatively, smaller fins than any of the related genera.

Calliurus (beautiful tail) is not at all characteristic of the genus, though the young of the small-mouthed species, in certain localities, has the tail marked as described by Rafinesque: " base yellow, middle blackish, tip white."

Grystes (growler) is certainly not applicable in this sense.

---

* To those anglers who are better posted in the technical terms of the great American "game" introduced to the nobility of England by General Schenck, than in the technical terms introduced here in reference to the nomenclature of the great American "game-fish," I need only say that *Micropterus*, and the specific names *dolomieu* and *salmoides*, " hold the *age*" over all other synonyms that have taken a hand, from time to time, in the "little game." This comparison may be more striking than ana-

I have never met an angler who had heard a Black Bass "growl," yet it was on the supposition that it did so, that Cuvier gave it this name. We had better stop here, for if we go farther we shall fare worse. We will therefore now refer to the objectionable features of the specific names *dolomieu* and *salmoides*.

Salmoides (trout-like; literally, salmon-like). Lacépède conferred this name simply (and appropriately, so far as he was concerned) because the figure was sent to him as the "Trout," or "Trout-Perch" of Carolina; (he *might* have called it *boscii*. It is my belief that if he had received Bosc's drawing prior to his specimen—*M. dolomieu*—he would have named *it*—the drawing—*Labrus dolomieu*.) If we take its game qualities into consideration, there is no fish that is so "salmon-like" as the Black Bass; none that exhibits so nearly the characteristic leap, the pluck, and the endurance of the "king of the waters." The name is, therefore, not altogether inappropriate.

Dolomieu being a French proper noun, without a Latin or genitive form, might be considered objectionable. Lacépède used the name, however, in this form, advisedly; not through ignorance, nor by accident, but for the sake of euphony, and to perpetuate the name of his friend in its integrity. In the original edition of his work he uses the French form *dolomieu*, but has the Latin form as a footnote under each specific heading; while in many of the reprints the editor has left out these Latin names as irrelevant.

In order to recognize and respect Lacépède's motive, it is best to let the name stand just as he wrote it, *dolomieu*.

---

logical, but as Jack Bunsby would say, its force "lies in the application of it."

As Dr. Vaillant adopts this form, and doubtless for the same reason, it is important for the sake of uniformity to allow it to stand. There is no lack of precedents for this form of specific title. I will merely mention as an example: *Icterus baltimore*—the Baltimore oriole. The title *baltimore*, as here used, is a proper noun, and was bestowed in honor of Lord Baltimore, whose livery was black and orange, the colors of the oriole or hanging-bird. Let the name of the small-mouthed Bass, then, stand as *dolomieu*— the name of a brave man for a brave fish.

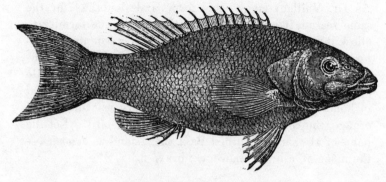

MICROPTERE DOLOMIEU.

(This engraving is a *fac-simile* of that in Lacépède's Hist. Nat. des Poissons, Vol. IV, pl. 3, fig. 3.)

LE MICROPTÈRE DOLOMIEU.*

Je desire que le nom de ce poisson, qu'aucun naturaliste n'a encore décrit, rappelle ma tendre amitié et ma profonde estime pour l'illustre Dolomieu, dont la victoire vient de briser les fers. En écrivant mon Discours sur la durée des espèces, j'ai exprimé la vive douleur que m'inspiroit son affreuse captivité, et l'admiration pour sa constance héroïque, que l'Europe mêloit à ses vœux pour lui. Qu'il m'est doux de ne pas terminer l'immense tableau que je tâche d'esquisser, sans avoir sente le bonheur de le serrer de nouveau dans mes bras!

Les microptères ressemblent beaucoup aux sciènes: mais la petitesse très-remarquable de leur seconde nageoire dorsale les en sépare; et c'est cette petitesse que désigne le nom générique que je leur ai donné.†

La collection du Muséum national d'histoire naturelle renferme un bel individu de l'espèce que nous décrivons dans cette article: Cette espèce, qui est encore la seule inscrite dans le nouveau genre des microptères, que nous avons cru devoir établir, a les deux

---

* Micropterus dolomieu.

† Μικρος, en grec, signifie *petit.*

mâchoires, le palais et la langue, garnis d'un très-grand nombre de rangées de dents petite, crochues et serrées; la langue est d'ailleurs très-libre dans ses mouvemens; et la mâchoire inférieure plus avancée que celle d'en-haut. La membrane branchiale disparoît entièrement sous l'opercule, qui présente deux pièces, dont la première est arrondie dans son contour, et la seconde anguleuse. Cet opercule est couvert de plusieurs écailles; celles de dos sont assez grandes et arrondies. La hauteur du corps proprement dit excède de beaucoup celle de l'origine de la queue. La ligne latérale se plie d'abord vers le bas, et se relève ensuite pour suivre la courbure du dos. Les nageoires pectorales et celle de l'anus sont très-arrondies; la première du dos ne commence qu'à une assez grande distance de la queue. Elle cesse d'être attachée au dos de l'animal, à l'endroit où elle parvient au-dessus de l'anale; mais elle ce prolonge en bande pointue et flottante jusqu'au-dessus de la seconde nageoire dorsale, qui est très-basse et très-petite, ainsi que nous venons de le dire, et que l'on croiroit au premier coup d'œil entièrement adipeuse.*—(LACEPEDE, *Hist. Nat. des Poiss.* Vol. IV, 325, 1802.)

---

* 5 rayons à la membrane branchiale.
16 rayons à chaque pectorale.
1 rayon aiguillonné et 5 rayons articulés à chaque thoracine.
17 rayons à la nageoire de la queue.
—[D. X, 7–4; A. II, 11.]

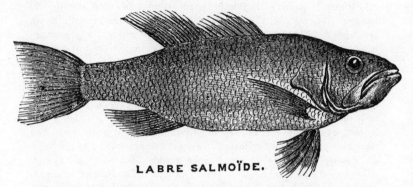

LABRE SALMOÏDE.

(This engraving is a *fac-simile* from Lacépède's Hist. Nat. des Poissons, Vol.
IV, pl. 5, fig. 2.)

LE LABRE SALMOÏDE.*

On devra au citoyen Bosc la connoissance du labre salmoïde et du
labre iris, qui tous les deux habitent dans les eaux de la Caroline.

Le salmoïde a une petite élévation sur le nez; l'ouverture de la
bouche fort large; la mâchoire inférieure un peu plus longue que la
supérieure; l'une et l'autre garnies d'une grande quantité de·dents
très-menues; la langue charnue; le palais hérissé de petites dents
que l'on voit disposées sur deux rangées et sur une plaque triangulaire; le gosier situé au-dessus et au-dessous de deux autres plaque
également hérissées; l'œil grand; les côtés de la tête, revêtus de
petite écailles; la ligne latérale parallèle au dos; une fossette
propre a recevoir la partie antérieure de la dorsale; les deux tho-
racines réunies par une membrane; l'iris jaune, et le ventre blanc.

On trouve un très-grand nombre d'individus de cette espèce dans
toutes les rivières de la Caroline; on leur donne le nom de *traut* ou
truite.   On les prend à l'hameçon; on les attire par le moyen de
morceaux de *cyprin.*   Ils parviennent à la longueur de six ou sept
décimètres; leur chair est ferme, et d'un goût très-agréable.—[Br. 6;
D. IX, 13; A. 13; P. 13; V. 6; C. 18.]—(LACEPEDE, *Hist. Nat. des
Poiss.* Vol. IV, 716, 1802.)

---

* Labrus salmoïdes.
  Perca trutta. *Manuscrits communiqués par le citoyen Bosc.*

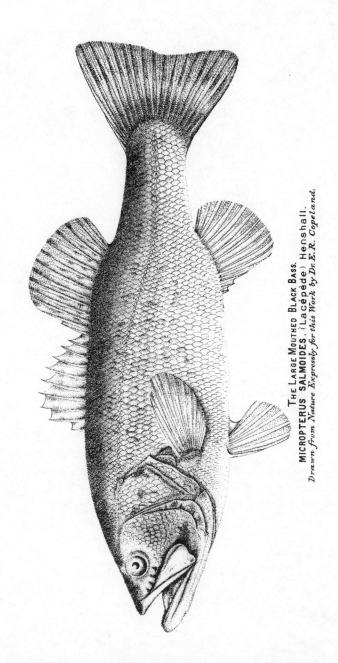

THE LARGE MOUTHED BLACK BASS.
MICROPTERUS SALMOIDES. (Lacépède) Henshall.
Drawn from Nature Expressly for this Work by Dr. E. R. Copeland.

CHAPTER II

Class PISCES.

Subclass TELEOSTEI.

Order ACANTHOPTERI.

Suborder PERCOMORPHI.

Family CENTRARCHIDÆ.

Subfamily MICROPTERINÆ.

Genus MICROPTERUS Lacépède.

SYNONYMY.

Micropterus Lacépède, Hist. Nat. des Poiss. IV, 325, 1802.
(Type *M. dolomieu* Lac.)
Labrus species, Lacépède, Hist. Nat. des Poiss. IV, 716, 1802.
(*L. salmoides* Lac.) (Not of Linnæus, the type *Labrus mixtus* L. belonging to the family of *Labridæ*, the common wrasse-fish of the coasts of Europe.)

6   (65)

Bodianus species, RAFINESQUE, Am. Mo. Mag. and Crit. Rev.
  II, 120, 1817. (*B. achigan* Raf.) (Not of Bloch, the
  type of *Bodianus*, being a marine fish of the family
  of *Serranidæ*.)

Calliurus RAFINESQUE, Jour. de Phys. V, 88, 420, June, 1819,
  and Ich. Ohi. 26, 1820. (Not of Agassiz, Girard,
  et al.) (Type *C. punctulatus* Raf.)

Lepomis RAFINESQUE, Ich. Ohi. 30, 1820. (Not *Lepomis* Raf.
  Jour. de Phys. II, 50, 1819, the original type *Labrus
  auritus* L. being a fresh water sunfish.)

Aplites RAFINESQUE, Ich. Ohi. 30, 1820. (As subgenus of *Lepomis.* Type *L. pallidus* Raf.)

Nemocampsis RAFINESQUE, Ich. Ohi. 31, 1820. (As subgenus
  of *Lepomis.* Type *L. flexuolaris* Raf.)

Dioplites RAFINESQUE, Ich. Ohi. 32, 1820. (As subgenus of
  Lepomis. Type *L. salmonea* Raf.)

Aplesion RAFINESQUE, Ich. Ohi. 36, 1820. (As subgenus of
  Etheostoma. Type *E. calliura* Raf.)

Cichla species, LE SUEUR, Jour. Ac. Nat. Sci. Phil. II, 216,
  1822. (*C. fasciata* Le S.) (Not of Cuvier, the type
  Cichla ocellaris Bloch, being a South American fresh
  water fish of the family of *Cichlidæ*.)

Huro CUVIER & VALENCIENNES, Hist. Nat. des Poiss. II, 124,
  1828. (Type *H. nigricans* C. & V.)

Grystes CUVIER & VALENCIENNES, Hist. Nat. des Poiss. III,
  54, 1829. (Type *Labrus salmoides* Lac.)

Huro SWAINSON, Nat. Hist. and Class. Fishes, etc., II, 200,
  1839.

Grystes SWAINSON, Nat. Hist. and Class. Fishes, etc., II, 202,
  1839.

Centrarchus species, KIRTLAND, Bost. Jour. Nat. Hist. V, 28,
  1842. (*C. fasciatus* K.) (Not of Cuvier, the type
  Labrus irideus Lac., being a fresh water sunfish.)

Centrarchus species, DeKay, Fishes N. Y. 28, 1842. (*C. fasciatus* DeK.*)

Grystes Agassiz, Am. Jour. Sci. and Arts. (2), XVII, 297, 1854.

Dioplites Girard, U. S. Pac. R. R. Surv. X, Fishes, 4, 1858.

Micropterus Cope, Pro. Ac. Nat. Sci. Phil. 83, 1865. (Name only.)

Micropterus Gill, Ann. Rep. Dept. Agric. 407, 1866.

Micropterus Gill, Pro. Am. Asso. Adv. Sci. XXII, B. 55, 1873.

Dioplites Vaillant & Bocourt MSS. Miss. Sci. au Mexique, 1874.

Huro Bleeker, Syst. Perc. Revis. <Ext. des Arc. Neer. XI, 15, 1875.

Micropterus Bleeker, Syst. Perc. Revis. <Ext. des Arc. Neer. XI, 15, 1875.

Micropterus Jordan, Ann. N. Y. Lyc. Nat. Hist. XI, 313, 1877.

Micropterus Jordan, Man. Vert. E. U. S. 229, 1876; and 2d ed. 232, 1878.

Micropterus Jordan, Pro. U. S. Nat. Mus. II, 218, 1880.

Micropterus Vaillant & Bocourt, Miss. Sci. au Mexique: ined.

Etymology: μικρός (*mikros*), small; πτερόν (*pteron*), fin.

Type: *Micropterus dolomieu* Lacépède.

Head well developed, its length varying from 3 to 3⅓ times in length of body; compressed; rather full between the eyes; snout rounded; profile straight; lower jaw prominent and projecting. Scales on cheek, opercle, subopercle, and interopercle, but none, or few, on the preopercle. Eye moderately large, nearly median, but rather nearer the snout than the preopercle. Nostrils round and normal.

Mouth large, with the cleft oblique; the posterior extremity of the upper jaw extends nearly to, or beyond, the posterior border of the eye. Lips but slightly developed. Preopercle smooth and rounding at its angle. Opercle nearly triangular, emarginate behind, ending in two flat points. Subopercle extends beyond the opercle, ending in a membranous point. Interopercle rounded below. Gill openings large. Branchiostegals six on each side. Scales on all of the opercular apparatus, except on the preopercular limb, where there are none, or very few.

Both jaws are armed with pointed, sharp, card-like teeth, curving backward. Patches of villiform teeth on vomer, palatine and pharyngeal bones. Gill-rakers long and stout, and armed with teeth. Tongue moderate and free; thick behind, narrow in front; its surface usually smooth.

Body elongate, ovate-fusiform, somewhat compressed; deepest just behind the ventrals. Scales moderate; smaller on breast and nape. Lateral line following curve of the back.

Dorsal fin with ten spines; a deep notch between the spinous and soft portions. Anal fin with three spines. Caudal emarginate.

Pyloric cœca fourteen or more. Air-bladder simple, slightly notched behind.

Generic Characterizations.

MICROPTERUS Lacépède, 1802.—"Un ou plusiers aiguillons, et point de dentelure aux opercules; un barbillon, ou point de barbillon aux mâchoires; deux nageoires dorsales; la seconde très-basse, très-courte, et comprenant au plus cinq rayons."— (LACÉPÈDE, *Hist. Nat. des Poiss.* IV, 325, 1802.)

CALLIURUS Rafinesque, 1819.—"Corps oblong comprimè. Tête et opercules écailleux, preopercule lisse, à 3 sutures carénées réunies en angle supérieurement, opercule postérieur à épine sur un appendice membraneux anguleux. Bouche très-fendue, mâchoires à grandes dents, sans lèvres, l'inférieure prolongée. Une nageoire dorsale deprimée au confluent des rayons épineux. Nageoires thoraciques à 5 rayons dont 1 épineux. Anus au mileu. A genre diffère principalement du genre *Etheostoma* par la forme du corps de la bouche et l'opercule ecailleux. *C. punctulatus.* Olivâtre, parsemé de points noirs très, rapprochés, ligne latérale peu courbée; queue bilobée, Jaune à la base noire au milieu, blanche au bout. D. $\frac{10}{14}$, A. $\frac{3}{10}$, P. 15, C. 24. Noms vulgaires de l'Ohio, Black-perch et Fine-tail."— (RAFINESQUE, *Jour. de Physique,* V, 88, 420, June, 1819.)

CALLIURUS Rafinesque, 1820.—" Body elongate, compressed, scaly; fore part of the head without scales, neck and gill-covers scaly ; mouth large with strong teeth in both jaws, and without lips. Gill-cover double, preopercle divided downwards into three curved and carinated sutures, without serrature; opercule with an acute and membranaceous appendage, before which stands a flat spine. One dorsal fin, spiny anteriorly, depressed in the middle. Anal fin with spiny rays, thoracic with none, and only five soft rays. Vent nearly medial.

The generic name means fine-tail. It differs principally from the genus *Holocentrus,* by the head, scaly gill-cover and singular preopercule : genus 12 of my 70 new genera of American animals."—(RAFINESQUE, *Ich. Ohi.* 26, 1820.)

LEPOMIS Rafinesque, 1820.—" This genus differs from *Holocentrus* by having the opercule scaly, from *Calliurus* by the opercule only being such, while the preopercule is simple and united above with a square suture over the head, besides the thoracic fins with 6 rays. Perhaps the *Calliurus* ought only to be a subgenus of this. From the G. *Icthelis* it differs by the large mouth and spines on the opercule.

The name means scaly gills. The species are numerous throughout the United States. They are permanent; but ramblers in the Ohio and tributary streams. They are fishes of prey, and easily caught with the hook. I shall divide them into two subgenera. I had wrongly blended this genus and the *Ictheli* under the name *Lepomis*. 13. G. of my Prodr. N. G." —(RAFINESQUE, *Ich. Ohi*. 30, 1820.)

APLITES Rafinesque, 1820.—" Only one flat spine on the opercule decurrent in a small medial opercule: first ray of the thoracic fins, soft or hardly spiny. Meaning, single weapon." —(RAFINESQUE, *Ich. Ohi*. 30, 1820.)

NEMOCAMPSIS Rafinesque, 1820.—" This fish [*Lepomis flexuolaris*] might perhaps form another subgenus, by the large month, head without upper sutures, spine hardly decurrent, nearly equal jaws, gill-covers, lateral line, etc. Its tail and preopecule are somewhat like *Calliurus*. It might be called *Nemocampsis*, meaning flexuose line."—(RAFINESQUE, *Ich. Ohi*. 31, 1820.)

DIOPLITES Rafinesque, 1820.—" Opercule with two spines above. First ray of the thoracic fins spiny. Lateral line curved as the back. Meaning two weapons."—(RAFINESQUE, *Ich. Ohi*. 32, 1820.)

ETHEOSTOMA . Rafinesque, 1820.—" Body nearly cylindrical and scaly. Mouth variable with small teeth. Gill cover double or triple unserrate, with a spine on the opercule and without scales. Six branchial rays. Thoracic fins with six rays, one of which is spiny. No appendage. One dorsal fin more or less divided in two parts, the anterior one with entirely spiny rays. Vent medial or rather anterior.

A singular new genus, of which I have already detected five species, so different from each other that they might form as many subgenera. Yet they agree in the above characters, and differ from the genus *Sciena* by the shape of the body and mouth, and the divided dorsal fin. The name means different mouths. I divide it into two subgenera. They are all very small fishes, hardly noticed, and only employed for bait; yet they are good to eat, fried, and may often be taken with baskets at the falls and mill races. They feed on worms and spawn."—(RAFINESQUE, *Ich. Ohi.* 35, 1820.)

APLESION Rafinesque, 1820.—(As subgenus of *Etheostoma*.) "Dorsal fin single, split in the middle. Meaning nearly simple."—(RAFINESQUE, *Ich. Ohi.* 36, 1820.)

HURO Cuvier and Valenciennes, 1828.—"Nous croyons pouvoir donner ce nom à un poisson que M. Richardson a pris récemment dans le lac Huron, et qui aurait tous les caractères de la perche, s'il ne manquait de dentelures aux os de la tête et de l'épaule, et spécialement au préopercule, qui n'en manque presque dans aucune espèce de cette famille.

"Less Anglais des environs de ce lac l'appellent *black-bass* ou *perche noire*, parce qu'il ressemble en effet assez pour le port et pour les teintes à un autre poisson qui porte le même nom aux Etats-Unis, et que nous décrirons plus loin dans notre genre *centropriste*, auquel il appartient."—(CUVIER AND VALENCIENNES, *Hist. Nat. des Poiss.* II, 124, 1828.)

GRYSTES Cuvier and Valenciennes, 1829.—"Comme il y a des poissons qui, avec tous les caractères des serrans, manquent de dentelures au préopercule, il y en a aussi qui joignent cette intégrité de préopercule à tous les caractères des centropristes. Ils sont à ces derniers ce que les bodians de Bloch étaient à ses holocentres; et si nous ne réunissons pas les Grystes et les centropristes en un seul genre, comme nous avons réuni les bodians et les holocentres dans notre genre serran, c'est que nous ne trouvons pas entre eux les mêmes passages insensibles."—(CUVIER AND VALENCIENNES, *Hist. Nat. des Poiss.* III, 54, 1829.)

HURO Swainson, 1839.—"Preoperculum entire; body fusiform, but broad in the middle; head large; mouth oblique, subvertical, large; lower jaw longest; chin projecting; dorsal fin, distinct, the first smallest; caudal emarginate."—(SWAINSON, *Nat. Hist. and Class. Fishes*, II, 200, 1839.)

GRYSTES Swainson, 1839.—"Dorsal fin almost divided into

two, the anterior or spinous division shortest, the posterior
lobed; preoperculum smooth; mouth large, sub-vertical; lower
jaw largest; caudal emarginate; sides of the head scaled; pectoral and ventrals small; anal fin shorter than the hind part of
the dorsal. Representing Huro in the circle of Percinæ."—
(SWAINSON, *Nat. Hist. and Class. Fishes*, II, 202, 1839.)

GRYSTES Agassiz, 1854.—"I have already shown in my
'Lake Superior' that the genera *Grystes* and *Huro* of Cuvier
do not differ essentially one from the other, and must therefore
be united into one natural group; moreover, when the fishes of
Kentucky shall be better known, it may become necessary to
substitute for either of them the name of *Lepomis*, introduced in
ichthyology by Rafinesque, as early as the year 1820, for the
western species of this genus. If I hesitate to make the change
now, it is simply because I have not the means of deciding
upon the value of his many species. The species of this group
are indeed very difficult to characterize. They differ chiefly in
the relative size of their scales, the presence or absence of teeth
upon the tongue, though Cuvier denies the presence of teeth on
the tongue of any of them, etc. There are, besides, marked
differences between the young and the adults. These circumstances render it impossible to characterize any one species
without comparative descriptions and figures."—(AGASSIZ, *Am.
Jour. Sci. and Arts*, (2), XVII, 297, 1854.)

GRYSTES Holbrook, 1855.—"Dorsal fin single, though deeply
notched; intermaxillary, maxillary, vomerine and palatine
teeth small and thickly set, or card-like; preopercle not serrated; branchiostegal rays, seven."*—(HOLBROOK, *Ichthy. Sou.
Car.* 25, 1855.)

DIOPLITES Girard, 1858.—"Body elongated, sub-fusiform in
profile, compressed. Head well developed. Preopercle smooth
and entire. Mouth large; lower jaw longest. Velvet-like teeth

---

* "Sometimes there are only six rays."—*Holbrook.*

on the jaws, front of vomer, and palatine bones. Tongue smooth. Cheeks and opercular apparatus scaly. Branchial apertures continuous under the throat. Two dorsal fins contiguous upon their base. Three small anal spines. Insertion of ventrals on a line immediately behind the base of pectorals. Caudal fin posteriorly sub-cresentic. Scales well developed and posteriorly ciliated."—(GIRARD, *U. S. Pac. R. R. Surv.* X, Fishes, 4, 1858.)

GRYSTES Günther, 1859.—" Six or seven branchiostegals. All the teeth villiform without canines; teeth on the palatine bones; tongue smooth. One dorsal, with ten spines, the anal fin with three. Operculum with two points, præoperculum with a single smooth-edged ridge. Scales moderate. The number of the pyloric appendages increased. Air-bladder simple, slightly notched behind."—(GÜNTHER, *Cat. Fishes Brit. Mus.* I, 252, 1859.)

HURO Günther, 1859.—" Six branchiostegals. All the teeth villiform, without canines; palatine bones ?; tongue ? Two dorsals, the first with six, the anal fin with three spines. No denticulations on the bones of the head; operculum with two flat obtuse points. Scales moderate."—(GÜNTHER, *Cat. Fishes Brit. Mus.* I, 252, 1859.)

MICROPTERUS Gill, 1873.—" Body ovate-fusiform, compressed, deepest behind the ventrals, with the caudal peduncle elongated, scarcely contracted towards the base of the fin.

" Scales small or moderate; quadrate, rather higher than long, with the exposed portion densely muricated, rounded behind and about twice as high as long; with the fan with few (4–9) folds; extending to the nape and throat.

" Lateral line regularly parallel with the back, in scales nearly like but smaller than the adjoining ones.

" Head compressed and oblong conic, with the lower jaw prominent and the profile rectilinear; with scales (more or less smaller than those of the trunk) on the cheeks, operculum, sub-

7

operculum and interoperculum ((1) none or (2) few on the pre-operculum); operculum ending in a flattened point (spine) and with the border above it emarginated; suboperculum with a pointed membrane extendihg beyond (behind and above) the opercular spine; preoperculum entire. Eyes moderate, about equidistant from the snout and preoperculum; notrils normal; anterior with a posterior lid; posterior patulous.

"Mouth, with the cleft moderately oblique, large (the supra-maxillary (1) nearly to or (2) beyond the vertical of the pos-terior border of the eye). Supramaxillary with the accessory ossicle well developed. Lips: upper, little developed; lower, moderate on the sides, but separated by a very wide isthmus.

" Tongue moderate and free.

"Teeth on the jaws in a broad band, acute, curved back-wards, and increasing in size towards inner rows; on the vomer, palatines and pterygoids, villiform.

" Branchiostegal rays six (exceptionally seven) on each side.

" Dorsal with its origin behind the axil of the ventral; (1) its spinous portion longer but much lower than the soft portion, with ten spines more or less graduated before as well as behind, and the ninth much shorter than the tenth; (2) the soft portion well developed.

" Anal with its base shorter than the soft portion of the dorsal, nearly coterminal with it, with three spines, of which the third is much the longest.

" Caudal emarginated and with obtuse lobes.

" Pectorals and ventrals normal.

" This enumeration of the characters common to the known forms of the genus has been drawn up with a view to exhibit the features differentiating the genus from the other representa-tives of the family Pomotidæ. The difference indicated by the general expression is coördinated with the greater distance of the eye from the preoperculum, the armature of the operculum, the peculiar form of the dorsal and the relatively small size of the anal fin. The elucidation of the anatomical characters of the genus and comparison thereof with those of other genera are reserved for a future occasion when the distinctive features can be illustrated."—(GILL, *Proc. Am. Asso. Adv. Sci.* XXII, B. 55, 1873.)

PHALANX GRYSTEINI (=*Micropterinæ* Gill.) Bleeker, 1875.— "Percæformes corpore oblongo vel subelongato, capite superne squamato vel lævi; dentibus maxillis; vomerinis et palatinis parvis; præoperculo edentulo inermi; squamis trunco parvis vel mediocribus sessilibus; anali spini 3." (BLEEKER, *Systema Percarum Revisum* <*Extrait des Archives Neerlandaises*, XI, 15, 1875.)

HURO Bleeker, 1875.—"Corpus oblongum. Caput vertice, regione temporali, genis ossibusque opercularibus tantum squamatum. Squamæ trunco cycloideæ? 65 circ. in serie longitudinali. Pinnæ dorsales non continuæ, anterior radiosa brevior spinis 6."— (BLEEKER, *Syst. Perc. Revis.* <*Ext. des Archiv. Neerland.* XI, 15, 1875.)

MICROPTERUS Bleeker, 1875.—"Corpus oblongum. Caput genis ossibusque opercularibus tantum squamatum. Squamæ trunco ctenoideæ 90 circ. in serie longitudinali. Pinna dorsalis parte spinosa et parte radiosa continuis subæquilongis, spinis 9 vel 10." — (BLEEKER, *Syst. Perc. Revis.* <*Ext. des Archiv. Neerland.* XI, 15, 1875.)

MICROPTERUS Jordan, 1878.— "Body elongate, not greatly compressed; spines little developed, those of the anal fin, three in number, small and weak; those of the dorsal, ten, low, the eighth and ninth quite short, so that there is a deep notch between the spinous and soft parts of the dorsal, almost breaking the continuity of the fin; caudal emarginate; operculum emarginate behind, ending in two flat points; mouth very large, the lower jaw longest; palatine teeth well developed; tongue and pterygoids toothless; gill-rakers long and stout, armed with teeth; supplemental maxillary bone well developed."—(JORDAN, *Man. Vert. E. U. S.*, 2d ed., 233, 1878.)

MICROPTERUS Vaillant & Bocourt: ined.

"Percoïdes à ventrales thoraciques; six ou sept rayons, branchiostéges, une seule dorsale, occupant la plus grande partie de la longueur du dos, avec la portion épineuse munie normalement de dix épines; anales présentant trois épines croisant en longeur de la prèmiere à la troisième et à peu près d'égal force; toutes les dents en velours; préopercule à bord lisse, angle operculaire en pointe arrondie ne formant pas une véritable épine. Ecailles médiocrement nombreuses, cténoïdes, polystiques.

"Ce genre, ainsi délimité, ne comprend qu'un petit nombre d'espèces propres aux cours d'eau de l'Amérique septentrionale.

. . . .

"Les écailles sont ctenoïdes, mais en général les spinules sont ou rudimèntaires ou incomplétement développés; les variations, que nous avons pu saisir, sont les suivantes. Tantôt les spinules ne sont nettement calcifiées que sur une zone plus ou moins étroite, bordant la portion libre de l'écaille et le reste de l'aire spinigère n'est qu' indistinctement hispide. Cette zone peut se réduire sur ses parties latérales et n'occuper que l'extrémité de l'écaille. D'autre fois le bord libre est sans spinules et celle ci ne ce rencontrent que vers le foyer dans un espace triangulaire formant la partie centripète d'un secteur; c'est sur le *Micropterus variabilis*, Le Sueur, que nous avons particulièrement observé cette disposition. Enfin, les spinules peuvent être à peine perceptibles et il faut y regarder de bien près pour ne pas croire les écailles de la ligne latérale sont toujours dépourvues de spinules, leur canal est à deux ouvertures comme chez les centropomes.

Ces variations, auxquelles on serait tenté d'attribuer une certaine valeur dans la distinction des espèces, ne nous ont malheureusement pas présenti une assez grande constance pour pouvoir être mises un usage, les observations devraient porter sur un plus grand nombre de sujets que ceux que nous avons eus à notre disposition.

La dénomination de *Micropterus* paraît devoir être adoptée préferablement à cell de *Grystes*, établie par Cuvier dans son *Règne animal* ou à celle de *Dioplites* Rafinesque, reprise par M. Girard. C'est sans doute une application en quelque sorte exagirée du droit de priorité, car les caractères du genre sont très-imparfaitement donnés par Lacépède et la dénomination même est fondée sur une anomalie évidente, cependant, l'individu type étant parfaitment connu, il peut y avoir avantage à reprendre ce nom, comme l'ont dégà fait plusieurs auteurs contemporains.

S'il est ainsi possible de limiter le genre, il n'est pas aussi aisé d'en distinguer les différentes espèces, lesquelles, aujourd'hui comme à l'époque ou l'écrivit L. Agassiz, sont excessivement difficiles à caractériser. Au premier abord, on reconnaît sans pcine plusieurs types, en ayant égardaux proportions du corps, au nombre des écailles et à diverses autres particularités, mais si on examine un certain nombre d'individus, les différences s'attenuent par des transitions graduelles.

. . . .

D'une manière générale, le *Micropterus variabilis* Le Sueur, a le corps le plus élevé et le *Micropterus salmoïdes* Lacép., le plus bas, les *Micropterus nuecensis* Grd., et *Micropterus dolomieu* Lacép., etant intermédiaires sous ce rapport. L'épaisseur donne des différences peu sensibles ; on sait d'ailleurs que ces variations, pouvant dépendre de la saison et du sexe, leur importance est moindre dans des espèces aussi voisines. La longueur de la tête rapporteé à la longueur totale donne les nombres extrêmes 29 et 25, peu différents l'un de l'autre et qui de plus se rencontrent tous deux sur une des espèces, la mieux caractérisée peut-être, le *Micropterus nuecensis* Grd., Le museau et la largeur de l'espece interorbitaire varient dans une assez grande mesure, 35 et 26 pour l'un, 29 et 20 pour l'autre ; mais il y a mélange entre les différentes especes, que nous croyons pouvoir distinguer, en sorte qu'il est assez difficile d'en faire emploi.

L'écart considérable que présente la formula de la ligne latérale est un des fait les plus importants, comme indiquant la distinction nécessaire de plusieurs types, puisque cette formule peut varier de 60 à 86. Il existe, il est vrai, un grand nombre d'intermédiaires, dont le tableau peut faire juger au premier coup d'œil. La formule de la ligne transversale suit une marche analogue, puisqu'au dessus de ligne latérale les chiffres varient de 7 á 11 et au-dessous, de 15 à 30. Il est aussi important de remarquer que la progression dans les deux formules est la même, c'est-à-dire que les écailles sont beaucoup plus petites pour les espéces citées les premières dans le tableau que pour les suivantes.

Quant aux formules des nageoires, la seule exception constatée pour les épines de la dorsale sur le premier exemplaire doit etreconsidérée comme une anomalie. Les rayons nous ne nous donnent que des différences peu significatives.

Enfin les dent linguales, par leur présence ou leur absence, four nissent un caractére spécifique de premier ordre, d'autant, comme le montre le tableau, qu'il a pu être abservé sur des individus de tailles très-variées et paraîtrait par conséquent ne pas subir de modifications avec l'âge.

En ayant égard à la combinaison de ces caractères on peut, croyons-nous, d'après les exemplaires de la collection de muséum, distinguer quatre espèces, que ne sont toutefois proposées qu'à titre provisoire, vu l'insuffisance des matériaux dont nous avons pu disposer. Le tableau dichotomique suivant donnera une idée de leur compréhension : "

Ligne transversale ayant pour formule.			
7 à 8	Ligne latérale;	Des dents linguales − − M. *nuecensis* Grd.	
15 à 20	60 à 70 écailles.	Pas de dents linguales − M. *salmoides* Lacép.	
9 à 11	Ligne latérale:	69 à 75 écailles − − − − M. *variabilis* Le S.	
25 à 30		80 à 86 écailles − − − − M. *dolomieu* Lacép.	

(VAILLANT & BOCOURT, *Mission Scientifique au Mexique*, IV, Zool.: ined.)

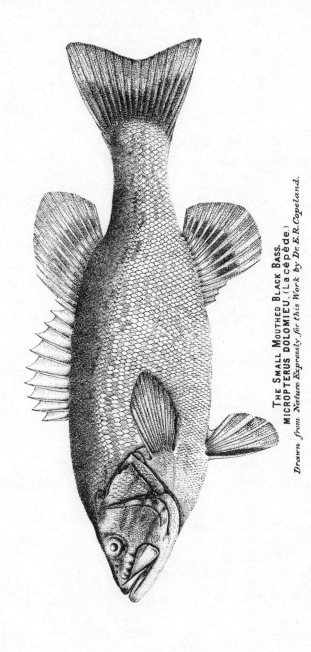

THE SMALL MOUTHED BLACK BASS.
MICROPTERUS DOLOMIEU. (Lacépède.)
Drawn from Nature Expressly for this Work by Dr. E. R. Copeland.

CHRONOLOGICAL CATALOGUE

Of the Nominal Species of Micropterus as noticed by various Authors, with Identifications.

NOMINAL SPECIES.	DATE	IDENTIFICATIONS.
Micropterus dolomieu Lacépède	1802	Micropterus dolomieu.
Labrus salmoides Lacépède	1802	Micropterus salmoides.
Bodianus achigan Rafinesque	1817	Micropterus dolomieu.
Calliurus punctulatus Rafinesque	1819	Micropterus dolomieu.
Lepomis pallida Rafinesque	1820	Micropterus salmoides.
Lepomis trifasciata Rafinesque	1820	Micropterus dolomieu.
Lepomis flexuolaris Rafinesque	1820	Micropterus dolomieu.
Lepomis salmonea Rafinesque	1820	Micropterus dolomieu.
Lepomis notata Rafinesque	1820	Micropterus dolomieu.
Etheostoma calliura Rafinesque	1820	Micropterus dolomieu.
Cichla variabilis Le Sueur, MSS.	1822	Micropterus dolomieu.
Cichla fasciata Le Sueur	1822	Micropterus dolomieu.
Cichla ohiensis Le Sueur	1822	Micropterus dolomieu.
Cichla minima Le Sueur	1822	Micropterus dolomieu.
Cichla floridana Le Sueur	1822	Micropterus salmoides.
Huro nigricans Cuvier & Valenciennes	1828	Micropterus salmoides.
Grystes salmoides Cuvier & Valenciennes	1829	Micropterus dolomieu?
Centrarchus obscurus DeKay	1842	Micropterus dolomieu.
Centrarchus fasciatus Kirtland	1842	Micropterus dolomieu.
Grystes nigricans Agassiz	1850	Micropterus salmoides.
Grytes fasciatus Agassiz	1850	Micropterus dolomieu.
Grystes nobilis Agassiz	1854	Micropterus salmoides.
Grystes nuecensis Baird & Girard	1854	Micropterus salmoides.
Grystes salmoides Holbrook	1855	Micropterus salmoides.
Grystes megastoma Garlick	1857	Micropterus salmoides.
Grystes nigricans Garlick	1857	Micropterus dolomieu.
Dioplites nuecensis Girard	1858	Micropterus salmoides.
Grystes salmonoides Günther	1859	Micropterus dolomieu.
Grystes nigricans Herbert	1859	Micropterus salmoides.
Lepomis achigan Gill	1860	Micropterus dolomieu.
Micropterus nigricans Cope	1865	Micropterus salmoides.

NOMINAL SPECIES.	DATE	IDENTIFICATIONS.
Micropterus fasciatus Cope..........................	1865	Micropterus dolomieu.
Micropterus achigan Gill...........................	1866	Micropterus dolomieu.
Micropterus salmoides Gill.........................	1873	Micropterus dolomieu.
Dioplites treculii Vaillant & Bocourt..........	1874	Micropterus salmoides.
Dioplites nuecensis Vaillant & Bocourt.........	1874	Micropterus salmoides.
Dioplites variabilis Vaillant & Bocourt......	1874	M. dolo. *var.* achigan.
Dioplites salmoides Vaillant & Bocourt.......	1874	Micropterus salmoides.
Micropterus floridanus Goode.....................	1876	Micropterus salmoides.
Micropterus pallidus Gill & Jordan............	1877	Micropterus salmoides.
Micropterus salmoides *var.* salmoides Jordan.	1878	M. dolomieu *var.* dolo.
Micropterus salmoides *var.* achigan Jordan.	1878	M. dolo. *var.* achigan.
Micropterus salmoides Vaillant & Bocourt...	ined.	Micropterus salmoides.
Micropterus nuecensis Vaillant & Bocourt...	ined.	Micropterus salmoides.
Micropterus variabilis Vaillant & Bocourt..	ined.	M. dolo. *var.* achigan.
Micropterus dolomieu Vaillant & Bocourt...	ined.	M. dolomieu *var.* dolo.

SYNOPSIS OF SPECIES OF MICROPTERUS.

Common Characters.—Body elongated, ovate-fusiform; slightly compressed; arched and thick along the back, thinner and straight along the belly; lower jaw longest; both jaws armed with broad bands of small, pointed, recurved, card-like teeth of uniform size; villiform teeth on vomer, palatine and pharyngeal bones; teeth on gill-rakers; spinous and soft portions of dorsal fin partly divided by a notch; anal fin with three spines; caudal fin emarginate; opercule emarginate behind, ending in two flat points; supplemental maxillary bone well developed.

* Mouth large; angle of mouth anterior to the posterior border of the eye.

† Third dorsal spine only one-half higher than the first.

a. Notch between spinous and soft rays of dorsal comparatively shallow.

b. Scales small on body, much smaller on breast and back of neck, and quite small on cheeks; eleven rows of scales between lateral line and dorsal fin; 70 to 80 scales along the lateral line (exclusive of small pre-caudal scales).

c. No scales on preopercular limb.

d. Anal fin almost without scales. (?)

e. Head moderate in size; slightly convex between the orbits.

f. Color, slaty or dusky green on back and sides, shading to white on belly and lower jaw; young brighter green, and more or less spotted and marked with vertical bars; tail in young (in some localities), yellow at base, middle black, tip white; opercle with several oblique olivaceous streaks; D. X, 13; A. III, 11.
.... DOLOMIEU.

** Mouth very large; angle of mouth extends beyond the posterior border of the eye.

†† Third dorsal spine twice (at least) as high as the first.

aa. Dorsal notch deep, almost dividing the fin into two.

bb. Scales moderate; not much smaller on cheeks, nape or breast; eight rows of scales between lateral line and dorsal fin; 65 to 70 scales along lateral line (exclusive of small pre-caudal scales).

cc. A single row of scales on preopercular limb.

dd. Anal fin somewhat scaly. (?)

ee. Head large; flat between the orbits.

ff. Color, olive green, darker on back and shading to white on belly and under side of lower jaw; more or less spotted when young; not barred, though sometimes an irregular dark lateral band; three oblique streaks on cheeks; these markings grow obscure with age ; D. X, 12; A. III, 10.......... ....SALMOIDES.

MICROPTERUS DOLOMIEU Lacépède.

THE SMALL-MOUTHED BLACK BASS.

SYNONOMY.

1802—*Micropterus dolomieu* Lacépède, Hist. Nat. des Poiss.,
IV, 325.
Micropterus dolomieu Vaillant & Bocourt, Miss. Sci.
au Mex., Zool.: ined.
1817—*Bodianus achigan* Rafinesque, Am. Mo. Mag. and Crit.
Rev. II, 120.
Lepomis achigan Gill, Pro. Ac. Nat. Sci. Phil. 20, 1860.
Micropterus achigan Gill, Rept. Com. Agri. 407, 1866.
Micropterus achigan Goode & Bean, Bull. Essex Inst.
XI, 19, 1879.*
1820—*Calliurus punctulatus* Rafinesque, Ich. Ohiensis, 26.
1820—*Lepomis trifasciata* Rafinesque, Ich. Ohiensis, 31.
1820—*Lepomis flexuolaris* Rafinesque, Ich. Ohiensis, 31.
1820—*Lepomis salmonea* Rafinesque, Ich. Ohiensis, 32.
1820—*Lepomis notata* Rafinesque, Ich. Ohiensis, 32.
1820—*Etheostoma calliura* Rafinesque, Ich. Ohiensis, 36.
1822—*Cichla variabilis* Le Sueur, MSS., in Museum d'Hist.
Nat. Paris.
Dioplites variabilis Vaillant & Bocourt, MSS. Miss.
Sci. au Mexique, 1874.
Micropterus variabilis Vaillant & Bocourt, Miss. Sci.
au Mexique: ined.
1822—*Cichla fasciata* Le Sueur, Jour. Ac. Nat. Sci. Phil. II, 216.
Cichla fasciata Kirtland, Zoology Ohio (2d An. Rept.
Geol. Surv. Ohio), 191, 1838.
Centrarchus fasciatus Kirtland, Bost. Jour. Nat. Hist.
V, 28, 1842.

---

* Used on the supposition that the name "*Labre salmoïde*" as used by
Lacépède was vernacular (French), unaccompanied by a classical form,
and therefore not available.

Centrarchus fasciatus DeKay, Fishes N. Y. 28, 1842.

Centrarchus fasciatus Storer, Syn. Fishes N. A. 38, 1846.

Grystes fasciatus Agassiz, Lake Superior, 295, 1850.

Centrarchus fasciatus Thompson, Hist. Vt. 131, 1853.

Grystes fasciatus Eoff, Smithsonian Report, 289, 1854.

Grystes fasciatus Gill, Smithsonian Report, 257, 1856.

Centrarchus fasciatus Günther, Cat. Fishes Brit. Mus. I, 258, 1859.

Grystes fasciatus Günther, Cat. Fishes Brit. Mus. I. 252, 1859. (Name only.)

Centrarchus fasciatus Roosevelt, Game Fish of North, 217, 1862.

Micropterus fasciatus Cope, Pro. Ac. Nat. Sci. Phil. 83, 1865. (Name only.)

Grystes fasciatus Putnam, Storer's Fish Mass. 278, 1867.

Micropterus fasciatus Cope, Jour. Ac. Nat. Sci. Phil. VI, 216, 1868.

Micropterus fasciatus Cope, Pro. Am. Phil. Soc. 450, 1870.

1822—*Cichla ohiensis* Le Sueur, Jour. Ac. Nat. Sci. Phil. II, 218.

Cichla ohiensis Kirtland, Rept. Zool. Ohio: 2d Geol. Rept. Ohio, 191, 1838.

1822—*Cichla minima* Le Sueur, Jour. Ac. Nat. Sci. Phil. II, 220.

Cichla minima Kirtland, Rept. Zool. Ohio: 2d Geol. Rept. Ohio, 191, 1838.

1829—?*Grystes salmoides* Cuvier & Valenciennes, Hist. Nat. des Poiss. III, 54.

Grystes salmoides Jardine, Nat. Lib. I, Perches, 158, 1835.

Grystes salmoides DeKay, Fishes N. Y. 26, 1842.

Grystes salmoides Storer, Synopsis Fishes N. A. 36, 1846.

Gristes salmoeides Herbert, Fish and Fishing, 197, 1859.

Grystes salmonoides Günther, Cat. Fishes Brit. Mus. I, 252, 1859.

Micropterus salmoides GILL, Pro. Am. Asso. Adv. Sci.
B 55, 1873.

Micropterus salmoides JORDAN, Ind. Geol. Surv. 214, 1874.

Micropterus salmoides JORDAN, Man. Vert. E. U. S. 230,
1876.

Micropterus salmoides UHLER & LUGGER, Fishes of Md.
111, 1876.

Micropterus salmoides JORDAN, Ann. N. Y. Lyc. Nat.
Hist. XI, 314, 1877.

Micropterus salmoides JORDAN, Bull. U. S. Nat. Mus. IX,
and X, 1877.

Micropterus salmoides HALLOCK, Sportsman's Gazetteer,
373, 1877. (In part.)

Micropterus salmoides JORDAN, Man. Vert. E. U. S. 2d
ed., 236, 1878.

Micropterus salmoides JORDAN, Bull. U. S. Nat. Mus.
XII, 30, 1878.

Micropterus salmoides HENSHALL, Rept. Ohio Fish Com.
31, 1879.

Micropterus salmoides JORDAN, Pro. U. S. Nat. Mus., II,
218, 1880.

1842—*Centrarchus obscurus* DEKAY, Fishes New York, 30.

Centrarchus obscurus STORER, Syn. Fishes N. A. 40, 1846.

Centrarchus obscurus GÜNTHER, Cat. Fishes Brit. Mus.
I, 258, 1859.

1857—*Grystes nigricans* GARLICK, Treat. Art. Prop. Fish, 105.

Grystes nigricans NORRIS, Am. Anglers' Book, 103, 1864.

ETYMOLOGY : *Dolomieu,* proper name (in honor of M. Dolomieu).

HABITAT : Canada to Alabama ; along the Appalachian Chain and west-
ward ; introduced eastward.

SPECIFIC DESCRIPTIONS.

MICROPTERUS DOLOMIEU Lacépède, 1802. — " Dix rayons
aiguillonés et sept rayons articulés à la premiére nageoire du dos ;

quatre rayons à la seconde; deux rayons aiguillonés et onze rayons
articulés à la nageoire de l'anus; la caudale en croissant; un
ou deux aiguillons à la seconde pièce de chaque opercule."—
[Br. 5; P. 16; V. I, 5; C. 17].—(LACÉPÈDE, *Hist. Nat. des
Poiss.*, IV, 325, 1801).

BODIANUS ACHIGAN Rafinesque, 1817. — "Lower jaw much
longer, gill-covers with two flat and short thorns, lateral line
nearly straight, base ascending diagonal; blackish with round
scattered fulvous spots, belly gray, fins brown, the dorsal depressed in the middle and with twenty-five rays, whereof ten are
spinescent, tail lunulated, with a gray edge.—*Obs.* vulgar names
in the United States Black Bass, Lake Bass, Big Bass, Oswego
Bass, Spotted Bass, etc., and in Canada Achigan or Achigan verd
or Achigan noir; but many species are probably blended under
those names, this is probably the Achigan of Charlevoix. It is a
fine fish, from one to three feet long, and weighing sometimes eight
to twelve pounds, affording a good food, etc. It is found in all
the large lakes of New York and Canada. It has many rows
of small teeth, and is voracious; eyes blue, iris gilt-brown; anal
fin with fifteen rays, whereof three are spinescent and short,
pectoral fins fulvous dotted of brown at the base, and with fifteen rays, thoracic fins with six rays, whereof the first is spinescent, caudal fins with twenty rays. This species and the foregoing have six branchial rays, and the gill-covers are composed of
four pieces, all scaly except the second. Body more cylindrical
than in the foregoing."—(RAFINESQUE, *Amer. Mon. Mag. and
Crit. Rev.* II, 120, 1817.)

CALLIURUS PUNCTULATUS Rafinesque, 1820. — "Lower jaw
longer; body olivaceous, crowded with blackish dots; head
brownish, flattened above; lateral line hardly curved upward
at the base; tail unequally bilobed, lower lobe larger, base yellow, middle blackish, tip white; dorsal fin yellow, with 24 rays,
of which ten are spiny.

An uncommon fish from four to twelve inches long. I observed it at the Falls; rare in the Ohio, more common in some

small streams. Vulgar names, Painted Tail or Bridge Perch; tail with two lobes, slightly unequal, base flexuose; belly and lower fins pale, anal fin with 13 rays, the three anterior spiny and shorter, behind rounded and far from the tail, although nearer than the dorsal fin; thoracic fin with five rays, none of which appear spiny, and no appendage; pectoral fins short, trapezoidal, with 15 rays; branchial rays concealed."—(RAFINESQUE, *Ich. Ohi.* 26, 1820.)

LEPOMIS TRIFASCIATA Rafinesque, 1820.—"Whitish, crowded with unequal and irregular specks of gilt olive color, none on the belly; gill covers with three large oblique streaks of the same color; opercule without appendage, spine acute, a faint brown spot below the lateral line; lower jaw longer; dorsal fin streaked behind; tail forked, yellow at the base, brown in the middle, tip pale.

"Found in the Ohio and many other streams; reaches over a foot in length sometimes; vulgar names, Yellow Bass, Gold Bass, Yellow Perch, Streaked Head, etc. Fins olivaceous; dorsal hardly depressed in the middle with 24 rays whereof 10 are spiny, hind part with three brownish and longitudinal streaks; anal fin rounded with 13 rays, 3 of which are spiny, 2 short and a long one; pectoral fins nearly triangular and acute, 16 rays; thoracics 6, tail 2, very broad, forks divaricate nearly lunulate; eyes small black, iris brown; lateral line following the back; diameter less than one-fourth of the length."—(RAFINESQUE, *Ich. Ohi.* 31, 1820.)

LEPOMIS FLEXUOLARIS Rafinesque, 1820.—"Olivaceous brown above, sides with some transversal and flexuose olive lines, belly white; lateral line nearly straight flexuose; spine broad acute, behind the base of the opercule, no appendage nor spot, pre-opercule forked downwards; upper jaw slightly longer; tail bi-lobed, base olive, middle brown, tip white.

"A fine species, reaching the length of two feet, and affording an excellent food. Common all over the Ohio and tributary streams; vulgar names, Black Bass, Brown Bass, Black Perch, etc.; fins olivaceous, dorsal with 23 rays, whereof 9 are spiny and rather shorter; anal with 12 rays, whereof 2 are spiny; pectorals trapezoidal, 16 rays; branchial rays uncovered; iris brown. This fish might perhaps form another subgenus, by the large mouth, head without upper sutures, spine hardly decurrent, nearly equal jaws, gill covers, lateral line, etc. Its tail and preopercule are somewhat like *Calliurus*. It might be called *Nemocampsis*, meaning flexuose line. Diameter one-fourth of the length."—(RAFINESQUE, *Ich. Ohi.* 31, 1820.)

LEPOMIS SALMONEA Rafinesque, 1820.—"Olivaceous brown above, sides pale with some round yellowish spots, beneath white; preopercule simple, head without sutures, lower jaw hardly longer, spines flat, short, acute, and decurrent above and beneath, opercule acute beneath the spines; tail lunulate, tip blackish; vent posterior.

"Length from 6 to 24 inches. Vulgar names White Trout, Brown Trout, Trout Pearch, Trout Bass, Brown Bass, Black Bass, Black Pearch, etc. Common in the Kentucky, Ohio, Green and Licking rivers, etc. It offers a delicate white flesh, similar to the *Perca salmonea*. It is a voracious fish, with many rows of sharp teeth on the jaws and in the throat. It bites easily at the hook, and eats suckers, minnows and chubs. Diameter one-fifth of the length. Fins olivaceous brown; dorsal with 25 rays, whereof 10 are spiny, slightly depressed between them; anal rounded small, 3 and 11 rays. Pectoral acute trapezoidal 18 rays. Thoracic 1 and 5, spiny ray half the length. Tail with 24 rays. Iris silvery."—(RAFINESQUE, *Ich. Ohi.* 32, 1820.)

LEPOMIS NOTATA Rafinesque, 1820.—"This species differs merely from the foregoing [*Lepomis salmonea*] by having a black spot on the margin of the opercule, two diagonal brown stripes on each side of the head below the eyes, and all the fins yellow, except the tail, which is black at the end, with a narrow white

8

tip. It is also smaller, from 3 to 8 inches long. It bears the
same vulgar names, and is found along with it, of which some
fishermen deem that it is the young. But I have seen so many
false assertions of the kind elsewhere that I am inclined to doubt
this fact, as it would be very strange that the gradual changes
should be so great. Yet this ought to be inquired into, since
many vulgar opinions are often found to be correct."—(RAFIN-
ESQUE, *Ich. Ohi.* 32, 1820.)

ETHEOSTOMA CALLIURA Rafinesque, 1820.—"Body slightly
fusiform and compressed, silvery, olivaceous above, some flexuose
transversal brownish lines on the sides; lower jaw longer, preopercule double, opercule with an angular appendage and an
obtuse spine behind it; scales smooth, lateral line flexuose; tail
forked, tricolored, and with a brown spot at the base.

"The largest species of the genus from 3 to 9 inches long.
It has some similarity with the *Lepomis flexuolaris*, and some
other river Bass, wherefore it is called Minny Bass, Little Bass,
Hog Bass, etc. Common in the Ohio, Salt River, etc. It has
sharp teeth. The head is large, rugose above; iris large, gilt
brown; branchial rays uncovered. Diameter one-seventh of
the length. Lateral line curved upwards at its base. Fins
olivaceous. Dorsal with 9 and 14 rays, beginning behind the
pectorals and ending far from the tail, like the anal, which has
12 rays, whereof one is spiny. Pectoral fins short, trapezoidal,
16 rays. Tail 24, fine, base with a yellow curved ring, followed
by a forked band of a pale violaceous color, tip hyalin. Mouth
straight."—(RAFINESQUE, *Ich. Ohi.* 36, 1820.)

CICHLA FASCIATA Le Sueur, 1822.—"Fourteen or fifteen
transverse brown bands on each side of the body, and two or
three oblique ones on the opercula, scaly margined with black;
spinous and soft parts of the dorsal fin equal in length, the fin
less arquated upward than the posterior one.

"Body elongated, compressed, tapering at the two extremities, three and one-half times the length of head, by one length

in depth; head of moderate size, narrow, destitute of scales between the eyes, and upon the snout, which is short; mouth extending beneath the eye; jaw large, truncated posteriorly, intermaxillary long and narrow; teeth very small, numerous pointed, curved and serrated in the manner of a card on the jaws, palate and extremity of the vomer; inferior jaw hardly longer than the superior jaw, mandible strong, enlarged, spoon-shaped; eye small and round; iris white, brown and red; pupil small and of a deep color; dorsal fin high, rounded behind, arquated before, and very low at its junction with the soft part, the spinous rays imbricated and reclined into the longitudinal cavity of the back; anal rounded, shorter than the soft part of the dorsal, with three spinous rays anteriorly; pectorals moderate, rounded; thoracics truncated, hardly longer than the pectorals, distant from the anal, and armed with a strong spinous ray; caudal slightly emarginate, lobes rounded with 17 principal rays, including the lateral flat ones, beyond which are 8 small ones; scales rounded, not denticulated, sub-irregularly placed, large on the sides, smaller on the back, small upon the back of the neck, very small under the belly, throat and cheek, and a little larger on the preoperculum and suboperculum; there are also very small ones between the rays of the anal and caudal fins; general color brownish-olivaceous, deep and fuliginous upon the back, lighter on the sides, the middle of the scales browned with a black margin; anal fin greenish; posterior part of the dorsal and the caudal violaceous, abdomen and throat bluish and violaceous, the 13, 14 and sometimes 15 bands with which this species is ornamented are a little deeper than the general tint; they are more perceptible in the fresh state of the fish, when but recently taken out of the water; the opercula are also traversed with many olivaceous bands, the lateral line is undulated oblique: the color changes in the dying fish, it is then sometimes all blue or bluish, or entirely black, and the transverse bands disappear. Length 18 or 20 inches.

"This is one of the best fish of Lake Erie for the table, and with that which the fishermen call Herring Salmon (*Coregonus Artedi* Le Sueur, Vol. I, par. II, p. 231), it is salted to preserve it till sold. They are taken at all seasons of the year by the seine, and hook and line. We observed them at Erie in the month of July, 1816, and at Buffalo, at which latter place we captured many with the seine. A variety occurred in Lake George, of which the specimens appeared to us to have the lower jaw more advanced. The fishermen name them Black Bass. B. 6; P. 18 to 20; T. 5; D. 10, 15; A. 3, 12; C. 17⅜."—(Le Sueur, *Jour. Ac. Nat. Sci. Phil.* II, 216, 1822.)

CICHLA OHIENSIS Le Sueur, 1822.—"Extremity of the anal fin sensibly more remote from the head than that of the dorsal; scales more regular than in the preceding species.

"The larger of the two individuals, which were brought from the Ohio River by Mr. Thomas Say, and deposited in the cabinet of the Academy, is 22 inches long by 5 deep, and about 3 in thickness; the skin of these two specimens is stronger in its texture than in specimens from Lake Erie; the scales are more uniformly disposed and equal; the anterior portion of the dorsal fin is not so much elevated, less arquated, but also furnished with 10 spinous rays; the soft part is equally long with the first, but is more elevated, rounded and composed of 14 branched rays; the anal fin is rounded, short with 14 rays, of which the 3 anterior ones are spinous; the extremity of this fin extends beyond that of the dorsal, in these individuals, further than in the species of Lake Erie. If this character is constant, we must regard it as belonging to a distinct species, but I think it is proper to wait for further observations for confirmation.

"The scales are in the same progression; large, rounded on the sides, moderate on the back towards the spinous portion of the dorsal fin, small upon the neck; upon the middle of the abdomen they are a little more elongated; very small between the thoracic and pectoral fins, on the throat, the cheek, and larger on the preoperculum and suboperculum; the teeth also differ little from the preceding species; the pectoral and thoracic fins are equal and similarly situate; lateral line near the back, a little undulated, originating from the angle of the opening of the operculum, passing on the middle of the tail; color in the dried specimens, yellowish brown; the scales did not appear to me to be margined with black as in the preceding species. B. 6; P. 18; T. 5; D. 10, 14; A. 3, 11; C. 16⅔."—(LE SUEUR, *Jour. Ac. Nat. Sci. Phil.* II, 218, 1822.)

CICHLA MINIMA Le Sueur, 1822.—" Dorsal long, spinous and soft parts of equal length, the former straight and very low; anal long, equal to the soft part of the dorsal; eye large.

" Body very long and subcompressed, more elevated towards the dorsal anteriorly; head arquated; eye very large; pupil and iris very large; dorsal fin long, divided into two equal parts, the anterior part of 9 spinous rays, and much lower than the soft part, which is rounded, with 14 divided rays; anal equal to the posterior part of the dorsal and of 13 rays, of which 3 are spinous, caudal of 15 to 18 rays; pectorals large, placed very low near the operculum; thoracic fin much smaller than the pectoral, and placed exactly beneath them; anal large; scales very small; color deep gray, tinted with bluish on the back, with metallic reflections on the sides and abdomen and back, and a spot upon the neck, lateral line straight, on the middle of the body; caudal fin subtruncated of 17 or 18 rays; teeth very small, in many ranges on the jaws and palate; mouth deeply divided.

" Lives in the small lagoons of tranquil water, which discharge by narrow channels into Lake Erie.   Length is 9 lines." —(LE SUEUR, *Jour. Ac. Nat. Sci. Phil.* II, 220, 1822.)

GRYSTES SALMOIDES Cuvier and Valenciennes, 1829.—" Tel est le *growler* de New York, dont nous devons la connaissance à M. Milbert, mais qui n'a point été décrit par M. Mitchill."

"Ce nom de *growler*, qui signife *grogneur*, vient peut-être de quelque bruit qu'il fait entendre comme les sciènes ou les trigles, mais nous n'avons à cet égard aucun renseignement positif. *Grystes* en est l'équivalent grec.

"M. Le Sueur, croyant l'espèce nouvelle, en a public une description dans le Journal des sciences de Philadelphie, sous le nom de *cichla variabilis;* mais nous avons tout lieu de croire que c'est ce poisson qui est représenté et décrit par M. de Lacépède (t. IV, p. 716 et 717, et pl. 5, fig. 2) sous le nom de *labre salmoïde*, d'après des notes et une figure fournies par M. Bosc, qui le nommait *perca trutta*. La figure en est un peu rude, mais la description s'accorde avec ce que nous avons vu, sauf quelques détails, qui tiennent peut-être moins au poisson même qu'à la manière dont il a éte observé.

"Ce prétendu labre, au rapport de M. Bosc, est très-commun dans les rivières de la Caroline, où on lui a transporté le nom de *trout* (c'est-à-dire *truite*). Il atteint deux pieds de longueur. C'est un excellent manger; sa chair est ferme et savoureuse. On le prend aisément à l'hameçon, surtout en mettant un morceau, de cyprin pour appât.

"Le growler a à peu près la forme d'un serran. Sa plus grande hauteur, qui est vers le milieu, ne fait pas tout-à-fait le quart de sa longueur, et son epaisseur ne fait pas moitié de sa hauteur. La longueur de sa tête n'est que trois fois et demie dans sa longueur totale. Son profil descend très-peu. Sa mâchoire inférieure est un peu plus longue que l'autre, et a quatre ou cinq pores sous chacune de ses branches. De larges bandes de dents en velours les garnissent toutes les deux, ainsi que le devant de son vomer et ses palatins. Le bord de son préopercule est parfaitement entier, et a l'angle un peu arrondi. L'opercule osseux se termine par deux pointes peu aiguës, dont la supérieure est la plus courte. La membrane branchiale a six et quelquefois sept rayons, variation qui est assez singulière, mais que nous avons constatée. Les os de l'épaule sont lisses, mais entiers, comme le préopercule. Le sous-orbitaire a quelques rides. Les écailles sont médiocres : il y en a quatre-vingt-dix sur une ligne longitudinale, et trente-six ou quarante sur une verticale. Son front, son museau, ses mâchoires, le limbe de son préopercule, la membrane des ouïes en manquent ; mais il y en a sur sa joue et ses pièces operculaires. Il en porte de petites sur les parties molles de sa dorsale et de son anale, et sur la caudale. Toutes sont finement ciliées et pointillées à leur partie visible, et ont huit crénelures à leur base. La ligne latérale, un peu arquée vers le bas, à son origine, suit du reste à peu près la courbure du dos. La dorsale ne commence que sur le milieu des pectorales. Les épines sont faibles ; la plus haute, qui est la quatrième, n'a pas le tiers de la hauteur du tronc sous elle. L'echancrure entre la pénultième et la dernière est prononcée ; l'anale ne commence que sous sa partie molle. Les deux nageoires finissent vis-à-vis l'une de l'autre, et laissent entre elles et la caudale un espace qui fait presque le quart de la longueur totale. La caudale se termine un peu en croissant ; les pectorales et les ventrales sont petites ou médiocres.

D. 10, 13 ou 14 ; A. 3, 11 ou 12 ; C. 17 ; P. 16 ; V. 1, 5.

"Tout ce poisson, devenu adulte, est d'un brun-verdâtre foncé, avec une tache d'un noir bleuâtre à la pointe de l'opercule.

"Nous avons reçu, par M. Milbert, un individu de huit à neuf pouces et un de six à sept. C'est ce dernier qui a six rayons à la membrane des ouïes et quatorze rayons mous à la dorsale.

"Plus tard, M. Le Sueur nous en a envoyé de la rivière Wabash un individu long de seize pouces, et trois autres qui n'en ont guère que cinq. Les jeunes sont d'un vert plus pâle, et ont sur chaque flanc vingt-cinq à trente lignes longitudinales et parallèles brunes, qui paraissent s'effacer avec l'âge.

" Le foie du growler est très-petit, presque entièrement placé dans le côte gauche ; l'œsophage, très-court, se dilate en un estomac ovale assez grand, à parois minces et sans plis. Le pylore, près du cardia, est large et entouré de quatorze appendices cœcales, dont dix à gauche et quatre à droite, assez grasses et assez longues. L'intestin remonte jusque sous le diaphragme, descend jusqu'auprès de l'anus, puis retourne jusqu'auprès du pylore, d'ou il va droit à l'anus. Son dernier repli a deux étranglemens assez marqués. La rate est petite, au milieu de l'abdomen, près de la pointe de l'estomac. La vessie natatoire, très-grande, mince, peu argentée, s'étend depuis le diaphragme jusqu'aupres de l'anus. Tout le péritoine a un bel éclat d'argent. L'estomac était rempli d'une grande quantité de fourmis ailées, de tipules de cousins et autres petits insectes volans, communs sur les eaux donces."—(CUVIER AND VALENCIENNES, *Hist. Nat. des Poiss.* III, 54, 1829.)

GRYSTES SALMOIDES Jardine, 1835.—"D. 10, 13 or 14; A. 3, 11 or 12; C. 17; P. 16; V. 1, 5.

"Growler is the provincial American name for this fish, which Cuvier thinks has been given from some noise or croaking sound uttered by it. Two fish only have yet been discovered which will rank under its character; the present a native of North America and another produced from the New Holland seas. In form of the body they somewhat resemble the last, but are at once distinguished from them and the preceding forms, by the smoothness and the want of any covering on the head; the opercle and preopercle having neither spines nor teeth on their margins. The present species, a native of the North American waters, and abundant in the neighborhood of New York, has been named *Salmoides*, from its resemblence to the salmon or trout, being in some parts termed 'Trout.' It reaches a length of two feet, is of excellent flavor, and is much esteemed as an article of food; and it affords sport to the angler, taking the hook readily. The general colors, an unobtrusive tint of olive, lightening towards the under parts where it becomes grayish white. The first dorsal fin is weaker in proportion than most of the forms we have already seen, but the last rises high behind

and assumes a shape somewhat like that of some of the Greylings. The tail is shaped a good deal like the *Salmoidæ*, and in
this fish has a dark bar across the center."—(JARDINE, *Nat. Lib.*
I, *Perches*, 158, 1835.)

CICHLA FASCIATA and CICHLA OHIENSIS Kirtland, 1838.—
"The Black Bass of the Lake and of the Ohio River. Le Sueur
has described them as distinct species. I have no doubt they
are specifically identical. They differ in form and color at different seasons and in different localities, and even the same individual will change its color repeatedly in a short space of time
if confined in a vessel of water.

"Rafinesque has described that from the Ohio under the
generic name of *Lepomis*, and taken these changings of color as
a distinction upon which he has founded several of his species.
His Lepomis notata is no other than the young of the common
Black Bass. Their appearance varies at different ages.

"This fish readily bites at a hook, and is valued as an article
of food."—(KIRTLAND, *Rept. Zool. Ohio,* 191, 1838.)

CICHLA MINIMA Kirtland, 1838.—"Le Sueur describes this
as an inhabitant of Lake Erie. I am suspicious it is only the
young of the preceding species, as I have never been able to find
it, though I have searched repeatedly in the lake and its tributaries."—(KIRTLAND, *Rept. Zool. Ohio,* in 2*d Geol. Rept. Ohio,*
191, 1838.)

CENTRARCHUS FASCIATUS Kirtland, 1842.—"This species
presents such a variety of forms, colors and habits, and is so
much influenced by age, sex, seasons and locality, it is not remarkable that its varieties should have been described as distinct species. Still I am convinced that the synonyms I have
enumerated embrace only one true species (these are *Lepomis
pallida, trifasciata* and *flexuolaris* Raf., Icth. Ohiensis, p. 30, 31;
Etheostoma calliura Raf., Icth. Ohiensis, p. 36; *Cichla fasciata*
Le Sueur, J. A. N. S.; *C. fasciata* Kirtland, Report Zool.
Ohio; *C. Ohiensis* Le Sueur, J. A. N. S.); and I am inclined to

add to them *C. minima* of Le Sueur, as I have never been able
to find in the lagoons about our rivers and the lake any fish
that answers to his description, except the young of the Black
Bass at a certain stage of growth.

"This species is found universally in our western waters. It
frequently is taken by hooks and in seines, and also gives amuse-
ment to our marksmen in the spring, when it runs into shallow
water for the purpose of spawning. At this time it is often
shot with rifles. Its flesh resembles in flavor that of the Black
Fish (*Tautoga Americana* Cuv.) and by many persons is esteemed as the best fish for the table that our western waters afford."—(KIRTLAND, *Bost. Jour. Nat. Hist.* V, 28, 1842.)

GRYSTES SALMOIDES DeKay, 1842.—"Greatest depth, to its
length as one to four nearly; its thickness not quite half of its
depth. Profile not very declivous. Lower jaw longest with 4
or 5 pores under each of its branches. Minute teeth in broad
bands. Opercle terminates in two moderate points, of which
the uppermost is short. Branchial rays six and occasionally
seven; a notable variation, but which is positively established.
Humeral bone smooth. Scales ciliate, moderate; ninety in a
longitudinal series and 36–40 in a vertical line. Scales only on
the opercular bones and cheeks; small ones on the soft portion of
dorsal, anal and caudal fins. Lateral line concurrent with the
back. Dorsal fin commences about the middle of the pectorals;
the fourth ray highest. Pectoral and ventral fins small. Caudal fin slightly crescent shaped.

"The adult, deep greenish brown, with a bluish black spot on
the point of the opercle; young with from 25–30 brownish longitudinal bands, which appear to become effaced with age. Length
6′0–24′0. (Copied from Cuvier.) Fin rays: D. 10, 13 or 14;
P. 16; V. 1, 5; A. 3, 11 or 12; C. 17."—(DeKAY, *Fishes
N. Y.* 26, 1842.)

CENTRARCHUS FASCIATUS DeKay, 1842.—"Body compressed;
back arched gibbous; profile descending obliquely to the rostrum,

which is moderately prolonged; scales large, truncate and with radiating plaits at the radical portion; the free portion small, rounded, concentrically striate, minutely denticulate on the margin; scales on the opercle large, with a single series on the subopercle, much smaller on the preopercle, and ascend high up on the membrane of the soft dorsal and caudal fins; the intraorbital region and the jaw scaleless; lateral line concurrent with the back; eyes moderate; nostrils double, vertical, contiguous; the anterior on its posterior border with a membranous valve, near these a few open pores; opercles pointed with a loose membrane; lower jaw somewhat advanced with a single series of from eight to ten distant pores beneath; both jaws armed with a broad patch of minute conic acute recurved teeth; an oblong patch of rasp-like teeth on the vomer, and a long band of similar teeth on the palatines; a transverse membrane on the anterior part of both jaws; a small patch of minute teeth on the center of the tongue, which is free and thin on the margins; branchial arches minutely toothed on the upper surface near the tongue, with long serrate, spinous processes above; pharyngeal teeth in rounded patches; branchial rays six. Dorsal fin commences slightly behind the pectorals; the anterior portion consists of nine stout spines, received into a sheath below; the first is shorter than the second, which again is not so long as the third, and this latter is subequal with the remainder; a small and not very evident depression separates it from the other portion, which consists of 1 spinous and 14 branched rays; it terminates above the end of the anal; this portion of the dorsal fin is high, and somewhat rounded; the second simply articulated, not branched, and the three posterior rays successively shorter; the pectorals under the posterior angle of the opercle broad and obtusely pointed; it contains 18 rays, of which the 5, 6, and 7 are the longest; ventral fins placed slightly behind the pectorals and composed of 5 robust branched rays; anal fin higher than long, commencing under the third soft ray of the dorsal and composed of 3 spinous and 12 articulated rays, of which latter the 4, 5, 6, 7 are longest; the first spinous ray very short, the second slightly longer, and the third double the length of the preceding; caudal fin emarginate, tips rounded, and composed of 16 flat robust, multifid and six accessory rays on each side; length 13.5; of head, 4.0; greatest depth, 4.2; fin rays, D. 9.1,14; P. 18; V. 5; A. 3, 12; C. 16⅚

This species is common in the great lakes and in the numerous smaller ones in this state, where it is generally known under the name of Black Bass. This species appears to differ very much in different localities, not only in color but in form, and according to Dr. Kirtland, the same individual will change its color repeatedly in a short space of time if confined in a vessel of water."—(DeKay, *Fishes N. Y.* 28, 1842.)

Centrarchus obscurus DeKay, 1842.—"Body compressed, regularly arched above, not gibbous, highest along the spinous portion of the dorsal fin; scales small, orbicular, concentrically striate on their free surfaces, covering the head and body and rising very slightly on the base of the dorsal; lateral line tubular above the upper margin of the opercle; makes a curve downwards over the point of the opercle, then rises a little anterior to the first spinous ray of the dorsal, and then becomes concurrent with the line of the back; head moderately small, and somewhat pointed, sloping gradually to the nape, thence ascending more rapidly to the dorsal ray; eyes very large; nostrils double, distant, the posterior largest; a small mucous pore below the anterior nostril; lower jaw longest; numerous fine teeth in both jaws, very acute and recurved, forming many rows in front and fewer on the sides of the jaw; still more minute teeth on the vomer and palatines; opercular bones scaly; the opercle with a membranous margin, and terminating in a flat point, which is occasionally double; the dorsal fin arises behind the base of the pectorals, composed of 9 spinous and 13 simple rays; the first spinous is shortest; the first of the soft portion simple, the remainder articulated and much higher than the spinous portion; it is coterminal with the anal fin; pectorals oblong and composed of 16 rays; the upper ray subspinous, simple; ventral fin pointed, contiguous, composed of 1 spinous and 5 branched rays; anal rounded of 3 spinous and 12 branched rays, the first spine short, the others gradually longer; caudal fin emarginate of 17 entire and 3 accessory rays on each side. All the rays of this fin are broad and compressed, with scales ascending high up towards their extremities; a general greenish brown or dark olive with a faint metallic bronze on the upper parts, beneath lighter; length, 6.0–8.0; fins, D. 9.1, 12; P. 16; V. 1, 5; A, 3, 12; C. $17\frac{3}{3}$. This species was obtained from Onondaga creek, there called Black Bass."—(DEKAY, *Fishes N. Y.* 30, 1842.)

GRYSTES SALMOIDES Storer, 1846.—"The adult fish is of a deep greenish brown color, with bluish black spot at the angle of the operculum; the posterior portion of the dorsal fin rises high, and resembles somewhat that of some of the Greylings; the tail is shaped much like that of the Salmonidæ, and has a dark brown band crossing its center. The young are marked with numerous longitudinal bands. D. 10, 13 or 14; P. 16; V. 1, 5; A. 3, 11 or 12; C. 17; length, 2 ft."—(STORER, *Synopsis Fish. N. A.* 36, 1846.) (Copied.)

CENTRARCHUS FASCIATUS Storer, 1846.—"Body compressed; back arched and gibbous; of a dusky bluish color, often with transverse bands; anal fin with three spines. D. 9, 1, 14; P. 18; V. 5; A. 3, 12; C. $16\frac{6}{6}$; length, 18 to 20 in."—(STORER, *Synopsis Fish. N. A.* 38, 1846.) (Copied.)

CENTRARCHUS OBSCURUS Storer, 1846.—"Body not gibbous, of a general greenish brown or dark olive color, with faint metallic bronze on upper parts; beneath lighter. D. 9, 1, 12; P. 16; V. 1, 5; A. 3, 12; C. $17\frac{3}{3}$; length, 6 in."—(STORER, *Synopsis Fishes N. A.* 40, 1846.) (Copied.)

GRYSTES FASCIATUS Agassiz, 1850. — "This species is very closely allied to the *Grystes salmoides* of the Southern States, from which it is,* however, distinguished by the profile of the more raised back, and of course by a broader body. The surface of the skull is uniformly rounded and not depressed, as in *G. salmoides;* the proportions of the head compared with the body are the same as in this latter, but the mouth is less opened, and the shorter labials do not reach a vertical line drawn across the hinder margin of the orbits, whilst they exceed such a line in *G. salmoides;* the teeth are arranged like cards, and are similar in both species. The fins upon the whole seem to be cut on the same pattern as in *G. salmoides,* but when we examine them attentively, we see that they are all stabbed like the body itself; the ventrals and pectorals shorter and more widened; the dorsal and anal lower. As for the other details of their structure they are about the same, as we may see from the following formula:

Br. 6; D. X, 14; A. III, 10; C. 7, 1, 8, 7, 1, 6; V. 1, 5; P. 16.

"The scales are a little smaller, but of the same form as in *G. salmoides;* the radiating striæ are perhaps less marked; they cover the opercular apparatus and the cheeks, but at this latter place their smaller size is quite remarkable; this latter character is very striking when we compare both species.

"Our specimens are from Lake Huron; one of them measures twelve inches, and the other seven. I have also received two specimens from Lake Michigan, through the care of Mr. Samuel C. Clarke, the largest of ,which measures eighteen inches. Professor Baird forwarded to me specimens from Lake Champlain. Dr. DeKay has found it in Lake Oneida. Finally, this species extends to Pennsylvania, as I was able to convince myself by two specimens collected at Toxburg, and for which

---

* " *Grystes salmoneus* does not occur in the Northern nor in the Middle States, although Dr. DeKay mentions it upon the authority of Cuvier, who probably mistook specimens of our *Grystes fasciatus* for the southern species. Having, however, failed to discover this confusion, Dr. DeKay describes the same fish again, under the name of *Centrarchus obscurus.*"— (AGASSIZ, *Lake Superior,* 295, 1850.)

I am under obligation to Professor Baird."—(AGASSIZ, *Lake Superior*, 295, 1850.)

CENTRARCHUS FASCIATUS Thompson, 1853.—"Form somewhat elliptical compressed, a little convex on the sides and pointed forwards; color dark greenish above, lighter and faintly mottled on the sides, and grayish white beneath; sides of the head fine light green; scales firm, moderate on the sides and operculum, but very small on the cheeks, back of the neck, throat, and belly; preoperculum with its upper limb nearly vertical and nearly at right angles with the lower, without spines or serratures; inter and suboperculum *upon the upper side and smooth below; operculum triangular, with a membranous prolongation posteriorly, and the bony part terminating posteriorly in two thin lobes with a deep notch between them, the lower lobe, which is the largest, ending in several short spines; teeth small, sharp, and numerous in both jaws, on the lower anterior edges of the palatine bones, and on the vomer, with a small cluster near the base of the triangular tongue, all standing like the pile on velvet, but looking a little inward, those on the jaws largest; fins small brownish and their soft parts covered with a rather thick mucous skin; the dorsal rounded behind, low at the junction of the spinous and soft parts, and the spinous rays capable of being reclined, imbricated, and concealed in a longitudinal groove along the back ; ventrals a little behind the pectorals; the anal under the posterior portion of the dorsal, and extending a little further back ; tail slightly emarginate, with the lobes rounded, vent a trifle nearest the posterior extremity; eyes moderately large ; lower jaw a trifle longer than the upper, with several visible pores along its margin ; length of the specimen before me, 19 in. The greatest depth equals one-third of the length, exclusive of the tail.—Rays: Br. 6; P. 17; B. 1, 5; D. 10, 15; A. 3, 11; C. 17.

"The Black Bass, by which name this fish is here generally known, ranks as one of the best fishes taken from our waters,

---

* The word "scaly" was evidently omitted here.—J. A. H.

but as is apt to be the case with good fishes, it is much less
abundant than several other species which are greatly its inferior
in point of quality. It is usually taken with the seine and its
weight varies from one to five or six pounds."—(THOMPSON, *Hist.
Vermont*, 131, 1853.)

GRYSTES NIGRICANS Garlick, 1857.—"The body is compressed, oval, back arched; of a dusky greenish color, often
with transverse bands, with 3 oblique stripes on the operculum
or cheek. . . . The Black Bass, when full grown, measures
from 12 to 18 inches in length. The largest one by far that I
have ever seen was caught last summer by Prof. Ackley in the
Cuyahoga River: its length was a little over 22 inches, and must
have weighed 8 pounds or more.

"This fish is found from the St. Lawrence to the tributaries
of the Ohio, and perhaps still further south; it is quite common
in all the rivers and lakes of Ohio and all the Western States.

"He is a bold biter, and when hooked fights with the most determined fury to the very last, affording the best of sport to the
angler, and is excelled but by a very few fish when placed upon
the table."—(GARLICK, *Treat. Art. Prop. Fish*, 105, 1857.)

GRISTES SALMOIEDES Herbert, 1859.—"This fish, in general
form, closely corresponds with that last described [*G. nigricans*].
It has the same gibbous back, with the lateral line following the
dorsal curve, and the same protruded lower jaw. Its teeth are,
set minutely in broad bands or patches. The operculum has
two moderate points.

"Its color is deep greenish brown, with a bluish black spot on
the point of the operculum. When young it has 25 or 30 longitudinal brownish bands, which become effaced by age.

"The first dorsal has 10 spines, the second 13 or 14 soft
rays; the pectorals 16 soft rays; the ventrals 1 spine and 5 soft
rays; the anal 3 spines and 11 or 12 soft rays; the caudal fin,
which is slightly lunate, has 17 soft rays."—(HERBERT, *Fish and
Fishing*, 197, 1859.)

GRYSTES SALMONOIDES Günther, 1859.—"B. 6–7; D. $\frac{10}{13.14}$; A. $\frac{3}{11.12}$; L. Lat. 90. Cæc. Pylor, 14 and more. The height of the body is nearly one-fourth of the total length; the length of the head is contained $3\frac{1}{2}$ therein. Lower jaw prominent. Preoperculum and suprascapular entire. Operculum with two spines. Præorbital with or without some slight denticulations; pectoral and ventral fins short. The fourth dorsal spine longest; the second of the anal much shorter than the third. Caudal is slightly notched. Uniform greenish brown, with a black spot at the posterior angle of the operculum. Young with indistinct longitudinal streaks."—(GÜNTHER, *Cat. Fishes Brit. Mus.* I, 252, 1859.)

CENTRARCHUS FASCIATUS Günther, 1859.—"D. $\frac{10}{14}$; A. $\frac{3}{12}$. Body gibbous; the height is $3\frac{1}{2}$ in the total length. Dusky bluish, often with transverse bands."—(GUNTHER, *Cat. Fishes Brit. Mus.* I, 258, 1859.)

CENTRARCHUS OBSCURUS Günther, 1859.—"D. $\frac{10}{12}$; A. $\frac{3}{12}$. Body rather elongate, not gibbous; the height is one-fourth of the total length. Uniform greenish brown."—(GÜNTHER, *Cat. Fishes Brit. Mus.* I, 258, 1859.)

LEPOMIS ACHIGAN Gill, 1860.—"Rafinesque first indicated the *Cichla fasciata* of Le Sueur, or *Centrarchus obscurus* of DeKay under the name of *Bodianus achigan*. His specific name must be preserved."—(GILL, *Pro. Ac. Nat. Sci. Phil.* 20, 1860.)

CENTRARCHUS FASCIATUS Roosevelt, 1862.—"The gill cover has two flat points, the teeth are minute, while the back fin, though single, is partly divided into 2. It contains 10 hard and 14 soft rays, the ventral 6, the first one almost spinous, the anal 3 spines, the first very short, and 12 soft rays, and the tail 16 soft rays."—(ROOSEVELT, *Game Fish of the North*, 218, 1862.)

GRYSTES NIGRICANS Norris, 1864.—"The color of this fish, which appears to vary with the locality or the season, is generally dark olive green on the back, shading gradually into a brownish yellow on the sides; belly opaque white. Body compressed oval, back arched, belly less curved than the superior outlines; breadth as 2 to 7. Lateral line concurrent with the back. Head small, little less than $\frac{1}{4}$ the length of body; preopercle covered with small scales, scales larger on opercle. The eye is on a line between the snout and posterior angle of the opercle, $\frac{1}{3}$ distant from snout, and is about $\frac{5}{8}$ of an inch in diameter; the irides are dark brown above and pale yellow below. Nostrils small, double. Tongue toothless; both jaws with small brush-like teeth, small patches of the same on each side the pharynx as well as on the branchial arches. Branchial rays 7. The first dorsal fin has 10 sharp spines, the anterior ray being short. The second dorsal is covered at its base with scales, and has 15 rays, preceded by an obtuse spine of $\frac{1}{2}$ their length; this fin is arched and rounded posteriorly. The pectorals beginning immediately beneath the point of the opercle are yellow, nearly obovate in shape, and have 18 rays. Ventrals commencing slightly posteriorly have 5 branched rays. The anal terminating beneath the posterior point of the second dorsal has 2 sharp, and 1 longer obtuse spine, and 12 branched rays. The caudal is very slightly forked and has 18 rays. . . . This fish differs from the Oswego Bass, to which it has so close a resemblance, in having a smaller head, and its belly less protuberant, though the position of the fins, their shape, and number of spines and rays, are almost identical."—(NORRIS, *Am. Angler's Book*, 103, 1864.)

MICROPTERUS ACHIGAN Gill, 1866.—"The common smallmouthed species (*Micropterus achigan*) is, in truth, well entitled to command the efforts of the pisiculturist, and could be introduced most advantageously into many sheets of water at present affording fishes of inferior quality."—(GILL, *Rept. Com. Agric.* 408, 1866.)

GRYSTES FASCIATUS Putnam, 1867.—"This species, which is the common Lake Bass and Black Bass of the great lakes, Lake

Champlain and several lakes in New York, and which also extends further south, has been introduced into Great Sandy Lake in Wareham. In the summer of 1862 a specimen of this fish was caught in Massachusetts Bay by one of the members of the state legislature, and is now in the state cabinet. The fish had evidently found the salt water not much to its liking, as it was much emaciated, and had changed so in its general appearance as at first sight hardly to be recognized."—(PUTNAM, *Storer's Fishes Mass.* 278, 1867.)

MICROPTERUS FASCIATUS Cope, 1868.—"This specimen is abundant in Holston River; individuals are identical with others from Miami River; Indiana; Wabash; Kiskiminitas; from Michigan and Lake George, N. Y. It grows to a considerable size and is much valued for food.

"The absence or rarity of this species and the *Ambloplites rupestris* in the Kanawha River, in Giles County and above is remarkable. During a residence of six weeks on its banks, I never caught or saw a specimen of either, and they are not clearly known to the fishermen."—(COPE, *Jour. Ac. Nat. Sci. Phil.* VI, 216, 1868.)

MICROPTERUS SALMOIDES Gill, 1873.—"Scales small, in about 70 to 80 oblique rows between the head and caudal, and 11 longitudinal ones between the back and lateral line, decreasing very much towards the nape and (especially) the breast; forming a sheath encroaching considerably upwards upon the soft portion and last spine of the dorsal. Head transversely (slightly) convex between the orbits, with (1) scales on the operculum larger than those of the nape, (2) on the suboperculum (in front) in two rows, (3) on the interoperculum narrow, mostly invested in the membrane (in one row), (4) on the cheeks very small (in about 17 to 20 rows), and (5) on the preoperculum none. Mouth moderate, the gape from the symphysis to the angle being little more than one-third (1: 2$\frac{1}{3}$) of the head's length. Supramaxillary ending in advance of vertical from the hinder margin of the orbit (about under the posterior border of the pupil).

"Dorsal fin with its anterior spines rapidly graduated (I=1; II=1·5; III=1·90; IV=2·05; V=2·30) to the fifth; fifth, sixth and seventh longest and about equal to the space between the back and lateral line; the succeeding ones very gradually diminishing to the ninth which is shortest (three-fourths—1: 1·25—of fifth) the tenth being about as long as the eighth and about a third shorter than the longest, *i. e.*, fifth.

"Dorsal fin with scales differentiated from those of the sheath, and advancing high up on the membrane behind each soft ray (except the last two or three).

"Anal fin with scales ascending high on the membrane behind the several rays.

"Color, in young and adolescent, bronzed grayish, with (1) irregular darker spots, tending to arrangement in three series alternating with each other above the lateral line, and (2) indistinctly maculated with darker and yellow below; head dark above, gray on sides, with three oblique or horizontal bands, viz.: (1) from margin of· upper jaw to below angle of preoperculum, (2) from lower angle of orbit to margin of preoperculum, (3) from hinder border of orbit to angle of operculum, and with a crescentiform band (curved forwards) in front of the forehead between the eyes; spinous dorsal simply punctulated with dark; the soft with a series of bronzed spots between the respective rays; and greenish with a marginal band of grayish-white; in adults the markings are more or less obliterated and the color a uniform dead green."—(GILL, *Pro. Am. Asso. Adv. Sci.* XXII, B. 69, 1873.)

MICROPTERUS SALMOIDES Uhler and Lugger, 1876.—"Elongated oval, arched; thick and rounded along the back; thinner and nearly straight at the belly. Head very large and thick, especially between the eyes, snout full and rounded; eyes very large. Head and body dusky above, with a greenish or bronzed tint; lower jaw and belly white; along the flanks runs a dusky band, more or less distinct according to the age of the fish; a bluish-black spot on the point of the opercle. Total length 14 inches, but occasionally 24 inches. "Fin rays :—D. 9, 14; P. 14; V. 1, 5; A. 3, 12; C. 19."— (UHLER & LUGGER, *Fishes of Md.* < *Rept. Fish Com. Md.* 111, 1876.)

MICROPTERUS SALMOIDES Jordan, 1877.—"In the Etowah, Oostanaula, and Coosa Rivers [Ga,], . . . The yellow and black caudal markings, so striking in young specimens from the Ohio River, and which suggested to Rafinesque the name of *Calliurus*, are not well shown by my specimens. The lower fins are unusually red, and there is a tendency to the formation of parallel lines of dusky spots along the rows of scales. These peculiarities perhaps indicate a permanent variety."—(JORDAN, *Ann. N. Y. Lyc. Nat. Hist.* XI, 315, 1877.)

MICROPTERUS SALMOIDES Jordan, 1877.—"The peculiar coloration of the caudal fin which suggested the name of *Calliurus*, 'base yellow, middle blackish, tip white,' belongs among Ohio fishes only to the young of the Black Bass. *Calliurus*, therefore, as shown by Professor Gill, is a synonym of *Micropterus*, and can not be applied to a distinct genus."—(JORDAN, *Contrib. N. A. Ich.* No. 1. < *Bull. U. S. Nat. Mus.* IX, 18, 1877.)

MICROPTERUS SALMOIDES Hallock, 1877.—"Head and body dusky above, often with a greenish or bronzed tint; lower jaw and belly white; opercle with a bluish-green spot at its angle. Along the flanks runs a dusky band, which is more or less apparent according to the age of the fish. It is most remarked in the young. Fins yellowish."—(HALLOCK, *Sportsman's Gazetteer*, 373, 1877.)

MICROPTERUS SALMOIDES Jordan, 1878.—"Dark green; young brighter and more or less barred and spotted, but without lateral band; tail yellow at base, then black, and edged with white; opercle with oblique olivaceous streaks; third dorsal spine half larger than first; dorsal notch rather shallow; scales smaller than in *M. pallidus*—eleven rows between lateral line and dorsal; mouth smaller; anal nearly scaleless; D. X, 13; A. III, 11; lat. l. 70 to 80. Great lakes and streams from L. Champlain S. and W.; common in New York and in most regions west of the Alleghanies; introduced eastward." — (JORDAN, *Manual Vertebrates E. U. S.* 2d ed. 236, 1878.)

MICROPTERUS SALMOIDES (LAC.) HENSHALL.

THE LARGE-MOUTHED BLACK BASS.

SYNONYMY.

1802—*Labrus salmoides* LACÉPÈDE, Hist. Nat. des Poiss. IV, 716.

Grystes salmoides AGASSIZ, Lake Superior, 295, 1850.

Grystes salmoides HOLBROOK, Ich. So. Car. 25, 1855, and 2d ed. 28, 1860.

Grystes salmoides NORRIS, Am. Angler's Book, 99, 1864. (In part.)

Dioplites salmoides VAILLANT & BOCOURT, MSS, Miss. Sci. au Mexique, 1874.

Micropterus salmoides VAILLANT & BOCOURT, Miss. Sci. au Mexique: ined.

1820—*Lepomis pallida* RAFINESQUE, Ich. Ohiensis, 30.

Micropterus pallidus JORDAN, Ann. N. Y. Lyc. Nat. Hist. XI, 314, 1877.

Micropterus pallidus JORDAN, Bull. U. S. Nat. Mus. IX and X, 1877.

Micropterus pallidus JORDAN, Bull. U. S. Nat. Mus. XII, 1878.

Micropterus pallidus JORDAN, Hayd. Geol. Surv. Ter. Bull. IV, No. 2, 435, 1878.

Micropterus pallidus JORDAN, Man. Vert. E. U. S. 2d ed., 236, 1878.

Micropterus pallidus GOODE, Pro. U. S. Nat. Mus. II, 115, 1879.

Micropterus pallidus GOODE & BEAN, Bull. Essex Inst. XI, 19, 1879.

Micropterus pallidus GOODE & BEAN, Pro. U. S. Nat. Mus. II, 138, 1879.

Micropterus pallidus HENSHALL, Rept. Fish Com. Ohio, 31, 1879.

Micropterus pallidus JORDAN, Pro. U. S. Nat. Mus. III, 17, 1880.

1822—*Cichla floridana* LE SUEUR, Jour. Ac. Nat. Sci. Phil. II, 219.

Micropterus floridanus GOODE, Bull. U. S. Nat. Mus. VI, 63, 1876. (Name only.)

1828—*Huro nigricans* CUVIER & VALENCIENNES, Hist. Nat. des Poiss. II, 124.

Huro nigricans JARDINE, Nat. Lib. I, Perches, 108, 1835.

Huro nigricans RICHARDSON, Fau. Bor. Am. III, 4, 1836.

Huro nigricans DEKAY, Fishes N. Y. 15, 1842.

Huro nigricans STORER, Syn. Fishes N. A. 25, 1846.

Grystes nigricans AGASSIZ, Lake Superior, 297, 1850.

Grystes nigricans HERBERT, Fish and Fishing, 195, 1859.

Huro nigricans GÜNTHER, Cat. Fishes Brit. Mus. I, 255, 1859.

Huro nigricans ROOSEVELT, Game Fish of the North, 219, 1862.

Micropterus nigricans COPE, Pro. Ac. Nat. Sci. Phil. 83, 1865. (Name only.)

Micropterus nigricans GILL, Rept. Com. Agric. 407, 1866.

Micropterus nigricans COPE, Pro. Am. Phil. Soc. 451, 1870.

Micropterus nigricans GILL, Pro. Am. Asso. Adv. Sci. B. 70, 1873.

Micropterus nigricans JORDAN, Ind. Geol. Surv. 214, 1874.

Micropterus nigricans JORDAN, Man. Vert. E. U. S. 229, 1876.

Micropterus nigricans HALLOCK, Sportsman's Gazetteer, 273, 1877. (In part.)

1854—*Grystes nobilis* AGASSIZ, Am. Jour. Sci. Art, XVII, 298.

Grystes nobilis PUTNAM, Bull. Mus. Comp. Zool. I, 6, 1863. (Name only.)

1854—*Grystes nuecensis* BAIRD & GIRARD, Pro. Ac. Nat. Sci. Phil. VII, 25.

Dioplites nuecensis GIRARD, U. S. Pac. R. R. Surv. X, Fishes, 4, 1858.

Grystes nuecensis GÜNTHER, Cat. Fishes Brit. Mus. I, 252, 1859. (Name only.)

Dioplites nuecensis GIRARD, U. S. Mex. Bound. Surv. II, 3, 1859.

Dioplites nuecensis VAILLANT & BOCOURT, MSS. Miss. Sci. au Mexique, 1874.

Micropterus nuecensis VAILLANT & BOCOURT, Miss. Sci. au Mexique : ined.

1857—*Grystes megastoma* GARLICK, Treat. Art. Prop. Fish, 108, 1857.

1874—*Dioplites treculii* VAILLANT & BOCOURT, MSS. Miss. Sci. au Mexique, 1874. (Zoölogie, pt. IV, plate IV, f. 2. No description ; the species since identified by its authors with *M. nuecensis.*)

ETYMOLOGY : *Salmoides*, trout-like ; salmon-like.

HABITAT : Red River of the North to Florida ; Virginia to Mexico ; introduced eastward.

Specific Descriptions.

LABRUS SALMOIDES Lacépède, 1802.—"Neuf rayons aiguillonés et treize rayons articulés à la nageoire du dos; treize rayon à la nageoire de l'anus; l'opercule composé de quatre lames, et terminé par une prolongation anguleuse; deux orifices à chaque narine; la couleur générale d'un brun noirâtre." [Br. 6; P. 13; V. 6; C. 18.]—(LACÉPÈDE, *Hist. Nat. des Poiss.* IV, 716, 1802.)

LEPOMIS PALLIDA Rafinesque, 1820.—"Olivaceous above, white beneath, a brown spot at the base of the lateral line, an obtuse appendage on the opercule, spine behind it: 3 faint obliqual streaks on the gill-covers; lower jaw longer: tail forked, pale yellow, tip brown.

"Not uncommon in the Ohio, Miami, Hockhocking, etc. Vulgar name, Yellow Bass; Common Bass, etc. Length from 4 to 12 inches. Shape elliptic, diameter one-fourth of the total length. Fins olivaceous, without streaks, dorsal depressed or interrupted in the middle, 9 spiny rays to the fore part, the medial longer, 1 spiny ray and 14 soft rays to the hind part. Anal fin rounded 13 rays, whereof 2 are spiny and short. Pectorals rounded with 14 rays; tail with 18; thoracics with 6. Eyes large, black, iris brown with a gold ring. Lateral line following the back, straight near the tail."—(RAFINESQUE, *Ich. Ohi.* 30, 1820.)

CICHLA FLORIDANA Le Sueur, 1822.—"Dorsal fin with 9 spinous rays anteriorly, and 15 soft ones posteriorly; anal with 3 spinous rays and twelve divided soft ones.

"The total length of this fish is one foot five inches, in depth 5 in. towards the dorsal fin; the body is attenuated; more obtuse anteriorly; snout short; inferior jaw a little longer than superior one; mouth deeply divided; intermaxillary bone long; maxillary bone prolonged unto the end of the eye; teeth very small, equal, approximate; card like before, smaller and more

10

delicate at the angles of the mouth, on the vomer and on the wings of the palate they are small and like velvet; eye round, near the summit of the head; scales rounded, large upon the sides near the pectoral fins, diminishing towards the back, and in approaching the tail and the abdomen, smaller, and subequal on all the pieces of the operculum; the snout and the upper part of the head are destitute of scales; mandible and post mandible very strong and broad; dorsal fin divided into two nearly equal parts, the anterior spinous, elevated before, very low behind and but little arquated; the posterior part more elevated and rounded; the anal fin short, extending beyond the dorsal as in the species of the Ohio, so that its middle corresponds with the posterior base of the dorsal; the rays of the fins are also much divided and articulated; pectorals small and rounded; thoracic fins subtriangular, as long as the pectorals; operculum without any denticulation, or spine; lateral line oblique, undulated; the color of this dried specimen is black on the back and lighter towards the abdomen.

" We are indebted for this species to the researches of Messrs. Maclure, Ord, Say, and Peale, who brought it from East Florida."—(Le Sueur, *Jour. Ac. Nat. Sci. Phil.* II, 219, 1822.)

Huro nigricans Cuvier & Valenciennes, 1828.—" Il a le corps un peu plus haut à proportion que la perche; le museau un peu plus court; le front moins concave; sa mâchoire inferieure se porte un peu plus en avant. Sur son front se voient des stries fines et nombreuses, mais toutes dirigées vers le bord de l'orbite. Il a des dents en velours aux mêmes endroits que la perche; son maxillaire a le bord supérieur dilaté; son front, son museau, ses mâchoires, n'ont point d'écailles; mais il y en a sur son crâne, sa tempe, toute sa joue et toutes ses piéces operculaires, leurs bords exceptés. Le limbe de l'opercule en est dépourvu, et son bord parfaitement entier et sans dentalures s'arrondit dans le bas, après avoir fait un très-léger arc rentrant. L'opercule osseux se termine en deux pointes plates, séparées par une petite énchancrure aiguë et oblique. Aucune des piéces de l'épaule n'a de dentelure. La première dorsale, beaucoup plus petite qu'à la perche, n'a que six rayons, et demeure assez éloignée de la seconde, qui est plus élevée, et peut avoir avec ses deux épines douze ou treize rayons mous. (Elle est en partie mutilée dans notre individu.) L'anale a trois épines et onze rayons mous; elle est aussi un peu plus grande à proportion qu'à la perche. Quant aux pectorales et aux ventrales, elles sont à peu près pareilles à celles de la perche, et la caudale aussi.

B. 7; D. 6.–2, 12? A. 3, 11; C. 17; P. 15; V. 1, 5.

"On compte soixante et quelques écailles entre l'ouïe et la caudale, et vingt-cinq ou vingt-six entre la première dorsale et le ventre. Elles paraissent toutes lisses et entières.

" La couleur de ce poisson, que nous n'avons vu que desséché, paraît avoir approché de celle de la carpe. Son dos est d'un brun verdâtre, qui s'affaiblit sur les côtés, et passe sous le ventre au blanc-jau nâtre argenté; une ligne grisâtre suit le milieu de chaque rangée longitudinale d'écailles.

" L'individu que nous avons eu sous les yeux, était long de seize pouces.

" Nous laisserons à l'espèce l'épithète qu'elle porte dans son pays natal, *Huro nigricans*."—(CUVIER & VALENCIENNES, *Hist. Nat. des Poiss*. II, 124, 1828.)

HURO NIGRICANS Jardine, 1835. — " The first is the Black Bass or Black Perch of the English residents on the banks of the Huron. Its flesh is firm and white, and it is much esteemed during the summer. The upper parts of the fish are of an olive brown, changing into yellowish white on the belly, and along the central ridge of each scale is a line of the same color with the upper parts, giving it a striped appearance on the sides; the body is rather deep in proportion ; the under jaw slightly projects, and the head, cheeks and opercles are scaled ; the teeth are nearly similar to those of the perch ; the first dorsal is much less, contains only six rays, and is placed at a considerable distance in front of the second; the anal fin is again considerably larger in proportion and has three spiny, with eleven soft rays; the others are very similar to those of the perch. Cuvier's specimen was 16 in. in length, and although the flesh is esteemed, and seems abundant in its native country, little is yet known regarding it."—(JARDINE, *Nat. Lib.* I, Perches, 108, 1835.)

HURO NIGRICANS Richardson, 1836.—"Profile elliptical, the ellipsis commencing acutely in the somewhat pointed chin and conical head, but passing gradually into the thickish tail; the depth of the body is greatest under the first dorsal and appears to be about equal to the length of the head, or one-third of the total length, excluding the caudal; head flat above, covered with scales as far as the posterior margin of the orbit; the forehead shows a slight median ridge with a more prominent lateral one, and there are many fine streaks on the upper margin of the orbit; the anterior suborbital bone is marked by some short diverging ridges, and the under and posterior margin of the orbit is more distinctly roughened by many small irregular prominences; the orbit is circular, situated close to the forehead, and two of its own diameters and one-half above the articulation of the lower jaw; it is also a diameter and one-half behind the extremity of the upper jaw, and four diameters from the point of the suboperculum or most posterior part of the gill cover; the mouth acquires a somewhat vertical aspect from the chin or tip of the lower jaw, projecting about a quarter of an inch beyond it, and from its opening descending from the plane of the forehead, at a considerable angle as it runs backwards; the articulation of the lower jaw is opposite the posterior margin of the orbit; the labials have a lengthened triangular form, the narrow apex only passing under the edge of the suborbital bone; the posterior dilated and truncated extremity projects considerably beyond the tip of the intermaxillary and extends further back than the orbit; it is further widened by the addition of a superior piece, or apoplysis whose corner is rounded; there are no pores

in the lower jaw, but two circular openings of canals in the
bone are visible through the dried skin which covers them.
The opposing surfaces of the intermaxillaries and lower jaw are
covered with densely-crowded, curved, fine card-like teeth, or
as they ought, perhaps, to be called, in conformity with Cuvier's
nomenclature, rather coarse "dents en velours;" the dental surface being broad anteriorly and narrowing to a point behind;
the transverse, anterior, projecting extremity of the vomer and
the outer edges of the palate bones are armed with fine teeth "en
velours;" the dental surface of the latter narrowing to a point,
posteriorly, like those of the mandibles; there is, however, a detached but contiguous patch just beyond this point on the edge of
the palate; the whole vault of the palate is smooth; the tongue, as
we have already mentioned, has been removed, and if Mr. Todd's
account of the pharyngeal teeth be correct, they are not distributed
into the same number of patches as in the perch. Preoperculum
having a narrow upright limb, covered with smooth skin, there
being a single scale only just above its angle; the lower limb is
wider and has three scales in a single row which does not cover
half its surface; the whole edge of the bone is smooth and even,
with the exception of a very shallow, wide notch at the base of
the upper limb. The interoperculum is comparatively broad, its
depth exceeding that of either the preoperculum or suboperculum,
it is covered by a row of ten scales, which leave its under border
naked; the bony operculum has an acute oblique notch in its
posterior margin, producing two thin points; the lower point is
closely applied to the apex of the suboperculum, forming with it
one obtuse thin plate, which, together with the upper point,
are concealed by the membrane which borders them; the under
margin of the suboperculum is slightly waved, forming two obscure lobes; as in many, or perhaps in most of the percoideæ
with scaly gill covers, the margins of the pieces composing them
are covered with a smooth skin; there is even a wider naked
place than usual behind the points of the operculum, and the

anterior border of that bone is as wide and prominent as the
limb of the preoperculum to which it adjoins; the forehead,
snout, infraorbital bones, and margins of the orbits, mandibles,
labials, branchiostegous membranes and edges of the different
opercular bones, are covered with a smooth skin; the rest of
the head, including the temples and the top of the cranium as
far as the "linea rostri basalis," are clothed with tiled scales;
the bones lining the posterior edge of the gill openings are likewise scaleless, and their edges, though undulated, are destitute
of spines or serratures; the nape is supported by a median ridge
of the cranium and a thin lateral one on each side equally high;
there are also several interspinous bones anterior to the first
dorsal; the branchiostegous membrane contains 6 curved rays,
the anterior ones cylindrical, the posterior ones becoming more
and more flat and wider. Br. 6; D. 6–2, 8?: P. 15; V. 1, 5;
A. 3, 11; C. 17$\frac{7}{4}$.

"The pectorals consist of fiften rays, the first of which is short
and its articulations very obscure, being visible only at the tip
and with a lens; the ventrals are attached directly under the
pectorals and contain 6 rays, of which the first is spinous and
one-third shorter than the succeeding ones; the first dorsal consists of 6 acute spinous rays, having the connecting membrane
notched between them; the first ray is one-third shorter than the
third, which is the longest and stands about an inch behind the
insertion of the pectorals and ventrals, the fourth and fifth are
nearly as long as the third; the second dorsal is one-third higher
than the first, and commences nearly an inch behind the posterior
insertion of the membrane of the latter, the 2 anterior rays
are spinous and separated by membrane—the first of them equal
in height to the corresponding ray of the first dorsal, the first
ray is simple but articulated; the succeeding ones are branched
at the tips, and nearly equal to each other, the seventh being,
however, rather the highest; the fifth ray is opposite the anus,
and the tenth . . . . is opposite to the fifth of the anal;

the anal contains 15 rays, the two first of them shorter, spinous, and very acute, the branched rays equal those of the dorsal in height; the first dorsal ray stands half an inch behind the anus. If the fish, exclusive of the caudal fin, be divided into three parts, the head will form one, and the first spine of the anal will stand at the commencement of the third ; the space between the anal and the caudal considerably exceeds that occupied by the attachment of the former; the caudal is somewhat rounded and very slightly emarginated, its base is covered with small scales, which terminate by an even line rounded off on the three exterior rays, while they cover the accessory short rays above and below to their tips, thus producing a notch at each end of the line.   The scales are rather large, the exterior edge forming a segment of a circle, and being quite smooth, the sides almost parallel, and the base truncated and crenated in correspondence with 10 or 11 furrows which diverge from the center, like the sticks of a fan; there are 60 scales on the lateral line exclusive of about 9 smaller ones, forming a continuation of the same row on the base of the caudal, and 26 in a vertical row beneath the first dorsal, of which 7 are above the row which forms the lateral line; a linear inch measured along the sides includes 5 scales and one-half; the scales on the gill covers are a little smaller than those on the body, those on the cheeks are still less, and the scales on the caudal and on the space before the ventrals are the smallest of all; a scale taken from the lateral line under the first dorsal is $4\frac{3}{4}$ lines wide and $3\frac{1}{2}$ lines long; the lateral line runs parallel to the curvature of the back and is distant from the belly—it is marked by a tubular elevation on each scale ; back and sides dark, with a faint longitudinal streak through the center of each row of scales; belly yellowish white."—(RICHARDSON, *Faun. Bor. Am.* III, 4, 1836.)

HURO NIGRICANS DeKay, 1842.—"General form that of the Perch; greatest depth of body under the first dorsal, and equal to one-third the length of body; scales large, smooth, covering the head as far as the orbit, and extending also on the opercles; lateral line tubular, concurrent with the dorsal outline; head flattened above with striæ diverging to the orbits. Lower jaw directed obliquely upwards and projecting 0.25 beyond the upper; velvet-like teeth on the jaws, vomer, and palatines; tongue ——; the bony opercle has an acute, oblique notch on its posterior margin, producing two thin points ; the branchial membrane, according to Cuvier, with 7 rays. Richardson enumerates but 6. The first dorsal small; its third ray longest, the fourth and fifth nearly as long; the second dorsal an inch behind the first and one-third higher; the two first rays spinous, short; the first ray articulated, simple, the remainder branched. In the only specimen hitherto examined the rays of this fin were injured, but Cuvier supposes there must have been 12 or 13, only 8 were visible; pectorals with the first ray very short; ventrals immediately beneath them ; anal, with its branched rays, equal in height to those of second dorsal; caudal slightly emarginate, with its tips rounded. Color, taken from a dried specimen, back and sides dark, with a faint longitudinal streak through the center of each row of scales; belly yellowish white. Length 17.5; Fins, D. 6–2, 8, or 12; P. 15; V. 1, 5; A. 3, 11; C. 17⅞.

"This is a remarkably firm and well flavored fish, taken readily with the hook during the summer months in Lake Huron, where it is called Black Bass. It will probably be found in Lake Erie, and of course within the limits of the State. As I have not seen it, I have availed myself of the descriptions and figure given by Cuvier and Valenciennes. Its history is yet imperfect, nor with our present knowledge can we assign it positively its proper place in the family."—(DeKay, *Fishes N. Y.* 15, 1842.)

HURO NIGRICANS Storer, 1846.—"Above of an olive brown, changing into yellowish white on the belly and along the central ridge of each scale is a line of the same color with the upper parts, giving it a striped appearance on the sides; the first dorsal fin is smaller than that of the Perch, and is placed at a considerable distance in front of the second; the anal fin is somewhat larger in proportion. D. 6–2, 12; P. 15; V. 1, 5; A. 3, 11; C. 17; Cuv. & Val. D. 6–2, 8; P. 15; V. 1, 5; A. 3, 11; C. 17$\frac{7}{4}$. Rich."—(STORER, *Synopsis Fish. N. A.* 25, 1846.) (Copied.)

GRYSTES NIGRICANS Agassiz, 1850.—" HURO NIGRICANS Cuv. is another species of the lower Canadian lakes, which occurs also in Lake Champlain. The generic distinctions from Grystes does not, however, rest upon sufficient characters to warrant its preservation in the system of fishes; I shall, therefore, call it in future *Grystes nigricans.* It is a very common fish in some of the lakes, and highly esteemed as an article of food. Throughout the lake region it is known under the name of Black Bass, and may be seen in large numbers in the enclosure under the gallery of the Cataract Hotel at Niagara. Dr. DeKay describes it as *Centrarchus fasciatus,* although he copies also Cuvier's description and figure of *Huro nigricans,* but without perceiving their indentity.

" In the northern lakes there is only one species of true Centrarchus found, the *Centrarchus æneus;* but it does not occur as far north as Lake Superior, though it is common in Lake Huron and the other great lakes."—(AGASSIZ, *Lake Superior,* 297, 1850.)

GRYSTES NOBILIS Agassiz, 1854.—" The species from Huntsville, known there under the name of trout, differs equally from the northern species mentioned in my 'Lake Superior,' and from that of the Southern States described by Cuvier and Valenciennes as *Grystes salmoneus.* Its snout is shorter, the posterior end of the upper maxillary extends beyond the hinder border of the eye, the head is higher, and the scales much larger in the dorsal as well as in the ventral regions. No teeth on the tongue. I call this species provisionally *Grystes nobilis* Ag. It reaches a large size, and weighs occasionally from 10 to 14 pounds."—(AGASSIZ, *Am. Jour. Sci. Arts,* XVII, 297, 1854.)

GRYSTES NUECENSIS Baird & Girard, 1854.—" Head forming
11

$\frac{4}{13}$ of the entire length. Mouth deeply cleft; its angle reaching a vertical passing backwards of the eye; lower jaw longer than upper. Eyes rather large; their diameter contained six times in the length of side of head. Scales on the cheeks a little smaller than those on the opercular apparatus. First dorsal lower than the second, caudal subcrescentic posteriorly. Anal extended a little further behind the second dorsal, though shorter and less deep. D. X, 13; A. III, 11; C. 4, 1, 8, 8, 1, 3; V. 1, 5; P. 15.

"Ground color of back, black clouded with greyish brown. Sides dull-yellow gray, with an interrupted darker band. Beneath light yellow. Rio Frio and Rio Nueces, Texas."—(BAIRD & GIRARD, *Pro. Ac. Nat. Sci. Phil.* VII. 25, 1854.)

GRYSTES SALMOIDES Holbrook, 1855.—"Head and body dusky above, often with a greenish or bronzed tint; lower jaw and belly white; opercle with a bluish-green spot at its angle. D. 9, 14; P. 14; V. 1, 5; A. 3, 12; C. 19.

"This fish is of an elongated oval form, arched; thick and rounded along the back, thinner and nearly straight at the belly. The head is very large and thick, especially between the eyes, and the 'snout is full and rounded; the facial outline is nearly straight, though the prominence of the intermaxillary bone gives it an incurved appearance. The eye is very large; it is placed one diameter and a quarter of the orbit from the snout, and two and a quarter diameters from the posterior extremity of the opercle, with its lower margin slightly above the medium plane of the head. The nostrils are round; the anterior and smaller is rather nearer to the eye than to the snout, and both are on a line within the orbit.

"The mouth is very large; the posterior extremity of the upper jaw extending behind the orbit; the lower jaw is the longest, and so projects as to make a part of the facial line when the mouth is shut. Both jaws are armed with numerous small conical, pointed recurved card-like teeth; they are all nearly of the same size, except some in the upper jaw, which are directed inwards and backwards. The vomer has in front a large arrow-headed group of minute villiform teeth; and the palate-bones have on each side a long and rather broad patch of similar teeth. The pharyngeal teeth resemble those of the jaws in size and form. The tongue is large and thick behind; thin, narrow and rounded in front, smooth and tolerably free.

" The preopercle is nearly semicircular at its angle, which is smooth or not serrated, but the ascending border is slightly emarginate above the angle. The opercle is subtriangular, with its base before and apex behind, and emarginate. The subopercle is quadrilateral, and extends as far back as the opercle. The interopercle is rounded below, and ascends for some distance between the preopercle and the opercle. The head is covered with scales above and at the sides as far as the posterior margin of the orbit, but the superior maxillary bone is naked. The gill openings are very large; there are 7 branched rays.

" The dorsal fin is very large and long; it begins rather behind the base of the pectoral, and is single, though deeply emarginate; its anterior portion has 9 spines, partially received in a groove; the posterior or soft portion of the dorsal fin is more elevated and has 14 articulated rays. The pectoral is broad, but short and rounded behind; it arises rather before the termination of the opercle, and has 14 rays. The ventral begins nearly even with the pectoral fin and is shorter; it has 1 spine and 5 soft rays, the internal of which is bound to the belly for half its length. The anal arises nearly in a line vertical with the root of the third dorsal ray, and has 3 spines and 12 branched rays. The caudal is large, broad, slightly crescentic, and has 19 rays.

" The scales are nearly semicircular in shape, with the diameter in front, straight and marked with 12 radiating lines. The lateral line is concurrent with the back, and runs along the superior fourth of the body; its scale is narrower behind than the others, and its excretory duct is placed obliquely.

"The head is dusky above, and silvery though slightly clouded on the sides, with a bluish green blotch at the opercle; the body is also dusky above or of a bronzed color (*sic*) with a greenish tint; the belly is silvery, and along the flanks runs a dusky band more or less evident according to the age of the animal; it is remarkable in the young. The dorsal fin is transparent, with only here and there dusky shades; the membrane of the pectoral is transparent, but the rays have a yellowish tint; the ventral is yellowish, and the anal is slightly tinted with the same color; the caudal is dusky, with a very obscure yellowish shade.

"The entire length from the opercle to the tip of the tail is equal to two heads and a half; the greatest elevation is seven eights of a head; total length 14 inches; specimens have been observed nearly 2 feet in length.

"The peritoneum is silvery. The liver is large, and of a very pale color; it consists of a single rhomboidal mass, as there are no marks of lobes; it is placed mostly in the left side, and projects but slightly into the right. The gall bladder is large, round, and is in great measure uncovered by the right margin of the liver. The œsophagus is large and broad. The stomach is large, and has thick, firm muscular walls, with deep folds of its mucous membrane within; the pyloric portion is short, thick, stout, and departs at a right angle at its posterior third. The intestine runs to the vent whence it is reflected to the pylorus, and then it turns backwards to end in the rectum; its walls are remarkably thick and firm, and its mucous membrane is beautifully reticulated, and presents numerous small areolæ for two-thirds of its length, and beyond this, longitudinal folds begin which are continued into the rectum. There are 11 primitive cœcal appendages, which soon divide into 2 or 3 others, so that as many as 28 may at times be counted. The spleen is rather small, very pale, and is situated so far back that its anterior extremity scarcely reaches the stomach. The air-bladder is large, and extends throughout the abdominal cavity; it is full in front, but is partially subdivided into two small pouches behind; within it is bright yellow at its superior and posterior part. The ovaries are suboval, rather broad, and unite in substance behind before they open."—(HOLBROOK, *Ich. So. Car.* 25, 1855, and 2d ed. 1860.)

GRYSTES MEGASTOMA Garlick, 1857.—"This fish has been identified with the common Black Bass (*Grystes fasciatus*), but is by no means the same fish, differing in many respects, both in its habits and physical structure, and has not been described in any work on American fishes, so far as I can learn.

"The great distinguishing feature of this Bass is its immense mouth, which has induced me to call it *Grystes megastoma*, or large-mouthed Bass.

"In its general form it resembles the common Black Bass, though somewhat thicker. The head is much larger in proportion to its size, and if a vertical line be drawn, passing through the center of the eye, we shall find that the end of the upper jaw projects back or behind the line quite a distance; whereas, in the common Bass the jaw will not reach as far back as the line. The scales are much larger, and thickly set over the gill covers. Back, of a dark greenish, olive color, fading gradually to white underneath. If found in dark-colored water, the white will be tinged with a pinkish hue. A darkish mottled band, of about half an inch in width, embracing the lateral line, traverses the whole length of the body.

"Br. rays, 6; Dor. 23: Sp. 9, Soft 14; A. 14: Sp. 3, Soft 11; C. 20; V. 6: Sp. 1, Soft 5; P. 13."—(GARLICK, *Treat. Art. Prop. Fish.* 108, 1857.)

DIOPLITES NUECENSIS Girard, 1858.—"Body elongated, subfusiform; head constituting a little less than the third of the entire length; posterior extremity of maxillary extending to a vertical line drawn posteriorly to the orbit; scales on the cheeks nearly equal in size to those on the gill covers; origin of ventrals posterior to the base of pectorals; upper regions, reddish brown, maculated; a lateral dark band; inferior regions whitish, uni-color.

"It is closely related to, if not identical, with *Grystes nobilis* Agassiz, from the southern bend of the Tennessee River. It has, also, much greater affinities with *D. fasciatus* than with *D. sal-moides*."—(GIRARD, *U. S. Pac. R. R. Exp. and Surv.* X; Fishes, 4, 1858.)

HURO NIGRICANS Günther, 1859.—"D. $6\frac{2}{10}$; A. $\frac{3}{11}$; L. lat. 60–65. Height of body equal to one-third of the total length, excluding the caudal; cleft of the mouth obliquely running up-wards towards the plane of the forehead; caudal slightly notched; coloration uniform."—GÜNTHER, *Cat. Fishes, Brit. Mus.* I, 255, 1859.)

DIOPLITES NUECENSIS Girard, 1859.—"Body elongated sub-fusiform; head constituting a little less than the third of the entire length; posterior extremity of maxillary extending to a vertical line drawn posteriorly to the orbit; scales on the cheeks nearly equal in size to those on the gill covers; origin of the ventrals placed posteriorly to the base of the pectorals; upper regions reddish brown, maculated; a lateral dark band; inferior regions whitish uni-color.

"This species is more closely related to *D. fasciatus* than to *D. salmoides*, and probably identical with *Grystes nobilis* (Ag.). At any rate the latter has greater affinities with *D. fasciatus* than with *D. salmoides*, the latter being restricted to its proper limits.

"The body is proportionally more elongated than in *D. fas-ciatus*, resembling more in that respect *D. salmoides*. It is com-pressed and sub-uniform when seen in profile. The greatest depth is somewhat less than the fourth of the total length, in which the head enters a little less than three times; the mouth is more deeply cleft than in any other of the known species of the genus, and its gap, is as usual, oblique upwards, owing to the constant protrusion of the lower jaw beyond the upper, which it does very prominently in this species. The posterior extremity of the maxillary is very much dilated, extending to a vertical line drawn considerably back of the whole orbit; the tongue is large and stout at its base, thinning and tapering towards its apex, which is broadly rounded; it is smooth anteriorly, being provided posteriorly and upon its middle with a narrow band of velvet-like teeth; both nostrils are nearer the anterior rim of the orbit than the extremity of the snout; the anterior one is a little smaller than the posterior, and placed more outwardly with reference to the middle of the snout; the eye is of moderate development, sub-circular in shape, reaching to the summit of the cranium, its diameter enters about six times and one-half in the length of the side of the head, twice in advance of the anterior rim of the orbit; the opercular apparatus is perfectly smooth and deprived of either spines or serratures; the scales upon the cheeks are but slightly smaller than those covering the opercular pieces; the gill openings are wide and continuous under the throat. The base of the first or spiny dorsal is longer than that of the second, but the fin itself is lower and more arched in its outline; the first and second spines are shorter than the third, which is the highest, the remaining ones diminishing gradually posteriorly; the tenth spine by its position belongs rather to the second than the first dorsal; the second dorsal is higher than long, sub-trapezoid, its upper edge being but slightly convex and the posterior rays almost as high as the anterior ones; the posterior margin of the caudal is sub-crescentic or sub-concave; the fin itself is contained $5\frac{1}{2}$ times in the total length; the origin of the anal corresponds to a vertical line intersecting the anterior third of the second dorsal; its base extends a little further back than that of the latter, although the tips of the posterior rays of both fins are nearly even, the anal being not quite so deep as the second dorsal is high; its whole base, including the three small and slender spines at its anterior margin, is shorter than that of the second dorsal; the

origin of the ventrals corresponds to a vertical line drawn immediately behind the base of the pectorals; the fins themselves are
broad and short, since their posterior margin does not reach the
vent, which is situated a little way in advance of the anterior
margin of the anal fin and under a vertical line drawn between
the two dorsal fins; the pectorals are of moderate development,
not extending quite as far back as the ventrals.

Br. VI; D. X, 13; A. III, 11; C. 4, 1, 8, 8, 1, 3; V. I, ·
5; P. 15. (Rio Cibolo.)

Br. VI; D. X, 13; A. III, 12; C. 4, 1, 9, 8, 1, 3; V. I,
5; P. 15. (Rio Blanco.)

"The scales are of moderate development, sub-oblique, deeper
than long, provided with radiating grooves on their anterior
section only, and pectinated posteriorly; the pectinations of the
scales of the dorsal region are either obsolete or else deciduous,
and easily removed with the epidermis. As a whole, the fish
has a rather smooth appearance, reminding us more of a Trout
than a Perch were it not for its anterior spiny dorsal fin. From
29 to 30 longitudinal rows of scales may be counted upon the
line of the greatest depth, 19 below and 9 above the lateral line;
the scales under the throat are quite reduced in size, those on
the cheeks being nearly as large as those on the opercle; minute
scales may be observed on the caudal fin to almost three-fourths
of the length of its rays, and a few scattered ones upon the base
of the second dorsal; the lateral line itself from the upper region
of the gill covers is slightly arched upwards until under the
second dorsal fin, hence runs nearly straightway along the middle
of the peduncle of the tail to the base of the caudal fin. The
upper regions are reddish brown, of a more or less deep hue,
and maculated with dark brown or black, while the inferior regions are whitish or yellowish and uni-color; a lateral, more or
less interrupted dark band may be traced from the black patch
at the posterior margin of the opercle to the base of the caudal
fin; three obsolete streaks may be seen upon the cheeks diverg-

ing from the orbit; the fins are uni-color except the second dorsal, which exhibits two longitudinal bars upon its base; the upper ones are greenish olive, the lower ones are yellowish olive."— (GIRARD, *U. S. Mex. Bound. Surv.* II, 3, 1859.)

GRISTES NIGRICANS Herbert, 1859.— "In color, this fish is of a dusky bluish black, sometimes with bronze reflections, the under parts bluish white, the cheeks and gill-covers nacreous, of a bluish color.

"The body is compressed; back arched and gibbous; profile descending obliquely to the rostrum, which is moderately prolonged; scales large, truncated; scales on the operculum large; a single series on the suboperculum, much smaller on the preoperculum, ascending high up on the membrane of the soft dorsal and caudal fins; eyes large; nostrils double; operculum pointed, with a loose membrane; the lower jaw is somewhat longest; the jaws are smooth and scaleless; both jaws are armed with a broad patch of minute conic acute reserved teeth; an oblong patch of rasp-like teeth on the vomer, and a band of the same kind on the palatines; branchial arches minutely toothed; pharyngeal teeth in rounded patches. The dorsal fin is composed of 9 stout spines; the second dorsal of 1 spine and 14 soft rays; the pectorals have 18 soft rays, the ventrals 1 spine and 5 soft rays, the anal 3 spines and 12 soft rays, and the caudal 16 soft rays."—(HERBERT, *Fish and Fishing*, 195, 1859.) —(I think this description more applicable to the large-mouthed Black Bass than the small-mouthed form, although Herbert copied it from DeKay's *C. fasciatus;* but I think he considered the latter the same as *H. nigricans* C. & V., on the strength of Professor Agassiz's estimate of, and statement concerning, the same species, viz: "Dr. DeKay describes it [*Huro nigricans*] as *Centrarchus fasciatus*, although he copies also Cuvier's description and figure of *Huro nigricans*, but without perceiving their identity."* It is also evident from the context of Herbert's descrip-

---

* "Lake Superior," p. 287, 1850.

tion that he means the large-mouthed Bass, though I am of the
opinion that he knew very little about either species of Black
Bass. Accordingly, I have used *Gristes nigricans* Herbert, as a
synonym of *M. salmoides* (Lac.) Henshall. J. A. H.)

GRYSTES SALMOIDES Norris, 1864. — "The following is an
abridgment of Holbrook's description, connected with a few
observations of the writer: Head and body dusky, olive above,
sometimes with a yellowish tint, lighter on the sides; belly
white; opercles light green or greenish yellow; first dorsal fin,
9 spines and 15 soft rays; pectorals 15; ventrals 1 spine and 5
rays; anal 3 spines and 12 rays; caudal 19 rays; body elongated, oval, straight on the belly; eye large; mouth very large,
lower jaw longer; the vomer has brush-like teeth in front; teeth
on the palatines and pharyngeal bones; tongue smooth, without
teeth in front."—(NORRIS, *Am. Angler's Book*, 99, 1864.)

MICROPTERUS NIGRICANS Cope, 1870. — "The Green Bass is
abundant in all rivers of the State [N. C.] I have it from the
Neuse, Yadkin, Catawba, upper and lower French Broad, and
from the Clinch in Tennessee. Specimens from the Neuse and
from near Norfolk, Virginia, six in number, differ from those
of the other rivers, in having a deeper body, and generally
longer and more prominent mandible. The depth enters the
length 2.75 times; in the more western forms always 3.25 times;
in the former it is greater than the length of the head, in the
latter it is considerably less. Other differences are not discover-
able, and I regard it as a marked variety only."—(COPE, *Pro.
Am. Phil. Soc.* 451, 1870.)

MICROPTERUS NIGRICANS Gill, 1873. — "Scales moderate, in
about sixty-five oblique rows between the head and caudal, and
eight (or seven and a half) longitudinal ones between the back
and lateral line, decreasing little towards the nape but more
towards the throat; with the sheath enveloping the base of the
soft portion of the dorsal very low and developed towards the
end of the fin. Head flat between the orbits, with (1) scales

on the operculum about the size of those of the nape, (2) on the suboperculum broad and in one row, (3) on the interoperculum broad, conspicuous and regularly imbricated, in one row, (4) on the cheeks moderate (in about ten rows in an oblique line, and five or six in a horizontal one), and (5) on the preoperculum (two to five) in an incomplete row. Mouth large, the gape from the symphysis to the angle of supramaxillary equaling nearly a half of the head's length. Supramaxillary not continued backwards decidedly beyond the vertical from the hinder border of the orbit.

" Dorsal fin with the anterior spines slowly graduated (the first being comparatively long) to the third ($I = 1$; $II = 1.30$; $III = 1.50$); fourth longest (but little more so than the third) and equal to or exceeding the interval between the back and lateral line; succeeding ones successively and in increased ratio abbreviated to the ninth, which is very short (two-sevenths— $1 : 3.5$—of fourth), the tenth being longer than the eighth (shorter than the seventh) and about two-thirds as long as the longest (i. e., fourth).

" Dorsal fin with scales ascending comparatively little behind on the membrane behind the soft rays (none behind last five or six).

" Anal fin with no (or very few) scales.

" Color, in young and adolescent, greenish-black, verging to yellowish-white on lower sides and abdomen, with (1) a series of large blotches arranged in a regular line, from shoulder to caudal, on the middle of sides, the posterior third of which becomes a continuous stripe and (2) below this middle series, rather irregular, small blotches, with tendency to become a continuous stripe on posterior third of body. Head dark above, white from lower half of maxillary bone, and suboperculum to chin and throat, and with three oblique and horizontal bands upon cheek, viz.: (1) one from angle of upper jaw to margin of preoperculum, (2) one from lower edge of orbit to angle of operculum, and (3) one radiating slightly upward from posterior margin of orbit to operculum.   Apex of operculum with large dark spot, upper fins dusky, lower yellowish-white.

" The stripes on the body frequently continue until the fish is well grown, though gradually becoming obsolete; black spots upon the scales remain more or less permanently, giving the appearance, in old fish, of fine lines or stripes. (Color *fide* J. W. Milner, MSS.) "—(GILL, *Pro. Am, Asso. Adv. Sci.* XXII, B. 71, 1873.)

MICROPTERUS PALLIDUS Jordan, 1877.—"Rafinesque's description of his *Lepomis pallida* seems to have been drawn from this species.   His specific name should therefore be adopted. This change is especially desirable, as it does away with the objectionable local name *floridanus* for this widely distributed species."—(JORDAN, *Bull. U. S. Nat. Mus.* X, 43, 1877.)

MICROPTERUS PALLIDUS Jordan, 1878.—" Dull olive green, more or less spotted when young, but not barred; usually with an irregular dark lateral band, and three oblique stripes on opercules; ends of caudal fin blackish, these markings growing obscure with age; third dorsal spine twice as high as first; notch between spines and soft rays deep; eight rows of scales between lateral line and dorsal; anal fin somewhat scaly; mouth very wide; D. X, 12; A. III, 10; lat. l. 65 to 70.   Great lakes and rivers of the West and South, abundant in most regions, and highly valued as a food fish."—(JORDAN, *Manual Vertebrates, E. U. S.* 2d ed. 236, 1878.)

MICROPTERUS PALLIDUS Goode & Bean, 1879.—"According to Mr. Stearns this species enters the brackish and salt waters of the Gulf of Mexico, whence he sends a specimen, No. 21,311, 12 inches in length.   D. IX, I, 13; A. III, 10; P. II, 12; V. I, 5; C.+17+.   L. lat. 65; L. trans. $\frac{7}{13}$."—(GOODE & BEAN, *Pro. U. S. Nat. Mus.* 138, 1879.)

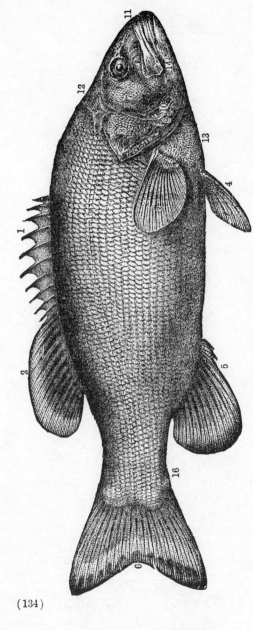

Small-mouthed Black Bass of Michigan.

(Furnished by A. B. Leet, Esq., Genl. Ticket Agent, Grand Rapids & Indiana R. R.)

1. Spinous dorsal fin. 2. Soft dorsal fin. 3. Pectoral fin. 4. Ventral fin. 5. Anal fin. 6. Caudal fin. 7. Cheek. 8. Opercle. Between 7 and 8 is the Preopercle. 9. Suboperele. 10. Interopercle. 11. Snout. 12. Nape. 13. Breast. 14. Angle of mouth. 15. Lateral line. 16. Tail (peduncle.) The Branchiostegals are below 9 and 10.

CHAPTER III.

GENERAL AND SPECIFIC FEATURES.

"Like—but oh! how different!"—WORDSWORTH.

As has been shown in the preceding chapter, the genus MICROPTERUS includes but two species, viz: *Micropterus dolomieu* Lacépède, the small-mouthed Black Bass, and *Micropterus salmoides* (Lacépède) Henshall, the large-mouthed Black Bass, or, as it is sometimes called, the Oswego Bass. The small-mouthed Bass, however, exhibits some minor points of difference between its Northern and Southern forms, which are now regarded as of varietal importance, and this species has consequently been divided into *Micropterus dolomieu* var. *achigan*, the small-mouthed Bass of the North, and *Micropterus dolomieu* var. *dolomieu*, the small-mouthed Bass of the South; the differences, however, are not of much moment, as they shade into each other, and are to be regarded as merely geographical variations.

Possibly no genus of fishes has been the occasion of so much confusion, scientifically and popularly, as the Black Bass. This is owing, no doubt, to its extensive habitat and wide-spread distribution; the original habitat of the species being the great basin of the St. Lawrence, the whole Mississippi Valley—or nearly the entire range of country lying between the Appalachian Chain and the Rocky Mountains—and the South Atlantic States from

(135)

Virginia to Florida; including also the widely-separated sections of the Red River of the North and East Mexico.

It would naturally be expected, in view of this extraordinary and expansive habitat, to find differences in color, habits and conformation; indeed, it is surprising that the variations are not more marked, and the number of species, consequently, greater, when one considers the great natural differences and conditions of the numerous waters, and the varieties of climate to which this genus is native. To the careless observer, however, there is but little to determine the differences between the two species of Black Bass. I have known anglers who had "slain their thousands" of both species, but who had never suspected that there was any difference except in color, until I pointed out to them the specific characteristics. Even those of more attentive observation, but who have never seen the two species together, find it difficult to readily comprehend the difference. To the trained observer, however, it is an easy task to distinguish the variations; and when specimens of equal weight, of both species, are placed side by side, the difference is at once apparent.

As widely distributed as the Black Bass is, we find that the most striking variation, in either species, is in color, which will run from almost black through all the shades of slate, green, olive and yellow to almost white; and indeed these variations in color can be found in almost any one State, and to a great extent in any one stream, or lake, at different seasons of the year. In some sections of the country one species may be more or less spotted or barred, while the other species may exhibit well-defined lateral bands of dark spots, though these peculiarities are more likely to occur in young or adolescent specimens.

The fins will also be found to vary somewhat in coloring, while the scales and fin-rays may differ slightly in number, as a variation of one-sixth, more or less, from established formulas is not unusual. Slight dissimilarities of contour, and some diversities of habits, also, exist. But all of these differences obtain, not only with regard to the Black Bass, but to most other species of fresh water fishes, and depend on well-known natural causes.

I resided for ten years in Wisconsin, where there were twenty lakes, abounding in Black Bass, within a radius of eight miles of my residence; and from close and constant observation of the characteristics of the Bass inhabiting them, I could almost invariably tell, upon being shown a string of Black Bass, in what particular lake they had been caught.

Where both species co-exist in the same waters, the small-mouthed Bass is generally of a darker or more somber hue than the large-mouthed Bass, whose color is more inclined to shades of green. The coloration of the small-mouthed Bass, however, in some localities, approaches shades of olive or yellow, and there will often be more or less red in the iris of the eye, in some instances shading down to orange or yellow; this latter distinction, though, like the double curve at the base of the caudal fin, and the more forked tail—which have been regarded by some anglers as distinguishing characteristics of this species— can not be depended on, as one or all of these distinctions are often lacking.

The most distinctive feature, as between the two species, is the gape of the mouth, which in the large-mouthed Bass seems simply enormous to those who have previously seen but the small-mouthed species. The contrast in build,

12

and external conformation, of the two species, is at once striking and characteristic. The large-mouthed Bass is thicker, especially through the shoulders, deeper in the body, with a more pendulous abdomen, and seems a heavier fish for its length than the other species, conveying the impression that it is the stronger and more powerful fish, as, indeed, it is; while the small-mouthed Bass, owing to its trim, slender and more graceful shape, truly convinces one that it is the more active and agile.

The relative size of the scales is all important in the differentiation of the two species. In the large-mouthed Bass these are much larger, there being but from sixty-five to seventy scales along the lateral line, running from the head to the tail; while in the small-mouthed species there are from seventy to eighty. Between the lateral line and the base of the dorsal fin there are but eight horizontal rows of scales in the large-mouthed Bass, while there are eleven similar rows in the small-mouthed Bass. The scales on the nape and breast in the large-mouthed species are not much smaller than those of the sides; but in the other species they are *very much* smaller; and while the scales on the cheeks and gill-covers of the large-mouthed Bass are small, those of corresponding situations in the small-mouthed Bass are quite minute, with a small portion of the gill-covers (preopercular limb) entirely bare.

The size and shape of the fins also differ somewhat, especially the dorsal, which in the small-mouthed Bass has the rays of the spinous portion higher and more uniform in size, rendering this fin higher, not so arching, and with a shallower notch than in the large-mouthed form.

The differences, then, in the form, gape of mouth, and size of scales and fins of the two species of Black Bass, without reference to color, are sufficiently pronounced to enable the angler to readily determine, by comparison, the small-mouthed from the large-mouthed Bass; for these differences are constant wherever the Black Bass exists, from Maine to Mexico, or from Canada to Florida. To the specialist there are other points of differentiation as detailed in the preceding chapter.

In preparing tables of exact measurements of the species, as also tables showing the relative weight as to length, I found so much discrepancy in these respects, in the same species from different localities, owing to slight variations of shape and conformation, that I concluded they would not subserve the purposes of a general guide, and so omitted them.

Both species are remarkably active, muscular and voracious, with large, hard and tough mouths; are very bold in biting, and when hooked exhibit gameness and endurance second to no other fish. Both species give off the characteristic musky odor when caught.

Both species generally inhabit the same waters, and there is a slight diversity in their habits where they co-exist together. Naturally, the small-mouthed Bass prefers rocky streams or the gravelly shoals and bottom springs of lakes and ponds, while its large-mouthed congener lurks about the submerged roots of trees or sunken logs in rivers, and delights in the beds of rushes and aquatic plants of lacustrine waters; but they readily adapt themselves to waters of various conditions, when transplanted, easily accommodating themselves to their surroundings, and have a happy faculty of making themselves at home wherever placed, so that in some localities their habits are as anomalous as their colors.

There is a wide-spread and prevalent notion that the small-mouthed Bass is the "game" species *par excellence*, but I doubt if this distinction is well founded. In common with most anglers I at one time shared this belief, but from a long series of observations I am now of the opinion that the large-mouthed Bass, all things being equal, displays as much pluck, and exhibits as untiring fighting qualities as its small-mouthed congener.

Fish inhabiting swiftly running streams are always more vigorous and gamy than those in still waters, and it is probable that where the large-mouthed Bass exists alone in very shallow and sluggish waters, of high temperature and thickly grown with algæ, it will exhibit less combative qualities, consequent on the enervating influences of its surroundings; but where both species inhabit the same waters, and are subject to the same conditions, I am convinced that no angler can tell whether he has hooked a large-mouthed or a small-mouthed Bass, from their resistance and mode of fighting, provided they are of equal weight, until he has the ocular evidence.

I use the expression "equal weight" advisedly, for most anglers must have remarked that the largest Bass of either species are not necessarily the hardest fighters; on the contrary, a Bass of two or two and a half pounds weight will usually make a more gallant fight than one of twice the size, and this fact, I think, will account in a great measure for the popular idea that the small-mouthed Bass is the "gamest" species for this reason:

Where the two species co-exist in the same stream or lake, the large-mouthed Bass always grows to a larger size than the other species, and an angler having just landed a two pound small-mouthed Bass after a long struggle, next hooks a large-mouthed Bass weighing four or five pounds, and is surprised, probably, that it " fights " no harder or perhaps not so hard as the smaller fish—in fact, seems " logy "; he, therefore, reiterates the cry that the small-mouthed Bass is the gamest fish.

But, now, if he next succeeds in hooking a large-mouthed Bass of the same size as the first one caught, he is certain that he is playing a small-mouthed Bass until it is landed, when to his astonishment it proves to be a large-mouthed Bass; he merely says, " he fought well for one of his kind," still basing his opinion of the fighting qualities of the two species upon the first two caught.

Perhaps his next catch may be a small-mouthed Bass of four pounds, and which, though twice the weight of the large-mouthed Bass just landed, does not offer any greater resistance, and he sets it down in his mind as a large-mouthed Bass; imagine the angler's surprise, then, upon taking it into the landing net, to find it a small-mouthed Bass, and one which, from its large size and the angler's preconceived opinion of this species should have fought like a Trojan.

Now, one would think that the angler would be some-what staggered in his former belief; but no, he is equal to the occasion, and in compliance with the popular idea, he merely suggests that " he is out of condition, somehow," or " was hooked so as to drown him early in the struggle ; " and so, as his largest fish will necessarily be big-mouthed, and because they do not fight in proportion to their size, they are set down as lacking in game qualities—of course, leaving the largest small-mouthed Bass out of the calculation.

Gentle reader, this is not a case of special pleading, nor

is the angler a creation of the imagination lugged in as an apologist for the large-mouthed Bass; he is a veritable creature of flesh and blood, of earth earthy, and with the self-conceit, weaknesses and shortcomings characteristic of the genus *homo ;* I have met him and heard his arguments and sage expressions scores of times, and if you will think a moment I am sure you have met him yourself.

Icthyologists have at various times given to the genus *Micropterus* numerous appellatives, and to the species more than fifty specific names, while laymen in different sections of the country have contributed their quota of vernacular names, among which may be mentioned : Bass, Black Bass, Green Bass, Yellow Bass, River Bass, Bayou Bass, Slough Bass, Lake Bass, Moss Bass, Grass Bass, Marsh Bass, Oswego Bass, Perch, Black Perch, Yellow Perch, Trout Perch, Jumping Perch, Welshman, Salmon, Trout, Black Trout, White Trout, Chub, Southern Chub, Roanoke Chub, etc., etc.

In addition to this formidable and perplexing array of names, there are other evils which add very much to the confusion attending the nomenclature of the Black Bass. Among them is the careless habit of many correspondents of our sportsmen's journals, who write of Bass, Bass tackle, Bass fishing, etc., meaning Black Bass in each instance, but leave it to the imagination of the readers of those journals as to what particular kind of "Bass" is meant.

Now this is all wrong, and is owing to gross carelessness, or perhaps in some instances to a want of proper information, and is a habit that ought to be reformed. We should learn to call things by their right names. A rose by any other name may smell as sweet, but as there are many varieties of roses they must be distinguished by correct and

specific names, and not by their odors. It is just as easy
to write the distinctive name "Black Bass" as the general
name "Bass."

Bass is a very vague term at best, meaning one thing in
one part of the country, and a totally different thing in
another. Along the eastern coast it means a Striped Bass
(*Roccus lineatus*), or a Sea Bass (*Centropristes atrarius*); in
Florida it means a Channel Bass (*Sciænops ocellatus*); in
the west it may be either a Black Bass (*Micropterus*), a
Rock Bass (*Ambloplites rupestris*), a White Bass (*Roccus
chrysops*), or a Calico Bass (*Pomoxys nigromaculatus*);
while in Otsego County, New York, it means an Otsego
Bass (*Coregonus clupeiformis* var. *otsego*), which is not a
Bass at all but a white fish.

Then, again, some of these correspondents write of the
real Black Bass, meaning usually *M. dolomieu*, the small-
mouthed species, seeming to imply that the other species is
not real, or at least is not *the* Black Bass, but something
else—a kind of *pseudo* variety. Others in writing of the
large-mouthed species, *M. salmoides*—owing to its former
name, *M. nigricans*—have called *it* the real Black Bass,
under the impression that as it was named *nigricans*—*i. e.*,
black—the other species must be some other color, and
could not be the simon-pure article. Now, one species is
not more *real* than the other; the small-mouthed Bass is
regarded as the type species because it was the first to be
described by a naturalist, and given a specific and generic
name.

The term "Black Bass," then, is distinctive, and should
always be used when alluding to the genus generally.
The different species should be mentioned as the small-
mouthed Black Bass or the large-mouthed Black Bass, as

the case may be, no matter whether the color be black, green or yellow.   Every one will then know exactly what is meant, and much of the confusion and uncertainty that now prevail in connection with the nomenclature of the Black Bass will be cleared away.

> " Not chaos-like, together crush'd and bruis'd,
> But, as the world, harmoniously confus'd,
> Where order in variety we see,
> And where, though all things differ, all agree."—*Pope.*

CHAPTER IV.

COLORATION OF THE BLACK BASS.

*"And it is so with many kinds of fish, and of trouts especially; which differ in their bigness and shape, and spots and color."—*IZAAK WALTON.

THE external appearance of the Black Bass, as exhibited in the colors and markings, differs so greatly and constantly in different sections of our country, that it would be useless to describe them minutely in a specimen from any given locality; for as the vernacular names of fishes are usually bestowed with reference to the outward peculiarities of coloring, this has already given rise to much confusion in naming the species. Thus they are called black, green, or yellow Bass, respectively, in different sections of the United States, and not without reason, for black, green and yellow are the predominating primary colors of the two species, though these colors are often toned down to any of the intermediate shades, with plumbeous, olivaceous or ochreous tints.

The color, however, is always darkest on the back, with a gradual shading or paling towards the belly or abdomen, which is always white or whitish. Where the two species of Black Bass are common to the same stream or lake, the small-mouthed Bass is generally the darkest in color, though this is by no means an invariable rule; for in other waters the small-mouthed Bass may be of a lighter or paler hue than the other species—usually yellowish-

13   (145)

olive or yellowish-white, but often pale green—while the large-mouthed Bass will be of a dark green coloration, and sometimes quite dusky.

Then, again, in some waters, no distinct coloring is apparent, the fish presenting merely a pale or faded appearance; especially is this likely to be the case in large streams much subject to overflow, and whose waters are often muddy or discolored. Hence, as may be surmised, color is not an important factor in the differentiation of the Black Bass species.

While some have no distinct markings, others are marked by dark, maculated, transverse or vertical bars; some, again, by longitudinal or lateral bands; and still others by mottled lines, dusky spots, or finger marks. Usually when Bass are so marked, the mottled bands run lengthwise in the large-mouthed species, while the small-mouthed Bass is marked by transverse bars or finger marks; but these distinctions are not infallible, for the small-mouthed Bass of the Southern States often exhibits well-defined mottled lines running lengthwise along the series of scales.

After being taken out of the water, the colors and markings change materially; generally, the brighter colors fade rapidly, while the dusky spots, bars, or bands become more distinct; this change of color is more frequently observed in the small-mouthed species. Sometimes, however, the markings will disappear, and the sides of the fish will assume a uniform coloration.

Then, again, the colors of the Black Bass frequently change with each season of the year; and there is, moreover, always a marked difference in the colors and markings of the fish at different stages of its growth. In the young, the colors are brighter and the markings more distinct than in the adult fish, and it is my opinion that the latter become entirely obsolete with age.

The fins are likewise subject to variation in coloring and markings; they may be either dusky or greenish; reddish or yellowish; and are, usually, more or less punctulated or spotted. The tail is often lighter in color at the base and outer edge, and dark or dusky between; thus one of the names proposed by Rafinesque for the small-mouthed species—*Calliurus punctulatus, i. e.,* "dotted painted-tail"—was founded upon the peculiar coloration of the tail of a young Bass, his description of the caudal fin being: "base yellow, middle blackish, tip white." Sometimes, however, especially in mature specimens, the tail has a dark border, while the middle is of a lighter tinge; and often the entire caudal fin will have a uniform coloration.

There are commonly, several—usually three—dusky or olivaceous streaks along the cheeks and gill-covers.

Inconstancy of coloration is not exceptional with the Black Bass, for all other genera of fresh water and anadromous fishes exhibit this peculiarity in a greater or less degree. Among the causes assigned for this phenomenal feature, and which have been either proven true or made tenable by actual experiment and careful observation, are: (1) character of food; (2) condition, depth and temperature of water; (3) color and character of beds of streams, lakes or ponds; (4) atmospheric conditions; (5) age; (6) season of the year; and (7) the changes incident to the breeding season; while some assume that (8) the power of changing color is voluntary with some, if not all, fishes.

Professor Richard Owen, in his admirable work, "Anatomy of the Vertebrates," Vol. I, says:—

"The varied, and often brilliant colors of fishes, are due to pigment cells at different depths of the skin, but chiefly in the active or differentiating area. Those of silvery or golden luster are mostly on the surface of the scales. The silvery pigment called 'argentine' is an article of commerce used for the coloring of fictitious pearls, and offers a crystalline character under the microscope. The blue, red, green, or other bright-colored pigment is usually associated with fine oil, and occupies areolæ favoring accumulation at, or retreat from, the superficies, and thus effecting changes in the color of the fish, harmonizing their exterior with the hue of the bottom of their haunts."

From the nature of the pigment cells, as portrayed in this description, it is easy to imagine how susceptible they are to the influences of such causes as those above enumerated.

The *Salmonidæ* have been more studied, perhaps, than any other family of fishes, and yet in none has there been more confusion in classification, owing in a great measure to the differences of external appearance, as caused by these various influences.

The eminent German naturalist, Seibold, says:—"In none of our native [German] fish is there such variety of color, according to the different influences of food, water, light and temperature, as in the toothed salmons."

Another able German scientist, Carl Peyrer, says of the common brook trout of Germany (*Trutta fario*):—"The color, and partly also the size which it reaches, vary according to its location, the influences of light, the season, water, and food, and therefore several varieties are dis-

tinguished, such as the forest or stone trout, the alpine or
mountain trout, the gold or pond trout, the lake trout, and,
according to the lighter or darker coloring, the white
trout, the black trout, etc." Truly almost as polyonomous
as our Black Bass.

That *difference in food* produces difference in coloration
does not admit of a doubt. Those of the *Salmonidæ* which
feed upon crustacea and larvæ exhibit the most brilliant
colors, while those which live upon insects, minnows,
worms, etc., are much duller in hue.

Sir Humphrey Davy, in his familiar work, "Salmonia,"
says: " I think it possible when trout feed much on hard
substances, such as larvæ and their cases, and the ova of
other fish, they have more red spots and redder fins. This
is the case with the gillaroo and the char, who feed on
analogous substances; and the trout that have similar
habits might be expected to resemble them. When trout
feed on small fish, as minnows, and on flies, they have
more tendency to become spotted with small black spots,
and are generally more silvery."

The well-known artist and angler, Charles Lanman,
states: " Various causes have been assigned for the great
variety in the color of the brook trout. One great cause
is the difference of food; such as live upon fresh water
shrimps and other crustacea, are the brightest; those which
feed upon May-flies and other aquatic insects are the next;
and those which feed upon worms are the dullest and darkest of all."

Dr. A. T. Thompson, the author of " Treasury of Natural History," observes: " That each species of trout has
its peculiarities of color, but the common trout is the most
beautiful of its class; the variations of its tints and spots,

from golden-yellow to crimson and greenish-black, are almost infinite, and depend in a great measure on the nature of its food, for the colors are always the most brilliant in those fish that feed on the water shrimp."

Near Waterville, Waukesha County, Wisconsin, is the extensive trout hatching establishment of Mr. H. F. Dousman, where a number of fine springs form a considerable stream after leaving the ponds and flumes, and into which a number of brook trout have escaped at various times, so that finally it became well stocked with trout, which propagate naturally in the stream. The trout which are reared artificially are kept in covered plank flumes, and in open ponds, and are fed principally on chopped liver; those in the ponds getting some addition to this fare, however, in aquatic flies, insects, etc. The stream contains a great many crawfish, which often do much damage to the dams and ditches of adjacent cranberry marshes. Upon visiting this establishment, I was at once struck with the remarkable difference in the colors of the trout in the flumes, in the ponds, and in the stream. Those in the flumes were quite dull in appearance; those in the ponds were brighter; while those in the stream were the most brilliantly colored trout I ever saw, caused, no doubt, by their feeding upon the crustacea with which the stream abounded. The dull color of the trout in the flumes was partly owing to their shaded condition.

Not only does the character of the food influence the external coloring of the *Salmonidæ*, but the tint of the flesh, if I may so call it, is also affected by the same cause; thus Professor Agassiz states that the most beautiful salmon-trout are found in waters which abound in crustacea, direct experiments having shown to his satisfaction that the intensity of the red colors of their flesh depends upon the quantity of *Gammaridæ* which they have devoured.

A striking instance of the difference in coloring of the flesh from the *influence of age or season,* is related by the well-known European ichthyologist, Dr. Fric, in regard to the salmon of Bohemia. He says that there are three different ascents of the salmon during the year: The first ascent begins in February or March under the ice, and lasts till May. These salmon weigh from twenty-five to fifty pounds, and are famous under the name of "Violet-salmon." The second ascent begins in June and lasts till August. These fish have a reddish flesh, and weigh from twelve to twenty-two pounds, and are known as "Rose-salmon." The third ascent is from September until December. These fish are mostly weak, weighing from three to fifteen pounds. Their flesh is pale, and they are usually called "Silver-salmon."

The trout of the mountain lakes of the Alps (*Salmo salvelinus*), according to the season and the nature of the water they inhabit, have their flesh whitish or reddish.

The *color and condition of the water* has likewise a very marked effect upon the external appearance of the *Salmon-idæ.* Agassiz found that the color of brook trout of neighboring streams was influenced by the color and quantity of the water, and that even trout of the same stream differed in color as they frequented the shady or sunny side. He also found that fish in clear, sunny waters, with gravelly bottoms, were highly and brightly colored; while those in shady streams, or where the bottom was dark or muddy, and the water not so clear, were correspondingly dusky in hue ; and that bright fish taken from waters of the former character and placed in those of the latter, would begin to fade in a few hours, and in a few days or weeks would become entirely changed in hue.

The great lake trout (*Cristivomer namaycush*) exists in three different states of color, according to situations in which it is found, and were thought by the French *habitans* of the great lakes to be three distinct fishes, known as *Truite de Greve,* or trout of the muddy bottom; *Truite des Battures,* or trout of the rocky shores; and *Truite du Large,* or trout of the deep, open waters; the first being dull-colored, the second bright and handsomely mottled, and the last bluish and silvery.

Charles Lanman truly observes, that the fish of streams rushing rapidly over pebbly beds, are superior both in appearance and quality to those of ponds or semi-stagnant brooks. But this may arise, not so much from any particular components of the waters themselves, as from the fact that rapidly running and falling water is more highly aerated, the atmosphere being more freely intermingled with it, and therefore more conducive to the health and condition of all that inhabit it.

The *influence of light* in producing color in fishes is very evident when we reflect that fishes are always colored upon the back, which is exposed to the direct rays of light, and pale underneath, usually being quite white on the abdomen. This fact is especially pronounced in the flat fishes, which swim upon the side; thus the flounder, the sole, the turbot, the halibut, etc., are dark and variously colored upon the side presented to the light, while they are quite pale or white on the under side. Fishes which inhabit dark caves, owing to the absence of light, are entirely colorless.

That the *age of fish* has much to do with their color is

well known ; a familiar example being the common gold-fish, which in early youth is black or dark colored, and only assumes its beautiful golden hue at maturity.

During *the breeding season* of fishes their colors become much heightened, but they lose their brightness and brilliancy in many cases when the season is over. A salmon fresh-run from the sea is justly considered the most beautiful of fishes, but after the spawning season there is none more sorry and ill-looking. Darwin mentions some very interesting particulars, among which, that the pike, especially the male, during the breeding season, exhibits colors exceedingly intense, brilliant and iridescent.

Another striking instance out of many is afforded by the male stickleback, which is described by Mr. Warrington (England) as being then beautiful beyond description: " The back and eyes of the female, on the other hand, are the most splendid green, having a metallic luster like the green feather of humming-birds. The throat and belly are of a bright crimson, the back of an ashy green, and the whole fish appears as though it was somewhat trans-lucent, and glowed with an internal incandescence. After the breeding season, these colors all change; the throat and belly become of a paler red, the back more green, and the glowing tints subside."

The well-known and beautiful spring, or breeding dresses of many of our darters and minnows, are common illustrations of the influence of the breeding season upon the change of color in fishes.

CHAPTER V.

GEOGRAPHICAL DISTRIBUTION.

"You may remember that I told you, Gesner says there are no pikes in Spain; and doubtless, there was a time, about a hundred or a few more years ago, when there were no carps in England."—IZAAK WALTON.

THE Black Bass is wholly unknown in the Old World, except where recently introduced, and exists, naturally, only in America. The original habitat of the species is remarkable for its extent, for, with the exception of the New England States and the Atlantic seaboard of the Middle States, it comprises the whole of the United States east of the Rocky Mountains, Ontario (Canada), and East Mexico. So far, but one species, the large-mouthed Bass, is known to inhabit Florida, but it is my opinion that the small-mouthed species will also be found in some of the streams in the western part of that State.

Of late years the range of the Black Bass has been extended through the efforts of public-spirited individuals, and by the Fish Commissioners of various States; so that at the present time this noble fish may be said to have a "local habitation and a name" in every State of the Union. It has also been successfully introduced into England.

The following account, by the late James W. Milner, Assistant U. S. Fish Commissioner, of the introduction of the Black Bass into new waters, will be found very interesting and instructive, and is taken from the Report of the U. S. Fish Commissioner for the years 1872–73:—

(154)

"Among numerous records of their introduction, in very few instances discriminating properly between the two species, we give the following: In 1850, twenty-seven live Bass were brought by Mr. Samuel Tisdale, of East Wareham, Mass., from Saratoga Lake and put into Flax Lake, near his home. In the years 1851 and 1852, others were brought to the number of two hundred and reared in ponds in the vicinity. The matter was kept quiet and fishing discouraged for five years, when the fish were found to have increased very rapidly. Some twenty-five ponds were stocked in the same county after Mr. Tisdale had initiated the experiment. Afterward, Black Bass from Mr. Tisdale's ponds were supplied to a lake in New Hampshire in 1867, and to waters in Connecticut and Massachusetts. In 1866 the Cuttyhunk Club, of Massachusetts introduced Black Bass into a pond in their grounds. In the year 1869 the Commissioners of the State, together with private parties, stocked several ponds and the Concord River with Black Bass, and in the following year other waters were stocked.

"In Connecticut, in the winter of 1852–53, the Black Bass was introduced into Waramang Lake, in Litchfield County. They were brought from a small lake in Dutchess County, New York. A few years later they were said to have increased greatly. Another lake in the same county was stocked not long afterward.

"Salstonstall Lake, near New Haven; East Hampton Pond, in Chatham; Winsted Pond, in Winchester, and many ponds and lakes of the State, particularly in the northwest portion, were stocked with the Black Bass previous to the year 1867.

"In the years 1869, 1870, 1871, and 1872, thirty-seven

lakes and ponds in different parts of the State were supplied with Black Bass.

"As early as 1864 or 1865 Black Bass had been put
into Rust's Pond, near Wolfborough, New Hampshire; in
1868 a few were brought to Charlestown and Lakes Massabesic, Sunapee, Pennacook, and Echo, and Enfield,
Wilson's and Cocheco Ponds were well stocked; in 1870
and 1871 the New Hampshire Commissioners introduced
the Black Bass from Lake Champlain into the waters of
the State at Meredith, Canaan, Webster, Canterbury, Har-
risville, Munsonville, Hillsborough, Warner, Sutton, New
London, Andover, Loudon, Concord, and in Croydon. In
Massabesic and Sunapee Lakes, where they had been introduced, in 1868 and 1869, they were found to have
increased, and, on the authority of Dr. W. W. Fletcher,
they have become exceedingly numerous in Sunapee
Lake.

" The Commissioners of the State of Rhode Island, since
1870, have stocked thirty ponds or small lakes in different
parts of the State with the Black Bass.

" In Maine, in the fall of 1869, the State Commissioners
and the Oquossoc Angling Association introduced from
Newburgh, New York, a quantity of Black Bass. The
waters of Duck Pond, at Falmouth; Fitz Pond, in Ded-
ham; Newport and Philips Ponds, Cochnewagan Pond, in
Monmouth; Cobbosseecontee Lake, in Winthrop and adjoining towns, were stocked, and a few years afterward
were reported to have increased largely in numbers.

"Since the year 1871, Black Bass (*Micropterus salmoides*)
and Oswego Bass (*Micropterus nigricans*) have been put
into seventy lakes, ponds, or streams of the State of New
York by the Commissioners. They had made their way of

their own accord through the canals connecting Lake Erie with the Hudson, into that stream.

" Private citizens of Pennsylvania introduced the Black Bass (*Micropterus salmoides*) into the Susquehanna about 1869, at Harrisburg. In 1873 the tributaries of the Susquehanna, the Potomac, and Delaware Rivers were supplied with Black Bass by the Commissioners at thirty-five different points.

" In the year 1854, Mr. William Shriver, of Wheeling, Virginia, planted in the canal basin at Cumberland, Maryland, his former home, a number of the Black Bass (*Micropterus salmoides*); from the basin they escaped into the Potomac River, where they have increased immensely at the present day. They were moved from the waters of the Ohio River to their new locality in the tank of a locomotive. Numerous cases have also occurred of transfer from one locality in the Southern States to another.

" There have been very many transfers of these valuable species that have not been recorded, as they are easily kept alive while being moved from one place to another, and propagate surely and rapidly in ponds, lakes, and rivers.

" These details are given because they show the facility with which comparatively barren waters may be stocked to a considerable extent with good food-fishes, and they exhibit the general interest and attention that have been given to this mode of propagation."

In the account above given, reference is made to the stocking of the Potomac River with Black Bass by General W. W. Shriver, of Wheeling, West Virginia. As this matter is often alluded to on account of the marvelous increase of the fish from so small a beginning—less than thirty Bass having been originally transplanted—and as other parties have been accredited with the praiseworthy act who had nothing whatever to do with it, and whom I will not even mention here, it may not seem out of place to give the subject a little more space in this connection.

The earliest reference to the matter, of which I have any knowledge, is contained in a letter describing the habits of the Black Bass, written by Mr. John Eoff, of Wheeling, West Virginia, and published in the Report of the Smithsonian Institution for 1854, and is as follows:—

" Mr. William Shriver, a gentleman of this place, and son of the late David Shriver, Esq., of Cumberland, Maryland, thinking the Potomac River admirably suited to the cultivation of the Bass, has commenced the laudable undertaking of stocking that river with them; he has already taken, this last season, some twenty or more in a live box, in the water-tank on the locomotive, and placed them in the canal basin at Cumberland, where we are in hopes they will expand and do well, and be a nucleus from which the stock will soon spread."

General Shriver, himself, in a letter to Philip T. Tyson, of Baltimore, Agricultural Chemist of Maryland, in September, 1860, says:—

" * * * The enterprise or experiment was contemplated by me long before the completion of the Baltimore and Ohio Railroad to the Ohio River at Wheeling, but no satisfactory mode of transportation presented itself to my mind until after the completion of the great work (in, I believe, the year 1853), and in the following year I made my first trip (although I made several afterwards in the same year), carrying with me my first lot of fish in a large tin bucket, perforated, and which I made to fit the opening in the water-tank attached to the locomotive, which was supplied with fresh water at the regular water stations along the line of the road, and thereby succeeded well in keeping the fish (which were young and small, having been selected for the purpose) alive, fresh, and sound.

"This lot of fish, as well as every subsequent one, on my arrival at Cumberland, were put into the basin of the Chesapeake & Ohio Canal, from which they had free egress and ingress to the Potomac River and its tributaries, both above and below the dam. * * *"

General Shriver also states in a subsequent letter to Dr. Asa Wall, of Winchester, Virginia, dated September 17, 1867 :—

"The number of these Black Bass taken to the Potomac River by me, as well as I can now recollect, was about thirty. * * *"

Mr. Edward Stabler, a well-known and reliable gentleman of Baltimore, in a letter to G. T. Hopkins, of the Board of Water Commissioners of Baltimore City, dated, "Baltimore, 10th Mo., 28, '65," and published in the *Baltimore Sun* during the same month, says :—

"After much delay and frequent disappointments and loss, from the lack of suitable transportation, I have succeeded in taking in the Upper Potomac, and safely transporting to Baltimore, a fine lot of 'Black Bass' (*Grystes nigricans* Agassiz), with which to stock 'Swan Lake,' and also those in Druid Hill Park.

"As a brief history of the introduction of this superior fish into the tributaries of the Chesapeake, and east of the Alleghanies—for they are, in my opinion, before the Trout, both for sport and the table—may not be without interest to some, it may be stated that some thirteen years since, my son, A. G. Stabler, then a conductor on the

Baltimore & Ohio Railroad, in connection with two public-spirited gentlemen of Wheeling (Forsythe and Shriver),
brought from Wheeling Creek, West Virginia, a small lot
of Bass in the water-tank of his tender. They were placed
in the Potomac, near Cumberland, and from this stock,
the Potomac, for more than two hundred miles, and all its
large tributaries—the Seneca, Shenandoah, Cherry Creek,
Sleepy Creek, Great and Little Cacapon, Patterson's Creek,
South and North Branch, etc.—afford fine fishing.

" They are, I know, from the Great Falls to a considerable distance west of Cumberland, for I have recently so
taken them, and often weighing from five to seven pounds
—from four to five pounds is not unusual. * * *"

The *Baltimore American* in June, 1874, in an article on
Fish Culture, remarked incidentally :—

" It was twenty years ago, that Alban G. Stabler and
J. P. Dukehart, together with Forsythe and Shriver,
brought a small lot of Black Bass in the tender of a locomotive from Wheeling Creek, West Virginia, and put
them in the Potomac. From this small beginning, sprang
the noble race of fish which now swarm in the river."

It is certain from the above evidence, that General
Shriver was the leading spirit in the enterprise, assisted,
no doubt, by Mr. Forsythe, of Wheeling, and Mr. A. G.
Stabler, of Baltimore. The latter gentleman, being the
conductor of the train which carried the Bass—and there
is no evidence showing that more than one lot was taken—
certainly had some share in the transaction ; and if he was
a " chip off the old block "—for his father, above-mentioned, was an enthusiastic angler—it would naturally be
expected that he would have taken a lively interest in the
affair.

The circumstance is one in which I have always felt the greatest interest, for it occurred at the time when I first left my native city of Baltimore for a home in the West; and I have a distinct impression of the matter, made at the time of its occurrence, either from having heard it frequently spoken of, or from reading accounts of it in the public prints of the day; and my early impressions have always connected the name of Mr. Stabler, then a conductor of the Baltimore & Ohio Railroad Company, with the praiseworthy act.

At all events, it excited my curiosity as to the Black Bass, which I had then never seen, and prompted me to seek the acquaintance of that grand game-fish, which I very soon afterwards proceeded to do, in the Miami River, near Cincinnati. It is scarcely necessary to say that I have ever since been on terms of the closest intimacy with him, he having entirely supplanted, in my affections, the love I once bore my former piscatorial friends, the Striped Bass, the Blue Fish, and the White Perch of the Chesapeake and the Patapsco; but I must confess to an occasional retrospective weakness, and a kindly yearning for the old-time friends of my boyish days, not excepting the diminutive, but delicious "Gudgeon" of the Upper Patapsco and Herring Run.

14

CHAPTER VI.

HABITS OF THE BLACK BASS.

"* * * they mutually labor, both the spawner and the melter,—to cover their spawn with sand,—or, watch it,—or hide it in some secret place, unfrequented by vermin or by any fish but themselves."—IZAAK WALTON.

SPAWNING AND HATCHING.

BLACK BASS are very prolific, the females yielding fully one-fourth of their weight in spawn. The period of spawning extends from early Spring to Midsummer, according to the section of country, and temperature of the water and without regard to species; in the Southern States occurring as early as March, and in the Northern States and Canada, from the middle of May until the middle of July, always earlier in very shallow waters, and somewhat later in those of great depth.

In Waukesha County, Wisconsin, I have observed a difference of from one to four weeks in the time of spawning, in the numerous lakes of that locality, owing to the difference in temperature of said lakes, caused by their varying depths.

The Bass leave their Winter quarters in deep water about a month or six weeks previous to the spawning season, at which times they can be seen running up streams and in the shallow portions of lakes, in great numbers. Soon afterwards, the males and females pair off and prepare for breeding.

They select suitable spots for their nests, usually upon a

(162)

gravelly or sandy bottom, or on rocky ledges, in water from eighteen inches to three feet deep in rivers, and from three to six feet deep in lakes and ponds; and, if possible, adjacent to deep water, or patches of aquatic plants, to which the parent fish retire if disturbed.

The nests are circular, saucer-like depressions, varying from one to three feet (usually about twice the length of the fish) in diameter, which are formed by the Bass, by fanning and scouring from the pebbles all sand, silt, and vegetable debris, by means of their tails and fins, and by removing larger obstacles with their mouths. This gives to the beds a bright, clean, and white appearance, which in clear water can be seen at a distance of several score yards. I have seen hundreds of such nests, in groups, almost touching each other, in the clear-water lakes of Wisconsin, Michigan, and Minnesota.

Sometimes the nests are formed upon a muddy bottom, with a pavement or foundation of small sticks and leaves, from which the mud and slime have been washed and scoured; and as this often seems to be a matter of choice, there being beds upon gravelly situations in the same waters, I have sometimes thought that this discrimination in the location of the nests, might be owing to some difference of habits in this respect, in the two species of Black Bass; but of this I am by no means sure.

The females deposit their eggs on the bottom of the nests, usually in rows, which are fecundated by the male and become glued to the pebbles or sticks contained therein. The eggs are hatched in from one to two weeks, depending on the temperature of the water, but usually in from eight to ten days.

When hatched, the young Bass are almost perfectly

formed, from one-fourth to one-half of an inch in length, and cover the entire bed, where they can be easily detected by their constant motion. After hatching, the young fry remain over the bed from two to seven days, usually three or four, when they retire into deep water, or take refuge in the weeds, or under stones, logs, and other hiding-places.

During the period of incubation the nests are carefully guarded by the parent fish, who remain over them, and by a constant motion of the fins, create a current which keeps the eggs free from all sediment and debris. After the eggs are hatched, and while the young remain on the nests, the vigilance of the parent fish becomes increased and unceasing, and all suspicious and predatory intruders are driven away.

Their anxiety and solicitude for their eggs and young, and their apparent disregard of their own safety at this time, is well-known to poachers and pot-fishers, who take advantage of this trait and spear or gig them on their nests. I have known, also, some who call themselves anglers—Heaven save the mark!—who take the Bass at this time in large numbers, with the minnow or crawfish. Of course the Bass do not "bite" at this season, voluntarily, but when the bait is persistently held under their noses, they at first endeavor to drive it away or remove it from the nests, and finally, I think, swallow it in sheer desperation.

FOOD AND GROWTH.

After the young Bass leave the spawning beds their food at first consists of animalculæ, larvæ, insects, and the ova of other fish ; as they grow older and larger they devour worms, tadpoles, small fish, etc.; and, in later life,

they vary their diet with crawfish, frogs, mussels, and
water-snakes, until, attaining a weight of two pounds, they
will bolt any thing from an angle-worm to a young musk-
rat.

Where food is plentiful they grow rapidly, reaching a
length of two inches in a few months after hatching, and
at a year old, will measure, at least, four inches. At two
years of age, they will be found from eight to twelve
inches in length, weighing about a pound, and will grow
nearly or quite a pound a year thereafter, until they attain
their maximum weight.

They arrive at maturity in from two to three years, according as the conditions for their growth were favorable
or otherwise. The maximum weight of the small-mouthed
form of the North and West may be said to be four or
five pounds, and of the large-mouthed form, from six to
eight pounds, though there are rare exceptions to this
rule.

An instance, showing the rapid growth of Black Bass,
is related by Mr. Charles J. Pearson, at that time Fish
Warden for Morris County, New Jersey: He states that
in the fall of 1876, fifty Black Bass, measuring from two
and a half to four inches in length, were placed in D. L.
Miller's pond at Madison, Morris County, New Jersey.
On October 17th, 1877, about one year from the time of
putting them in, Mr. Miller had occasion to draw the
water down, for some repairs. He had the flume so arranged as to take any fish that might run out. Eleven
Bass were caught. They measured from ten to thirteen
inches in length, and were undoubtedly the same fish
which were put in the year before, as none of this species
of fish were ever known in the pond before.

There is not an absolute uniformity of growth in fishes, any more than in other creatures; thus, some fish will outgrow others of the same hatching until double their size, a fact made very apparent in the artificial culture of brook Trout, Salmon, etc.; but Black Bass will grow with wonderful rapidity where an equable temperature of water and an abundance of food obtain. As an instance of the influence of an abundant supply of food upon the growth of Black Bass, A. N. Cheney, Esq., of Glens Falls, New York, related to me the following circumstance, and presented me with a fine photograph of the two fish alluded to:—

"I send you a photograph of two large-mouthed Bass caught by myself. They are, or, rather, one of them is, the largest Bass ever caught in any waters about here, weighing seven pounds and fourteen ounces, and the other six and a quarter pounds. The most remarkable fact is, perhaps, the effect of food upon the growth of fish. The two fish in question were caught in Long Pond, near here, August 1, 1877. Long Pond was stocked with six small Bass from Lake George, New York, in 1866, they having been put into a stream emptying into the Pond by some gentlemen, who, on their way from camping a week at Lake George, had to cross this stream to reach home; and the putting the fish into the stream was suggested by their catching a number of small Bass during the last day in camp.

"The fact of their deposit was almost forgotten, when, in 1874–'75, quantities of Bass was discovered in the Pond, which had hitherto been inhabited by Pickerel, Perch, and quantities of bait fish, minnows, silver and gold shiners, etc. While Lake George had never been known to yield a Bass over six and a half pounds, Long Pond has turned out at least a dozen over that weight.

"The largest small-mouthed Bass ever caught in this region, was a five pound fish from the Hudson River, taken by Colonel Jeptha Garrard, of Cincinnati, with a fly, while fishing with me. Two years later, I caught one of equal weight, near the same place."

The following very interesting account of the food and growth of the Black Bass, and which, at the same time, exhibits its voracity and pugnacity, was contributed to the columns of *Forest and Stream*, by William A. Mynster, of Council Bluffs, Iowa. Mr. Mynster is an exceptionally close observer, and takes especial delight in watching and tending his "finny pets:"

I had a dam constructed in my spring branch, immediately below my fish ponds, in such a manner as to form a small body of pure, clear water. In this I placed some seven or eight hundred native fish of different varieties, embracing the black bass, sheepsheads, buffaloes, and pickerel. From the banks of this body of clear water I was enabled to see every movement of my finny pets, and many moments of leisure have I spent in watching their habits. The Black Bass (*Micropterus pallidus*) would usually swim into the current, where he would sport about on the gravelly bottom, while the buffalo would retire into stiller water and browse in the grass and water-cress growing on the bottom.

Thus I ascertained their habits of feeding, and was enabled to determine what growth they would make in a given time without being fed artificially. Hence I seldom, if ever gave them any food. The Buffalo (*Bubalichthys bubalus*), in a few weeks became attenuated, and began dying. This I attributed to their being in cold spring water with a current too rapid, and their not being able to procure sufficient food. The Black Bass, on the other hand, thrived amazingly well, and were making a most marvelous growth. This I attributed to the fact that they were in pure water of a uniform temperature. The Bass, although found in all kinds of water, undoubtedly thrive best in clear, pure, spring brooks with gravelly bottom. The size of these Bass when I first put them in this place was from four to six inches in length, and in less than three weeks had grown upwards of an inch.

This, I must confess, notwithstanding I had implicit confidence in their making a rapid growth, astonished me much. I had always been a believer in heavy feeding, and felt satisfied that the amount of growth that would be derived in a certain time depended mainly upon the quantity of feed that had been consumed. This led me to speculate where these Bass obtained their food, confined as they were in a very small body of water containing some eight hundred fish, and immediately below my ponds containing some 40,000 salmon, young and older. For the purpose of ascertaining this, I made my Bass frequent visits, and by remaining quietly secreted on the banks, soon discovered the source of their food supply.

One day as I was thus occupied, in company with my eldest boy, he called my attention to the fact that a snake (*Tropidonotus grahami*) was leisurely swimming through their midst. At first I felt inclined to pursue the snake, fearing that he might in some manner injure, if not destroy, a large portion of my native stock. My fears were, however, speedily terminated by one of my larger Bass making a rapid dart at the snake with open mouth, and nearly severing its head quite close to the body. The scene that then ensued beggared description. Never shall I forget it—such a floundering and splashing! The surface of the water for an instant seemed literally covered with perpendicular tails enveloped in foam. So great was the commotion that we were compelled to retire to a greater distance in order to avoid being thoroughly drenched.

After the disturbed waters had become somewhat calmed, we resumed our former position in order to make further observations, and found our large Bass hero, with one end of the snake in its mouth, rapidly making away with it, and a smaller, but not less pretentious brother, at the other end, endeavoring with all his might and main to eat even with him. Thus these gamey lads continued for some time, swimming up and down the stream, like two boys running with a rope. The distance between them, however, rapidly diminished.

This had continued for some time, when we saw emerging from under a log at the edge of the banks one of my pike (*Esox lucius*). At first he came slowly but steadily, when he made a rapid dart, with open mouth, at my smaller Bass, and, at a single gulp, placed himself outside of it! Then he came face to face with our hero. It was an awful moment of suspense for some time. Our finny gladiators remained motionless, eyeing each other, measuring the dimensions of each other's mouth, as it were. The crisis at length came. The Bass, by force of digestion, had made way with his part of the snake rope, and making one mighty effort, stretching maxillary and dental to their utmost capacity, soon enveloped the pike to a point just below the operculum. At this point we departed, feeling perfectly satisfied that our hero would take care of himself.

I presume it is unnecessary to say that I no longer entertain any doubts as to the ability of the Bass to take care of himself, and that heavy feeding is indispensable to a rapid growth.

The above may, perhaps, seem somewhat fishy to a great many, but when we consider the structure of the Bass, our doubts will be, in a great measure, abated. The variety above-mentioned has a very large mouth—in fact, they seem all mouth, thus enabling them to envelop any thing not exceeding their own circumference, with ample room for respiration through the gills. The œsophagus is very large (about the size of the stomach) and short. This enables them to take into the stomach all that may be embraced by the mouth.

In the warm waters of the extreme South, which preserve a more equable temperature than those of the Northern States, the Black Bass grow to an immense size, their maximum weight, in Florida, being from twelve to fourteen pounds; but while I have seen them of these weights, I never took one, there, weighing more than nine pounds, with the artificial fly, but, doubtless, I could have done so with live bait or the trolling spoon.

In Northern waters they do not grow nearly so large, six to eight pounds being the limit. Under conditions and circumstances favorable to their growth they will increase in weight, as before stated, about a pound a year;

15

but under adverse circumstances or unfavorable conditions their growth is much slower; therefore, no rule of general application can be established from any single instance, or as the result of any exclusively local test or experiment.

The growth of Black Bass is affected not only by the supply of food and temperature of water, but also by the extent of range. Bass in small ponds do not thrive so well, nor grow so fast; the smaller the extent of their range, the slower will be their growth, and, indeed, this is true of any other fish; for it is well known that fish confined in aquaria, in springs or wells, grow so very slowly, that their increase in size is hardly appreciable from year to year, even though their supply of food be abundant.

An equally well-attested fact is, that the largest Bass are found in the largest bodies of water, or where the range is extensive; extreme depth of water seeming to be more favorable to their growth than mere extent of surface. For example, I know of several shallow lakes in Wisconsin, where the Bass seldom grow to exceed two pounds, while in deeper lakes in the same vicinity they attain the usual maximum weight of four or five pounds; and in Green Lake, a large and deep lake near Ripon, in the same State, I once caught a string of thirty Black Bass, mostly of the large-mouthed species, weighing from four to eight pounds each, and fully averaging six pounds.

HIBERNATION.

Black Bass undoubtedly hibernate, except in the extreme Southern and South-western States; but in the colder climate of the North and West, it has been proven in numerous instances, that they bury themselves in the mud, in the crevices of rocks, under masses of weeds, or sunken logs, in the deepest water, and remain dormant until spring.

This habit has been doubted by some, inasmuch as an occasional Bass has been caught through the ice; though such instances are rare indeed, and all those of which I have any knowledge occurred late in the winter, or early in the spring. As one swallow does not make a summer, these unusual cases must be considered as merely exceptions to the general rule.

During a residence of ten years in Wisconsin, where fishing through the ice was constantly practiced during the winter, and where tons of pickerel, pike-perch and yellow-perch were so taken in a single season, I never knew of a single Black Bass being so taken except very late in the winter, or in early spring, say in March, just before the breaking up of the ice; and even those instances were of rare occurrence, and happened only during unusually mild weather; and these same waters, be it remembered, afforded the finest Black Bass fishing during the summer and fall.

Dr. D. C. Estes, of Lake City, Minnesota, an accomplished angler and naturalist, records a similar experience in regard to Lake Pepin; he says:—

"The Pike and Pickerel are the only fish taken here in the winter. It is strange to many what becomes of the countless numbers of other game fish that throng these waters in the summer season. Bass, which are so numerous then, are never seen in winter. I am quite sure that not a single Bass was ever caught here through the ice.

I have for years tried all depths of water to raise one, or to discover one, but have thus far failed. I must believe, then, that they hibernate."

Genio C. Scott, in "Fishing in American Waters," quotes an intelligent and veteran Black Bass angler of Central New York, in regard to this habit, and who furnishes the following conclusive evidence:—

" I have never known them [Black Bass] to be taken in winter, and I think they seek a particular location and remain torpid during winter. My attention was directed to this fact about thirty years since. At that time I was in the habit of spearing fish in a mill-dam on the outlet of Seneca Lake, at Waterloo, Seneca County, New York. From April to November I found numbers of Bass; from December to March I found all other varieties, but no Bass.

" In the winter of 1837, the water was shut off at the lake for the purpose of deepening the channel to improve the navigation. This was considered a favorable time to quarry the limestone in the bed of the river; and upon moving the loose rock in the above-named mill-dam, where the ledges cropped out, there were found hundreds of Bass imbedded in their slime, and positively packed together in the crevices and fissures of the rocks. My subsequent experience has done much to convince me that my theory is correct."

On this point, A. N. Cheney, Esq., of Glens Falls, New York, related to me the following incidents:—

"A few years ago a man, Seth Whipple, living on the Hudson River, near Glens Falls, in drawing some sunken logs from the river, during the winter, for firewood, found in the hollow of one of the logs, six Black Bass (small-mouthed), weighing from a half to two pounds; they were nearly dormant.

"The father of Pension Commissioner Bentley, who lives at Glens Falls, and has some Trout ponds on his place, to gratify a boy bought of him a Black Bass, and placed the fish in a spring. When autumn came the fish was missing, and was supposed to be stolen. During the succeeding winter the spring partly dried up, and to restore the water supply the spring was dug deeper. During the operation it was found necessary to remove an old stump in the side of the spring, when to his surprise the Bass was found underneath the stump, in a hole, evidently prepared for winter burrow."

Mr. John Eoff, of Wheeling, West Virginia, a remarkably close observer, says, in the "Report of the Smithsonian Institution," for 1854 :—

"In the winter season they retire to deep and still water, and apparently hide under rocks, logs, etc., and remain there until the first of April."

I could multiply evidence on this point, if necessary, but these several opinions, founded upon observations made in the widely separated States of Wisconsin and Minnesota in the northwest, New York in the north, and West Virginia in the middle section of our country must suffice.

That Black Bass do not hibernate in the extreme South, is well-known; and to this circumstance, perhaps, may be attributed, in a measure, their larger growth. Still it is not unreasonable to suppose, that the Black Bass of that section have a period of repose and seclusion, analogous to hibernation, at some other season of the year, possibly during the fervid heat of the summer solstice; for it is usual for the Bass of the North-west to cease biting and retire to the deepest water during an unusually heated term in summer.

The fact that the best season for Black Bass fishing varies in different sections—in the North being from July till October; in the West and most northerly of the Southern States in the spring and fall; and in the extreme South during the winter season—would naturally lead one to suppose that the period of dormancy in the Black Bass occurs at different seasons in different localities, and is influenced by climatic conditions, or the supply of food.

CHAPTER VII.

INTELLIGENCE AND SPECIAL SENSES.

Venator. But, master! do not trouts see us, in the night?
Piscator. Yes; and hear, and smell, too, both then and in the day-time.—
Izaak Walton.

THE brain of fishes differs so materially in size, conformation, substance and analogy from that of other animals, that it has been the rule of specialists to attribute to this class of vertebrates a very low order of intelligence. In opposition to this theory, however, Dr. F. Day recently read a paper before the Linnæan Society of London, England, in which he endeavored to show that fishes possessed a far higher order of intelligence than is usually accorded them.

He claimed that the experience of himself and others indicated that they possessed emotions and affections, and in support of that view he showed that they constructed nests, transported and defended their eggs, protected their young, manifested their affections for each other, recognized human beings, could be tamed, exhibited the emotions of fear, anger, and revenge, uttered sounds, hid from danger, sought protection by attaching themselves to the bodies of other animals, and had peculiar modes of defense; that they left the water in search of food, and that they sometimes combined for attack and defense.

Every observant angler and naturalist has, in his own

(175)

experience, proved the truth of many of the above assertions, and, no doubt, some have observed traits of intelligence still more convincing.

The wonderful faculty of anadromous fishes, seeking out and ascending their native streams during the breeding season, even after being purposely carried hundreds of miles away, has commanded the admiration of biologists, yet they can see nothing in the small and jelly-like brain of the fish to account for the marvelous habit, but instinct; on the same principle, perhaps, that Coleridge accounts for the blindness of Love:

"His eyes are in his mind."

SENSE OF SIGHT.

We are led to believe, from the investigations of anatomists, that the organs of special sense in fishes are very imperfectly developed; but while this may be true, in the main, as regards the special senses of touch and taste, I am constrained to believe, from the observations of myself and many others, that fishes, in general, have the senses of sight, hearing, and smell developed in a much greater degree than is generally supposed.

The diversities in form and position of the eyes of different fishes, prove that they are of the greatest use to them, in procuring food, and in escaping from their enemies; and are placed "where they will do the most good."

In the majority of fishes, which are constantly moving about, and frequent alike the surface and bottom of streams, the eyes are placed in the usual position of most other animals, one on each side of the head. In those which stay more constantly in the lower depth of waters, the eyes are placed on top of the head, as in the star-gazers; while in the flat fishes, which recline or swim on one side near the bottom, both eyes are placed on the same side of the head, enabling them to obtain the benefit of both eyes while in that position. In the Pike-perch, which is nocturnal in its habits, the eyes are unusually large, as is the case with other animals who seek their food mostly at night.

It is a popular idea that fish are necessarily near-sighted on account of the conformation of the eye, which is large, round and prominent; and the main argument adduced to support this theory, is the readiness with which they will take an artificial fly, trolling spoon or other artificial bait, which resemble in but slight degree the natural objects of food that they are intended to represent, if, indeed, they are intended to represent any thing.

It is very often the case that those anglers who are most strenuous in their theory that fish are near-sighted, stultify themselves by carrying a large and most varied assortment of artificial flies, of all shapes and colors, in order to meet the "fastidious taste" of the fish, that often refuse one pattern or color, and rise eagerly to another, which could not be the fact were they so near-sighted as many believe. The consistency of these anglers would be more apparent, if they would adopt Mr. Cholmondely Pennell's theory of artificial flies, and confine themselves exclusively to his three typical flies—brown, yellow, and green hackles.

Now, I am not of those who believe that our brave game fishes possess such extreme gullibility, as to mistake an artificial lure for the genuine article, upon the hypothesis of near-sightedness. My opinion, founded upon numerous experiments, is, that fishes see and hear as well in and through the medium of the water, for all practical purposes, as the angler does through the medium of the atmosphere; the clearer and more rarified the medium, the clearer and greater the range of vision in both instances.

In muddy or turbid waters the sight of fishes is necessarily limited, as ours would be in hazy or foggy weather. It is neither fair nor logical to presume that fishes, in water, ought to discern objects in the atmosphere above, any clearer or plainer than we can perceive objects in the water, while standing on the brink.

We are altogether too prone to judge every thing from our own standpoint, and to attribute to our own cleverness results that in all probability depend upon other and extraneous circumstances. Who, of us, could tell a skillfully tied artificial fly from a real one, beneath the water, when its surface was ruffled by a brisk breeze, shadowed by drifting clouds, covered with the froth and suds of an eddy, or surmounted by the foam and bubbles of a rapid ?

Yet, there are those who contend, because fish fail to detect this difference through the same obstacles to clear vision, that they are of a verity near-sighted, and easily fooled by the very poorest semblance of a fly or feathery nondescript; but let one of these persons try a cast of the best flies upon a bright, still day, when the water is perfectly clear and the surface like a mirror, and if he expects to get a rise under such conditions, he himself must be very near-sighted indeed.

On the other hand, any one who has seen a Black Bass

dart like an arrow and seize a minnow swimming quietly thirty feet away, or a Brook Trout flash like a meteor for a dragon fly hovering near the water at the same distance, must admit that their visual powers are sufficient for all practical purposes.

It is quite amusing to hear an angler expatiate learnedly on the dimness of sight and dullness of hearing in fishes, and in the next breath caution the tyro to have his clothing conform as nearly as possible with the hues of the foliage skirting the stream; to keep out of sight, tread lightly, and make as little noise as possible; and to assure him, that, even then, the chances are that the fish will see the novice before he sees the fish.

It is a curious contradiction of theory and practice, a fishy illustration of the abstract and concrete. The explanation I conceive to be this: Our Piscator would be considered a scientific angler, which, in his case, becomes a contradiction of terms; for while blindly holding to the opinions of some closet naturalist, he is practically following the dictates of his own experience and common sense.

Now, it is possible to be scientific and an angler, too, but our science, like our angling, must be practical, and must of necessity be learned by close observation and study of the habits of the fishes as they exist in nature, and not alone from the study of the physical construction of a preserved specimen.

I am well aware that scientists consider fish myopic, or near-sighted; not, however, on account of excessive convexity of the cornea, as is popularly supposed, for it is an exploded theory in medical science that myopia depends necessarily upon this condition; indeed, in fishes the cornea is almost flat, while in birds of prey, which have a very extended range of vision, the cornea is quite convex.

From the lack of analogy, from the great difference in construction of the ocular and auditory apparatuses of fishes and terrestrial animals, and from the wide difference in the properties of the media of air and water, I am convinced that the organs of the special senses of sight and hearing in fishes are not well understood at the present day; and I am confident that future investigations will prove them to be possessed of much greater acuteness of vision and hearing, than is now accorded them.

It is a well-known fact that fishes are attracted by any gay, bright, or glittering substance, as a finger-ring, a sleeve-button, or a coin, and have deliberately swallowed them when dropped in the water. I have caught Brook Trout with wintergreen and partridge berries, the bright scarlet color seeming to allure them, and I have even caught them with a naked bright fish-hook; but all this does not prove that they were the victims of a myopic mistake, or that in their near-sightedness they mistook these various articles for something else; neither does it prove that a Black Bass will grab at a trolling spoon, a Bluefish snap at a bone squid, or a Spanish Mackerel seize a metal or pearl troll under the delusion that they are really choice shiners, or delicate piscatorial tidbits.

A camel, it is said, will bolt all sorts of substances, as metal, glass, stones, leather, etc., but when were his short-comings attributed to short-sightedness? Our dogs will often refuse good, clean food and hunt up an old dry bone, a stone, an old shoe, or a stick, and will gnaw them with delight, and even swallow them with evident gratification. Birds will peck at and swallow bright beads, colored threads, etc., and kittens will seize, claw and bite almost any moving small object; but these vagaries are attributed to the idiosyncracies of the animals mentioned, while in fishes they are ascribed to defective sight.

But what are a fish's eyes for? According to our present knowledge they are to enable him to become "a snapper-up of unconsidered trifles" with hooks attached to them!

Now, so far as the artificial fly is concerned, when it is cast lightly upon a fretted surface, I think it is generally taken by a fish under the impression that it is a natural insect; but with regard to trolls of all kinds, as spoons, squids, spinners, propellers, etc., and very often with regard to the artificial fly, I am of the opinion that they are taken through a spirit of mere bravado, curiosity or wantonness, and not with the idea that they are living objects of prey. They are seized by the fish because they are bright, attractive and in motion; not because they are hungry, but because they are in a biting mood, for we often find, nay, most always find, that fish so taken are already gorged with food.

Sense of Hearing.

There is no external ear in fishes, the internal ear alone existing, and which is extremely delicate in its construction.

Dr. John Hunter observed that it varied much in the different genera of fishes, but that in all it consisted of three curved tubes, which united one with another. The whole organ is composed of a kind of cartilaginous substance, and in some fishes is crusted over with a thin lamella to keep it from collapsing.

The canals terminate in a cavity, in which cavity there is a bone or bones. These ear-bones are familiar to most anglers, and are sometimes very beautiful, resembling porcelain, and are often called "brain-ivory;" those of the sheepshead (*Haploidonotus grunniens*) of our Western waters are known as "lucky stones," and are highly prized by boys as pocket pieces.

A remarkable instance, demonstrating the acuteness of the sense of hearing in fishes, has recently occurred in California. As it is an exceedingly interesting and well-authenticated fact, and one so totally at variance with pre-conceived notions, I feel justified in reproducing it here. The account was published in the San Francisco *Chronicle*, upon the authority of Mr. B. B. Redding, one of the Fish Commissioners of California :

In Siskiyou County there is a caravansary kept by George Campbell, and known as the Upper Soda Springs Hotel, which is situated on a semicircle of land formed by a bend in the Sacramento River. Wishing to have a supply of fresh Trout close at hand, Mr. Campbell had a supply of water conducted through a board flume from the river to a natural depression in the ground, thereby creating an excellent fish pond of about half an acre in extent, which he supplied with full-grown Trout caught in the river. The supply flume is, for some distance, raised about four feet above the ground. About four hundred feet from the pond, a small rivulet, which is an outlet for irrigating water, flows under the flume, crossing it at right angles and about four feet below it, and empties into the river.

The fall of water from the end of the flume to the surface of the pond is two feet, the water in the flume flowing with a velocity of three miles an hour. The pond has an outlet, which is screened to prevent the escape of the Trout. Shortly after the pond was established, the discovery was made that numbers of fish were missing from it. Mr. Campbell instituted an investigation, which resulted in discovering that the fish, dissatisfied with their new quarters, had leaped through the waterfall two feet into the flume, and, swimming against the strong current until they reached where the stream crosses under the flume, they had leaped out of the latter to the stream four feet beneath.

Upon discovering the method of flight adopted by his finny acrobats, Mr. Campbell prevented further escape by placing a screen at the mouth of the flume. Up to last accounts the dissatisfied fish had discovered no other method of getting into their favorite Sacramento. The questions immediately suggest themselves: How could the fish know that a stream flowed under the flume, the sides of which were considerably above the surface of the water, and if they possessed that knowledge, how were they to know that they were immediately over it? Mr. Redding examined the ground carefully along the flume, and could not discover a single instance of a Trout having jumped out at any other place.

Mr. Redding subsequently communicated to the *Forest and Stream* the following solution of the matter:—

The attention of Prof. E. D. Cope, the eminent naturalist, having been called to the above facts, he has given me an explanation which seems entirely satisfactory. He tells me that at the base of every scale of the Trout, at a point where the scale is united with the skin, is a nerve; that all these nerves, from the base of every scale, lead to a large ganglion situated on the center of the forehead of the fish below the eyes; and that nerves from this ganglion communicate to the internal ear. These nerves, at the base of each scale, are formed to receive vibrations in water. Any vibration in water reaching the scales of the fish is thus communicated to the internal ear. If, as was the fact, one of the timbers that supported the flume rested in the running water on the ground, the vibrations of this running water on the ground would be carried by this timber to the flume and to the water in it, four feet above, and the ear of the fish would separate and take cognizance of the difference in the vibrations, as the human ear in the air distinguishes the difference between the voices of friends.

It has, generally, been conceded that fish can hear sounds or vibrations produced on, or in, the water, but that they can hear sounds produced in the air is doubted by many; but every observant angler can recall instances where this doubt has been refuted.

It is well known to many, though still doubted by some, that fish can be tamed and taught to come to the surface of the water to be fed, answering promptly to the sounds of the voice, a bell, or a whistle. I have observed instances of this kind, myself, and under such circumstances as rendered it impossible for the fish to see the person producing the sounds mentioned.

I have frequently observed fish exhibit symptoms of great fright or alarm at the report of fire-arms, or other loud noises, and to be scared and dart away at the sound of the human voice, or the barking of a dog, when the fish could not see the originators of the noises.

CHAPTER VIII.

ON STOCKING INLAND WATERS WITH BLACK BASS.

"And it is observed, that in some ponds Carps will not breed, especially in cold ponds; but where they will breed, they breed innumerably."—IZAAK WALTON.

THE Black Bass is peculiarly adapted, in every respect, for stocking inland waters. There is no fish that will give more abundant and satisfactory returns, and none in which the labor and expense attending its introduction is so very slight.

As a food fish, there are very few more palatable fresh-water fishes, its flesh being firm, white, and flaky, and when cooked, nutty, tender, and juicy; it has few bones and little offal, and as a pan-fish is unexcelled. Its game qualities are second to none, and it will thrive and multiply in waters where the *Salmonidæ* can not exist.

There are few fish more prolific, while there is none more hardy, healthy, and better able to take care of itself, and none that protects or cares more tenderly for its young; consequently, there is no limit to its production and increase in suitable waters, save from a lack of natural food.

In view, then, of its many good qualities, there is no fish more worthy of cultivation; none that can be so easily transplanted, and none that is so well adapted to the various waters of our country, for there is no game-fish that has such an extensive original habitat.

16   (185)

Every attempt that has been made, intelligently, to stock suitable waters with the Black Bass, has been crowned with signal success, which, unfortunately, has not been the case with the introduction of other game and food-fishes. The praiseworthy efforts that have hitherto been made to introduce the Salmon and Brook Trout, even in streams formerly inhabited by them, have either totally failed, or the results, in a majority of instances, have not been at all satisfactory; nor does it seem, now, as though these efforts will ever prove successful, owing to causes which I have mentioned elsewhere.

Streams which are necessarily obstructed by dams—even when the most approved fishways are provided—or whose waters are polluted by the refuse of manufactories, can never be successfully stocked with the salmonids; but the Black Bass seems to thrive wonderfully well in spite of these and other disadvantages.

From what has been said in regard to their habits, it will readily be seen that there is no necessity for hatching Black Bass artificially, in the manner practiced with the Salmon, Trout, or Shad, nor would the method be as successful, for reasons well known to fish culturists.

The *Salmonidæ* of the Eastern United States, with the exception of the grayling, prepare their beds and deposit their spawn late in the fall, or early winter. This being accomplished, all further interest in the procreation of their species, for the time, ceases; the eggs are left to themselves, and such as escape being devoured by their numerous enemies are hatched in from two to four months, according to species and temperature of water. The young are provided with a yolk-sack, which nourishes them for a period of from twenty-five to forty-five days, varying with the species, when they begin to look for other means of subsistence.

During all this time, from spawning until the absorption of the yolk-sac—from three to six months, as the case may be—the eggs and young are helplessly exposed to the ravages of predatory fish, reptiles, and birds. Under these circumstances, comparatively few fish arrive at maturity, and streams are soon depopulated by seining, injudicious angling, and natural vicissitudes; hence arises the necessity for their artificial cultivation and the re-stocking of such waters.

The eggs of the salmonids are of a separate and non-adhesive character, which admits of their being easily handled and managed for the purposes of artificial reproduction, while those of the Black Bass are glutinous and adhesive, which renders them very difficult to manipulate for similar purposes.

The Black Bass being hatched with but a rudimentary or very small umbilical vesicle or yolk-sack, needs the fostering care and attention of the parent fish, who teaches it how and where to find its food, and protects it from its enemies in the same way that a hen cares for her brood.

All that is required, then, to stock a stream or pond with Black Bass, is to procure a small number of the fish, at least a year old, and place them in the waters. If the water is of a suitable character, and possesses a sufficient supply of natural food, the Bass will propagate naturally, and rapidly increase in numbers.

The only considerations to be looked after are the character and conditions of the waters to be stocked—sufficient depth and extent of surface being more important than quality of water—and the supply of food contained in them. It is useless to attempt to stock very small and confined ponds of less than three acres in extent; for in such ponds, without communication with running water, the Bass will not increase beyond a certain limited number, which will usually be the number of fish originally planted; for the supply of natural food will soon become exhausted, and the old fish will prey upon the young, should any be hatched, until a certain average, proportionate to the supply of food, is established and maintained.

In the case of newly formed ponds, they should be well stocked with minnows, crustacea, frogs, etc., at least a year before the Bass are introduced. It is also necessary that there should be in all ponds, deep holes of not less than twelve feet in depth, to which the Bass can retire in very hot weather, and where they can also hibernate.

In some waters, one species of Black Bass may prosper better than the other; for instance, in large ponds or shallow lakes, with a sluggish current, muddy bottom, and abounding in fresh-water algæ, the large-mouthed Bass will thrive better, perhaps, than the small-mouthed species. But in streams, and ponds with a good supply of running water, either, or both species may be introduced.

The Black Bass has been successfully acclimatized in England; and at the proper season advertisements may now be found in English papers of young Bass from America for sale at high prices, for stocking English waters. Mr. Silk, fish-culturist to the Marquis of Exeter, has taken over two lots of young Bass from the Delaware River, the first in 1878, and the second in 1879. In a letter to the late Frank Buckland, Mr. Silk says:—

In 1879 I went again, and started from America with 1,200 Black Bass, and on arriving home I had 812, having done better than I did on the previous occasion.   All of the Black Bass were for the Marquis of Exeter, he having borne all the expense of the experiment.   Most of the fish were placed in a lake belonging to his lordship, called Whitewater, near Stamford.   Not any of them have been caught yet, but two of them were found dead in a pipe, where they had got jammed.   The pipe supplied a filterer, and they had got in and could not get out again.   From what I could learn they would be about half a pound each in weight, so that they had done very well.   The first lot that were put in will be three years old in April, when they are expected to commence breeding.

In transporting Black Bass for the purpose of stocking new waters, great foresight, care, and judgment must be used. The size and number of the fish, the distance they are to be carried, and the length of time to be consumed in the journey, must all be taken into consideration. The size and number of the fish will determine the size and number of the containers; thus, while a common wash-tub would be a safe receptacle to transport twenty-five Bass, six inches in length, for a long distance, it would not be sufficient for half the number of double the size, for it would require a vessel that would contain at least one and a half times the quantity of water. This is a safe rule to follow, and calculations can be made accordingly.

For small fish, six to eight inches long, the largest size wash-tubs are well adapted, but for larger fish the carrier must be much deeper. If barrels are used they should not be perfectly new, nor should they retain any vestige of their former contents, as vinegar, oil, whisky, etc., if old ones. The very best ones would be those that had been used to hold water for a long time. Wooden tanks, constructed for the purpose, are best, if they have been soaked in running water a sufficient length of time to take up and remove all the soluble matter of the wood, as tannic acid, etc. Metal tanks, constructed of galvanized iron, heavy tin, etc., though more expensive, are to be preferred, but they must be rendered perfectly clean before the fish are put into them.

If the number of fish to be carried is large, it is much better to provide a sufficient number of containers than to crowd the fish. There is no good plan yet devised for aerating water, while in transit, by forcing air into it, for most of it escapes at once, as the numerous bubbles that appear on the surface, testify. The better way is to expose the water to the air in finely divided particles, in the form of spray or small drops, as by forcing or pouring it through a fine rose. I have seen it successfully accomplished by dipping the water out of the container with a common sprinkling-can, or watering-pot, and pouring it back again through the rose, or sprinkler, from a considerable height; this is as simple and effectual a way as any yet devised.

It is a bad plan to change the water frequently, as is often done, for the change in the character and temperature of the water thus produced, affects the fish unfavorably. The best plan, by far, is to aerate the original water. If in warm weather, the temperature of the water should be noted, occasionally, and kept at its original temperature, or a little lower, by the addition of small pieces of ice, from time to time.

These instructions are only general, and must be varied to suit particular circumstances. Sometimes, for short distances, double the number of fish may be safely carried, in the space I have designated. Moreover, it is possible to be too attentive, and kill the fish with kindness. If the number of fish to be transported is large enough to justify the experiment, the best and safest plan would be to carry one vessel, with its allotted number, first, and, according to the operator's best judgment; then, as the experiment proved successful, or not, would depend the transportation of the balance, on the same, or some other plan of proceeding.

PART SECOND.

TOOLS, TACKLE, AND IMPLEMENTS.

CHAPTER IX.

FISHING RODS.

"And now, scholar! I think it will be time to repair to our angle-rods."—
IZAAK WALTON.

THE first and most important article in the angler's
outfit is the rod ; it takes precedence of every other tool or
implement in his *armamentarium*. A thoroughly good
and well-balanced rod is the angler's especial joy and
pride. A true and tried rod of graceful proportions and
known excellence, which has been the faithful companion
on many a jaunt by mountain stream, brawling river, or
quiet lake, and has taken its part, and shared the victory
in many a struggle with the game beauties of the waters,
at last comes to be looked upon as a tried and trusty
friend, in which the angler reposes the utmost confidence
and reliance, and which he regards with a love and affec-
tion that he bestows upon no other inanimate object.

I doubt if rifle, shot-gun, or fowling-piece ever becomes
so dear and near to the sportsman as the rod to the angler, for the rod really becomes a part of himself, as it were,
through which he feels every motion of the fish when
hooked, and which, being in a measure under the control
of his will, and responsive to the slightest motion of his
wrist, seems to be imbued with an intelligence almost life-
like.

The essential qualities of a fishing-rod are balance,

(195)

strength, elasticity, pliancy, and lightness, and in its construction such a wood, or combination of woods, must be
used as will best subserve these conditions. The natural
cane, or reed pole, when it is of good and true taper, is
the primitive model for a fishing rod, but it is not adapted
to all kinds of angling, being too long for one mode, too
stiff for another, and not well balanced for a third.

The nearest approach to a perfect rod, in theory, and
composed entirely and alone of any one variety of wood
proper, is a red cedar rod, made entirely of one piece from
butt to tip. It combines all of the essential qualities of a rod,
and can be made suitable for any method of angling, long
or short, stiff or pliant, and withal, is extremely light;
but in practice it is not tough or strong enough for the
ordinary angler. And so each and every kind of wood
has some objections when used, alone, in the construction
of a rod; most kinds of wood making a rod too heavy,
when other qualities are all right.

The next best thing is to use a combination of woods,
and this plan has been found by experience to be the best.
Another plan is to alter the natural conditions of a wood
by mechanical skill, as in the split bamboo rod, by which
the original natural good qualities are not only preserved,
but improved upon by the skill of the workman.

MATERIAL FOR RODS.

In order to get proper and desired action of combined
woods, and for convenience, portability, and ease of being
repaired, rods are very properly made in several pieces, or
joints. The fewer pieces used, however, the better will
be the action of the rod, and, in fact, two, or at most,

three pieces, are sufficient for all kinds of rods except Salmon-rods, which are of a necessity the longest rods made.

In the selection of woods for a rod, such kinds must be used as possess the principal attributes of a fishing-rod, which are toughness and elasticity; and when these qualities are combined with lightness, there is nothing more to be desired, for proper modeling will insure perfect balance and pliancy.

Many kinds of native and foreign woods have been tried and experimented with to produce a rod perfect in action, such as cane, ash, hickory, maple, basswood, ironwood, hornbeam, cedar, barberry, bamboo, memel, lancewood, mahoe, greenheart, bethabara, or wasahba, etc.

ASH.—For butts of rods there is no wood so suitable as good, close-grained, second-growth white-ash. It is straight-grained, light, springy, and strong, and in some kinds of rods it is also available for second pieces or joints, having a springy "snap" possessed by no other wood.

LANCEWOOD.—For second pieces and tips, lancewood, when of good quality, stands pre-eminent, being close-grained, tough, and extremely elastic, with sufficient spring and snap for small joints. It is used for tops, or tips, more universally than any other wood, on account of its superiority over all other varieties for this purpose. It is rather heavy for butts, though often used for this purpose, some fly-rods being constructed entirely of this fine wood, making very durable and beautiful rods, with a delightful action, but still rather heavy for most anglers. Mr. Orvis, of Manchester, Vermont, however, makes lancewood fly-rods with a short hand-piece of other material, which are most excellent and serviceable rods. I have used one with the utmost pleasure and satisfaction, and can fully recommend it.

GREENHEART is next to lancewood for tips, and for second joints is preferred by many; it is somewhat heavy, and quite tough and springy. Many rods are made entirely of this wood, and are excellent, too, by the way, but most too heavy for the admirers of light rods. It certainly forms very handsome rods, when nicely polished, and which are capable of good and hard service. In England it is a favorite wood for fly-rods, where, as a rule, much heavier rods are used than in our own country.

BETHABARA, or WASAHBA.—This wood was, I believe, introduced several years ago by A. B. Shipley & Son, of Philadelphia, who make a specialty of rods of this handsome material. It is very dark in color, resembling, somewhat, black-walnut in this respect. It is extremely hard and close-grained, almost like bone in density, though it is rather heavy, except for second pieces and tips. Messrs. Shipley say that no other wood can equal it for great strength, toughness, and elasticity. It is susceptible of a beautiful polish, and I know of no other wood that makes so handsome a rod in its natural color. Never having tried a rod of this material, I can not speak of its action, though I am sure, from its inherent qualities, as exhibited in some specimens of the wood which I have examined, that it is eminently serviceable for the smaller joints. I have seen some rods of this material, made by George B. Ellard, of Cincinnati, which have done good service, and are much admired.

CEDAR.—As before stated, red cedar makes a perfect rod, except in its lack of toughness or strength. For Trout fly-rods, in the hands of an expert with light rods, it is all that can be desired, but it needs to be handled with the skill of a master, and by one who loves his rod next to his wife, *de facto*, or intended.

HICKORY.—This wood was formerly much used, especially in the construction of certain parts of Salmon-rods, but its use has been entirely discontinued, in this country, at least. It is, of course, the toughest of woods, but lacks spring and elasticity, having a tendency to warp and become permanently bent, by the continual strain to which a rod is subjected.

HORNBEAM has been used to some extent in the manufacture of rods, and is well spoken of by those who have used it. It is very difficult, however, to procure it straight-grained, which it should be to make it available for fishing-rods. It is quite tough, but pretty heavy, and is in no way equal to lancewood for tips or second joints, for which purposes it has been mostly used, though there have been a few fly-rods constructed entirely of this wood. If perfectly straight-grained, it no doubt answers a good purpose.

MAHOE is a foreign wood now coming into vogue for rods, and more especially for fly-rods. It resembles ash somewhat in its qualities, being not very heavy, and quite springy and elastic. It is much used in Havana for springs of that queer looking, high-wheeled vehicle, the *volante*. It is much praised by some for producing rods of a superior action, but as I have had no personal experience with them, I am unable to say any thing for or against them.

MAPLE and BASSWOOD are used only in the construction of cheap and common rods, and need no further mention here, except that curly maple is sometimes used for short and ornamental butts, or hand-pieces.

CANE, or REED.— Native and foreign cane poles are much used for fishing-rods, especially in certain kinds of angling where no reel is required, and for such service answer a good purpose. The native canes are the lightest, though not so strong and durable as the Chinese or Japanese canes.

CALCUTTA BAMBOO.—The East Indian, or, as it is generally termed, the Calcutta bamboo, is the best of all material for the construction of a perfect rod when carefully made by a skillful and master workman. In its natural state it is almost perfect in its action, and possesses all the desired qualities for certain modes of angling, but for methods that require a shorter and lighter, or more pliant rod, these additional features can be secured by altering the original conditions of the cane, by sawing it into strips and accurately fitting and gluing them together; thus reducing the caliber, and, at the same time, preserving and enhancing all the essential and desirable qualities in a more compact form.

There are two kinds of Calcutta bamboo, known to the trade as "male" and "female" canes. The former is nearly solid, hard, and very tough, with large and protuberant knots or joints, where, when growing, are attached the leaves and tendril-like branches, which are so tough as to render it necessary to burn them off; this gives to these canes the peculiar clouded and burnt appearance, which adds so much to the beauty of the split bamboo rod. The female cane is hollow through its entire length, except just at the joints or bulges, which are not so prominent as in the male cane. The male cane is the best to use in its natural state, but for split bamboo rods, the selected female cane is to be preferred, as it makes the most perfect rod.

Origin of the Split Bamboo Rod.

The split bamboo rod being an American institution, and there being no reliable record of its early manufacture, I may be pardoned for giving a brief space to its consideration. I consider it the greatest invention ever made pertaining to the art of angling, equaling the invention of the breech-loading rifle and shot-gun for field sports.

The history of the " split bamboo," " section bamboo," or, as it is sometimes called, the " rent and glued bamboo" rod, although of recent origin — dating back only some thirty years—is somewhat obscure. Several persons have laid claim to the invention, though with what justice, it has, heretofore, never been clearly determined.

There is no important mechanical invention that has, in its inception and principle, sprung entirely and spontaneously from the brain of any single individual, and this will apply to the split bamboo rod as well; for though purely an American invention, as now constructed, the idea, or principle, is really of English origin. Rods formed of several pieces of wood, that is, from two to four longitudinal sections mitred and glued together, were made in England many years ago; and Aldred, of London, made rod tips, or, as they are called in England, " tops," of split bamboo, long before the split bamboo rod, proper, was made in this country. Aldred's tops, however, were necessarily a failure, from the faulty method of their construction. He made them of many short pieces, sawn from between the knots, or leaf-ridges, of the male cane, and spliced, to form continuous lengths. So much for the original idea.

It is not my province, nor desire, to detract one iota

from the credit or just due of any one in this matter, but rather to render unto Cæsar those things that belong to Cæsar. I will present only such evidence as is entirely trustworthy, having been obtained from authentic sources, and put it on record here as reliable data in regard to the early history of the American split bamboo rod; and in so doing I hope to do justice to an obscure, but worthy brother of the angle.

The first split bamboo rods were made by Mr. Samuel Phillippi, a gunsmith of Easton, Pennsylvania, about the year 1848. Mr. Phillippi was an angler of some local repute, and died about 1878. Mr. Charles H. Luke, a veteran angler of Newark, New Jersey, formerly lived in Easton, and was a near neighbor of Phillippi, with whom he fished and hunted on many occasions. He naturally spent much of his spare time at Phillippi's gun-shop, where, about 1850, he watched him for hours at a time making split bamboo trout fly-rods, in which, being a fine and exact workman, he took great pride.

Mr. Charles F. Murphy, of Newark, New Jersey, famous as one of the best makers of split bamboo rods, and who has few, if any, superiors as a fly-fisher, corroborates Mr. Luke's testimony, and says that Phillippi used split bamboo for fly-rods, certainly as far back as 1848, and further says: "I am certain you can give Phillippi credit for the discovery of split bamboo for fly-rods, without fear of contradiction."

Dr. W. W. Bowlby, of New York City, a gentleman well known as an angler, says: "My earliest recollection of the split bamboo rod dates back to about the year 1852. At that time I lived in New Jersey, near Easton, Pennsylvania, and fished in the same waters in New Jersey and

Pennsylvania with an old gunsmith, of Easton, known among us as " Old Sam Phillippi." It was about the year above named that I saw a split bamboo rod in his possession, and he informed me at that time, that he was the originator of the idea; and to him, I earnestly believe, belongs the credit of having first conceived the idea of constructing a rod from such material. Phillippi's rods were three joints, second joint and tip split bamboo; butt was made of ash."

I have similar statements from other gentlemen, whose names I do not feel at liberty to disclose, but their testimony is to the same effect, qualified in some instances by the remark that Phillippi's rods were crude affairs; and which, though true, does not detract in any degree from the credit due him. Phillippi's rods were made in three joints, or pieces, two of which, only, were of split bamboo, the butt being ash, and stained to imitate bamboo ; but the bamboo joints were made on the same principle as those of to-day, though composed of but four strips. Phillippi's rods seem poor things now, but at that time they seemed wonderful.

The first complete split bamboo rod, that is, all of the joints being of this material, seems to have been made by Mr. E. A. Green, of Newark, New Jersey, about 1860, though some claim that the late Mr. Thaddeus Norris, of Philadelphia, is entitled to this honor; however this may be, they were both subsequent to Mr. Phillippi, and their rods were merely improvements on his more primitive efforts. Whether either or both of these gentlemen had any knowledge of Mr. Phillippi's rods, or whether the idea was original with them, is not material, and does not affect Phillippi's claim of priority. Mr. Green being a skillful and ingenious mechanic, and a thorough and expert angler, produced excellent rods, though for his own use, only.

The first perfect split bamboo rods for the trade were made by Mr. Charles F. Murphy, of Newark, who, after seeing Mr. Green's rods, saw a chance for still greater improvement; and Mr. Green, knowing him to be an artistic and skillful wood-worker, encouraged him to undertake their manufacture, which he did about 1863-'64.

Mr. Murphy made the first split bamboo Salmon-rod in 1865, which Dr. Andrew Clerk took to Scotland, where it proved a success. Subsequently, Genio C. Scott took the same rod to the St. Lawrence, and, on his return, published an interesting account of his trip, and the use of the rod, in Wilkes' "Spirit of the Times," in the same year. The first split bamboo Black Bass rod was made by Mr. Murphy, in 1866.

Up to this time all split bamboo rods were composed of but four strips or sections. About 1870, Mr. H. L. Leonard, of Bangor, Maine, began making the six-strip bamboo rod, and Dr. A. H. Fowler soon followed him. Mr. Leonard is one of the most skillful makers of split bamboo rods in the country; the angler who is the fortunate possessor of one of his best rods ought to be a happy man; I speak from experience. Although Leonard's rods were the first six-strip rods put in the market, Mr. Murphy had perfected one some time before.

To Andrew Clerk & Co., and their successors, Abbey & Imbrie, 48 Maiden Lane, New York City, however, belong the credit and honor of bringing this rod to its present state of perfection and prominence. They were the first patrons of Phillippi, Murphy, and Leonard, and gave them every assistance and encouragement.

This firm was the first to make a specialty of the manufacture of the split bamboo rod, and was the first to introduce the six-section rod, those previously made for them by Phillippi and Murphy being four-section rods. They subsequently trained skilled mechanics to this branch of their business, and until they had made a success of the split bamboo rod, they stood alone in the enterprise, being ridiculed by other manufacturers and dealers for pursuing a phantom and a false idea.

They persisted in their course, however, in spite of opposition and ridicule, and to-day enjoy the fruits of their devotion to the idea of producing "the best rod in the world." And by their pluck and commendable enterprise and persistent endeavors, notwithstanding the repeated failures and petty annoyances incident to their experiments, they have at last the satisfaction of knowing that their efforts have been appreciated by anglers, and that their large experience has put them far in the advance as manufacturers of this unexcelled rod; and the fact that other manufacturers have since taken up the making of this rod as an important part of their business, proves that the original position and faith of Andrew Clerk & Co., and their successors, Abbey & Imbrie, in regard to the merits of the split bamboo rod, were well founded.

The best form of the split bamboo rod, as proved by actual service, is the round, six-section rod. Many experiments have been made to improve upon this method, but they have resulted in failure. The hexagonal rod is claimed by its supporters to be preferable to the round rod, inasmuch as there is no cutting away of the surface enamel or outside siliceous coating, at the angles.

as in the formation of the round rod, and therefore is a stronger rod.

While this looks plausible enough to the superficial reasoner, it has no foundation in fact. The hexagonal rod is not a true six-sided figure, but rather a round figure with six angles; for the face of each section is of course slightly rounded, or convex, as it originally existed in the cane, and the extremely small amount of outside surface that is taken off at the angles to make the rod perfectly round does not amount to any thing in reality, or weaken the rod a particle. On the contrary, it lessens the liability of the sections becoming separated by use, from the prominence of the jointed angles or seams, as in the hexagonal rod, which are liable to become bruised or chipped off by striking or rubbing against hard substances, as rocks, trees, boats, etc., and so exposing the seams to the action of air and moisture, which softens the glue and causes the strips to separate.

Another plan has been advocated, to reverse the process in sawing the strips, and place the enamel or outside coating at the interior of the rod. And still another, and somewhat better plan, by the way, has been proposed, more especially for tips, as follows:

The shaded sides of the sections represent the outer coating. The sections are to be pressed together, and glued in the position in which they are drawn in the figure, which brings the enamel of each strip partly inside and partly outside; the piece is then worked down

to a round form, having the center of enamel, and the
circumference of alternate strips of inside and a small
portion of the siliceous or outside layer.

Then these rods have been made of eight and nine
strips; but there is no real merit in any of these last-
mentioned plans, and the six-section, outside enamel,
hexagonal or round, is the only common-sense, practical
plan.

The following table of relative weights and measurements of section-bamboo fly-rods, which, however, can
only be approximate, is furnished by Messrs. Abbey &
Imbrie, No. 48 Maiden Lane, New York City:

LENGTH OF ROD.	WEIGHT OF REEL PLATE.	TOTAL WEIGHT.
11 feet	1¾ ounces.	9 ounces.
11½ feet	2 "	10 "
12 feet	2¼ "	12 "
14 feet	2½ "	18 "
16 feet	2¾ "	28 "
16½ feet	2¾ "	31 "
17 feet	3 "	36 "
17½ feet	3¼ "	40 "
18 feet	3½ "	44 "
19 feet	3¾ "	50 "
20 feet	4 "	54 "

BLACK BASS BAIT RODS.

The Black Bass and his mode of capture has hitherto
been altogether too much neglected, if not entirely
ignored, by most of our writers upon the gentle art,
either from a lack of interest, or a want of proper information, upon the subject. Some works, that have
been held in the highest esteem, contain the least infor-

mation upon Black Bass angling, and even that little is totally unreliable and unsatisfactory. As a rule, our angling authors have damned the Black Bass with faint praise, and have given but the most primitive methods for its capture.

Most writers have devoted their attention exclusively to the Salmon and Brook Trout, among the fresh-water game fishes, or to the Striped Bass, Blue Fish and Weak Fish, among the salt-water species. While acknowledging the game qualities and fine sport afforded the angler by these different species, and which acknowledgment is founded upon ample personal experience with them all — excepting the Salmon—I regard the Black Bass as one of our gamest fishes; and an experience of twenty-five years has convinced me that the sport afforded by it is not surpassed by the pursuit of any other member of the finny tribe, excepting possibly the Salmon, with which "King of the waters," as I have just stated, I have had no experience.

But in order to realize Black Bass fishing in its perfection, suitable tackle must be employed. Fishing for Brook Trout with a bean-pole for a rod, and a piece of raw meat for bait, would not be considered sport in the true meaning of the term, nor should the pursuit of the Black Bass, under similar conditions, be so regarded; yet the methods of Black Bass angling heretofore described by our angling authors, and practiced by most anglers, are open to the same objections.

Until within the past few years such primitive rods as the cane-pole of the South, the alder or hemlock of the Middle States, or the tamarack pole of the North-west, were, when well selected, light, and of true taper, equal to or superior to any thing offered by the dealers. Ten years ago, a person entering a tackle shop in a Western town, and inquiring for Bass tackle, would be presented with a rod from twelve to sixteen feet long, weighing from one to two pounds; a large brass reel, with a handle like a coffee-mill crank; a line like a chalk line, and a large ungainly hook with a side bend—-and all this formidable array of clumsy apparatus to do battle with such a thoroughbred and noble foe as the Black Bass! Combination rods, general rods, perch rods, cheap striped bass tackle, *et hoc genus omne*, had been, as a rule, manufactured for the Western market, and sold for Black Bass fishing.

This was the more surprising, as the Black Bass inhabited so many of the waters of the Union, from New England to Florida, and from Maryland to Missouri. He was, moreover, the acknowledged peer of the Brook Trout for gameness by those who knew him best; and it was "a consummation devoutly to be wished" that as much skill should be displayed in his capture, and as elegant and as suitable tackle employed for the purpose as in the case of his speckled rival.

Those enthusiastic and observant anglers, who learned from experience that there was a want not supplied in Black Bass rods, as offered by the trade, and who possessed sufficient ingenuity, constructed their own rods, and fished in their own way; and as these worthy souls were generally regarded as authority in their respective localities on the subject of Black Bass fishing, and not without reason, their particular style of rod was adopted in their particular locality as the "perfect bass rod." This will account for the marked difference of opinion

18

upon this subject in different sections of the country, for each such rod was made in accordance with the style of fishing, and the character of the waters to be fished.

Some years ago, while residing in Wisconsin, I conceived the idea of writing a book on the Black Bass, in order to do justice to a fish that seemed to be but little understood; and likewise to divest the sport of Black Bass angling—as it then existed—of some of its primitive and disagreeable features, and give it a higher place in the catalogue of noble sports.

I was convinced that it was only necessary to present the claims of the Black Bass in a proper light, and to give a description of the most suitable tackle for its capture, to induce the angling fraternity to accord full justice to a noble fish, which I was satisfied was, for many reasons, destined to become the leading game fish of America.

Accordingly, I began making notes of my observations of the habits of the Black Bass, and was collecting data for the intended treatise, when, fortunately and opportunely, Mr. Charles Hallock founded and established that excellent journal *Forest and Stream*, which came just when it was most needed. Here then was my opportunity to reach the anglers of the country, and I was not slow to embrace it, and at once began to champion the cause of the Black Bass.

I prepared a series of articles on the Black Bass and Black Bass angling, and described at some length the proper rod, reel, line, hook, etc., and mode of using them, to render it not only feasible, but practicable, to convince the angler of the high order of game qualities inherent to the Black Bass; and that by the use of suitable tackle it would not suffer by a comparison with other game fishes. The seed of these articles was sown in good ground, and yielded abundantly. I received letters from hundreds of Black Bass anglers, in all parts of the country, thanking and complimenting me for the ideas suggested, and for espousing the cause of their favorite fish, the Black Bass. The result proved far beyond my most hopeful anticipations, and I have the satisfaction of knowing that to-day there is no game fish more eagerly sought for, and none that is being more rapidly introduced into new, inland waters by the advocates and admirers of this truly game fish.

In February, 1875, I published an article, entitled, "The Coming Black Bass Rod," in *Forest and Stream*, which gave a description of my idea of a proper rod for Black Bass angling, founded on many years experience, and the use of many different rods for this purpose. Mr. C. F. Orvis, of Manchester, Vermont, an expert angler, as well as a maker of fine fishing-rods, at once began the manufacture of a Black Bass rod from those suggestions, and they are to-day to be found in all parts of the country, he having been remarkably successful in introducing them, for they supplied a want long felt.

Other manufacturers, seeing the necessity for a new departure from the old beaten path, soon began to make short and light Black Bass rods, more in accordance with the spirit of the age, and the demands of their customers, which they called the "Forest and Stream" Black Bass rod, thus honoring and doing justice to the admirable journal to whose columns are due the credit of completely reconstructing the Black Bass rod, and of replacing the former long, heavy and clumsy affair, by the elegant, short, light and pliant rod of the present day. And not only has the length and weight of bait rods been reduced, but fly-rods of all patterns have been reduced at least a foot in length, during the past five years, to their great advantage.

THE HENSHALL BLACK BASS MINNOW ROD.

While a rod may vary somewhat, according to the mode of angling, there is no good reason for such a wide diversity of opinion as obtains on the question of Black Bass rods. For instance: Fishing from the bank of a swift and narrow stream, wading the bars of a wide river, or fishing from a boat on a quiet lake, seem in themselves apparently very different processes; but in reality they are only slightly different means of securing the same end, viz: the capture of the Black Bass with a minnow for bait—for my remarks apply only to bait fishing—and a properly constructed rod would answer in either place and fulfill either condition, when accompanied by a light, freely rendering reel, together with a fine trout line. An artistic angler, fishing for Trout or Black Bass with the fly, would use his fly-rod in either place; from a boat, from the bank, or while wading the stream; he would use the same rod under any and every circumstance, wherever he had room to make a cast. The Black Bass bait fisher will in time become as consistent as the fly fisher, but it will only be when he adopts the proper rod, which rod I will now endeavor to describe.

I start out with the proposition that a first-class American, single-handed Trout fly-rod is, *per se*, the very perfection of rods and the *chef'dœuvre* of the rod-maker's art.

Such a rod is about eleven feet long, and is made of split bamboo, or a combination of ash and lancewood, and should weigh from seven to nine ounces. With such a rod, properly handled, either line, leader or hook may part, but the rod will remain intact. It combines all the essential qualities of a good rod, viz: balance, lightness, strength, elasticity, and pliancy. A Salmon rod is only a Trout rod enlarged, proportionately, in every particular, and made to be used with two hands instead of one.

Now, if all fish were caught with the fly, there would be no need for other rods than the Trout and Salmon fly-rods; but as such, unfortunately, is not the case, we are compelled to adopt other rods in accordance with the mode of fishing, the character of the fish to be caught, and the kind of bait to be used. But whatever may be the nature of the rod that is to be made, let this general rule or principle be followed in its construction: Let the rod conform as nearly as possible to the typical rod, *i. e.*, the Trout fly-rod, as is consistent with the manner of service required of it. If we follow this rule we can not go very far astray.

Acting upon this principle, then, I have found in my experience that the essential qualities or attributes of a good Black Bass rod for bait fishing, are just the same as the typical rod for balance, weight, strength, and elasticity, with a happy medium of pliancy, between a Trout fly-rod and a Trout bait-rod, which can hardly be expressed in words. But this slight stiffening of the rod makes it correspondingly heavier, and in order to maintain the same relative weight, we must cut down the length of the rod by taking off from two to three feet, thus reducing the rod to eight or nine feet in length, which is found by experience to be far superior to longer rods for Black Bass fishing.

As a long, withy, willowy rod is best for casting a fly, so is a short, stiffish rod best for casting a minnow. With a rod of this character, and a light-running, multiplying reel, it is an easy matter to cast from thirty to forty yards. The situation of the reel upon the butt must be a compromise between the single and double-handed fly-rods; for though the rod is used almost entirely with one hand, yet there are emergencies when both hands must be used, for occasionally a six-pound Bass or a fifteen-pound Pickerel, Pike-perch, or Catfish will be hooked; or an unusually bold or fierce fighting Bass may get the advantage of one and take to the weeds or rocks. It is also essential to have plenty of room for the hand below the reel in casting, as the thumb must control the running off of the line, and prevent the reel from overrunning, as in Striped-bass fishing. The rod must have light, standing guides, instead of rings as in the fly-rod.

The rod from which my original description of the " Coming Black Bass Rod " was taken is eight feet and three inches long, and is in three joints; the first joint or butt is composed of white ash, and the second joint and tip of lancewood; it weighs just eight ounces; it is finely balanced, and has a true bend from butt to tip; with it I have killed hundreds of Black Bass, weighing from two to four pounds, and occasionally heavier, and Pickerel from five to twelve pounds, with an occasional one scaling fifteen pounds. I have used it many seasons, and do not see where it can be improved; it is as firm and elastic as when first made. I have oftentimes cast out my entire line of fifty yards, when casting with the wind.

I feel justly proud of the merits of this rod, for I made it myself.

Messrs. Abbey & Imbrie, of 48 Maiden Lane, New York City, made me a rod from designs and specifications furnished by myself, which comes as near the embodiment of my ideas of a Black Bass minnow rod as any I have seen. After a season of hard usage and thoroughly practical tests, I am prepared to say that I do not see how it can well be improved. It is fully the equal of my own pet rod (which I made myself), and is of course more highly finished; indeed, in this latter respect it can not be excelled.

The materials and mountings of this rod are of the highest quality. The butt is prime white ash, and the second piece and tip are of selected Cuba lancewood. The mountings are German silver, solid and strong. The ferrules are milled, capped and banded, and the guides solid, light, and of a very graceful and new pattern, and are lashed on. The butt has a wound grip, or hand-piece, and the reel-bands and cap are very finely finished. The metal tip is of the four-ring pattern, light and strong.

The joints are made solid and flush, without tenons or dowels, or mortising. This I have found to be the best way for fitting the joints, for the boring not only weakens the joint, but the tapering tenon, acting like a wedge, will cause the joint to separate by the continual springing of the rod. Mr. C. F. Orvis, one of the best and most honest tackle makers living, also constructs the joints of his rods in this way.

The dimensions of the rod made by Abbey & Imbrie are as follows:—

Total length, when put together, 8 feet 3 inches.

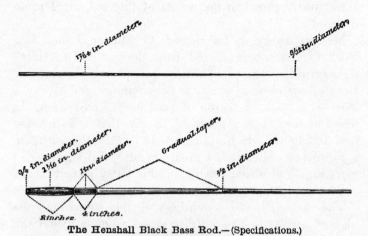

The Henshall Black Bass Rod.—(Specifications.)
(Abbey & Imbrie.)

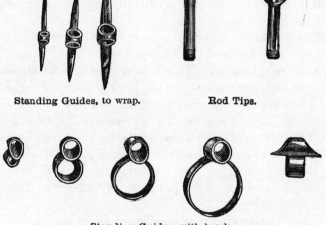

Standing Guides, to wrap.   Rod Tips.

Standing Guides, with bands.

Length of each piece, 34½ inches, including ferrules.
Butt: Extreme end of butt, ¾ inch in diameter.
      Small end of butt, ½ inch in diameter.
      Grip or hand-piece, $1\frac{1}{16}$ inch in diameter.
      Reel-seat, 1 inch in diameter.
Second piece: Large end, $\frac{7}{16}$ inch in diameter.
      Small end, $\frac{17}{64}$ inch in diameter.
Tip: Large end, ¼ inch in diameter.
      Small end, $\frac{3}{32}$ inch in diameter.
Reel-seat, 4 inches long.
From extreme butt to reel-seat, 7 (from 6 to 8) inches.

The weight of a rod made from these dimensions will be about nine ounces, depending upon the material employed in its construction. Its weight can be reduced to eight ounces by taking off a sixty-fourth of an inch from the several diameters, and can be increased to ten or eleven ounces by enlarging the diameters in the same ratio; but it must be remembered, that in altering the conditions of this rod, at all, in order to preserve its admirable balance and fine action, it is imperative that the diameters be increased or diminished, uniformly, throughout the entire length of the rod, from the extreme butt to the tip.

To attempt to secure lightness by reducing the caliber of the butt-piece alone, would result in spoiling the rod; and as Messrs. Abbey & Imbrie truly say: "The angler who seeks lightness in a rod at the expense of *any thing* else is worse than an infidel." While this rod *may* be reduced to even six ounces, if its proper proportions are observed in the modeling, and still be a good rod for Rock Bass, Croppies and White Bass, it would be too light for Black Bass angling.

19

This rod has a true and gradual taper from the reel-seat to the tip, which gives it a back, which, while just stiff enough for casting a minnow, is sufficiently pliable and yielding to give a correct working to the rod under the play of a lively fish. And just here is where so many rods fail. Many rods are made too weak in the butt, or the upper two-thirds of it, usually by a rapid and concave taper to reduce the caliber of the rod at this point, in order to gain lightness. But this can only be done at the expense of weakening the rod, and spoiling its action.

When a rod has too weak a back, or too slender a butt at this point, it causes the rod to be top-heavy, and produces what is known as a "double action" in the rod, or a "kick in the handle;" qualities which were sought for in some Salmon fly-rods in the old country, as it was supposed that a fly could be cast farther with rods of this character. But it was necessary that the angler should become thoroughly educated in the handling of a rod with this peculiarity, to be enabled to use it with any degree of satisfaction.

However much this principle may have been desired by British Salmon fishers, it becomes the very worst feature in a Black Bass minnow rod. With this defect in a bait rod, it is impossible to cast with any accuracy, or to any great distance. And, moreover, it produces in the angler a lack of confidence in his rod, for it "feels weak" to him at the very point where it should feel the strongest, and really the rod would give way at just this very point under a heavy strain.

But, to refer to my rod again : I can easily cast a minnow from forty to fifty yards, and with great accuracy, with this rod, the back being just stiff and yielding enough for this purpose. The bend from the last third of the butt piece to the tip forms a true and perfect arch under the strain of a hard-pulling fish, which is the bend so desirable, and so hard to obtain in a fishing-rod. The strain falls equally upon the entire rod, so that it is impossible for me to tell just where it would break under a sufficient strain. The weak part of an imperfect rod can always be felt by an expert angler, and he knows perfectly well, while playing a fish, just where the rod is weakest, and just where it would fail.

In giving a description of this rod, I have given the description of what I call a perfect Black Bass minnow rod, and the reader can rely upon it as being correct in principle, and satisfactory in practice. And should he ever become possessed of such a treasure, he will, in the fullness of his heart, be prepared to hold up both hands for me.

This same style of rod can be procured from any first-class maker, as Conroy, Bissett & Malleson, No. 65 Fulton Street, New York; Charles F. Orvis, of Manchester, Vermont; or S. W. Goodridge, of Grafton, Vermont, all of whom make excellent rods, from specifications furnished by myself. I have examined and tested rods made by all of them, and know whereof I speak.

Mr. Orvis informs me that some of his customers ordered rods with the butt extending below the reel clamps a foot or more, so as to reach under the elbow, and thus form a *point d'appui*. This demand is founded upon laziness, carelessness, or "pure cussedness," which was first induced by using the old-style rods, which were so heavy and long as to require either this support, or, what was worse, the holding of the rod with both hands.

Now, the object of the modern Black Bass rod is to dispense entirely with this ungraceful and clumsy style, and enable the rod to be used with the hand alone, as in fly fishing. I sincerely hope that my brother anglers will not thus handicap their skill, nor encourage this needless extension of butt. It will be well to remember, in this connection, that no excellence is gained but by great labor, and no skill attained but by careful practice. There may be born poets, but I doubt if there are born fishermen; the love may be innate, but its confirmation requires patience, perseverance and elbow-grease.

The novice will be sometimes told by theoretical anglers that he must procure a rod which accords with his size, strength, and general build; that a rod which suits one angler, will be too long, too short, too heavy, or too light for another. Now, this is all gammon; a rod must be made to suit the kind of fish, and the mode of fishing, without any reference whatever to the angler himself.

In ordering a shot-gun that is to be used on all kinds of game, from the lordly buck to the dainty quail, it is of the highest importance that the gun should be built to fit the sportsman in every particular, and he then varies the charge according to the game. But there is no analogy between a shot-gun and a fishing-rod; the latter weighs but ounces, where the former weighs pounds, and the weight of a rod for Black Bass angling will suit a weakly youth, or the strongest man, as well. A half-pound in weight is of no moment as compared to the strength of a man; and it is all stuff, and the sheerest nonsense, to talk of making a rod of this weight conform to the muscular requirements of any individual. A well-balanced rod feels the same to the weakest man or strongest, the tallest man or shortest; while a rod that lacks this quality will feel right to no one. I have no patience or sympathy with those visionary book-anglers, who talk or write such ridiculous nonsense, or spin such fine-drawn theories.

A Home-made Black Bass Rod.

As the Black Bass anglers of Ohio, Kentucky, Tennessee, Northern Alabama, and the South-west generally are extremely partial to a natural cane or bamboo rod, I desire to tell them how to make a good one of this material at little cost, and which, though not a "thing of beauty," will prove itself a "joy forever," in comparison with the cane-rod, as generally used. After using such a rod as I am about to describe for one season, the angler will be ready to advance another step, and adopt a good ash and lancewood rod, which contingency, I am free to admit, is the principal motive for this information.

A natural bamboo-cane, as it is procured at the tackle stores, is from fifteen to twenty feet in length; and it is the custom, in the localities named, to use from ten to twelve feet of the smaller or upper end of such a cane for a Black Bass rod, after attaching standing guides and a reel fastening. While such a rod is strong and light, with a moderate degree of pliancy and elasticity, it entirely lacks the great desideratum, balance, being decidedly top-heavy, and is too small at the butt to allow of a firm grasp of the hand, generally necessitating the use of both hands to hold it. Now, to obtain the greatest amount of good and pleasure from a rod of this character, proceed as follows:

Select a genuine Calcutta bamboo-cane, which may be known by its dark, mottled markings, caused by its having been burnt about the leaf-ridges, or knots. Select one that is hard and elastic, with a good taper, and quite small at the tip; those known as "male" canes are the best, having larger bulges, or leaf-ridges, and being much tougher than the "female" canes. Having chosen a good one, cut off six and a half feet of the smaller end for the rod, the remaining larger portion of the cane will make a good handle for a landing-net.

Now make a wooden butt of white-ash or black-walnut, from eighteen to twenty inches long, of the following diameters: At the extreme butt end, seven-eighths of an inch; now increase the diameter by a gradual taper to an inch and one-eighth at a distance of five inches from the extreme butt; then decrease the taper to an inch at a distance of seven inches from extreme butt. The next four inches forms the reel seat, and is one inch in diameter throughout its length; now decrease the diameter by a rapid, concave taper for a distance of two inches, to three-fourths of an inch, and thence a gradual taper to the smaller end of the butt, which must exceed the diameter of the large end of the cane about one-sixteenth of an inch; the diameter of the large end of the cane-joint— where cut in two—will be from half an inch to five-eighths of an inch.

Having proceeded according to the instructions just given, we have a cane-joint six feet and six inches long, and a wooden butt say twenty inches long, with the grip of one and one-eighth of an inch in diameter, and the reel seat of one inch diameter. Now procure a set of reel bands one inch inside diameter; a pair of ferrules for the joint—the inside diameter of the smaller or male ferrule being of the same diameter as the large end of the cane piece, which can readily be ascertained with a pair of calipers; five standing guides, graduated sizes, and a solid metal tip. These mountings should be brass or German silver. The guides should be attached at equal distances from the reel seat to the tip; and, having properly fitted the ferrules and reel bands, give the rod two coats of shellac or coach varnish. When dry, the rod is ready for use, and will be about eight feet in length, and weighing not more than eight ounces—a single-handed rod equal to any rod made for casting, will be well-balanced and strong, but will lack the pliancy, elasticity and perfect working of a good ash and lancewood rod, yet it will be such a great improvement on the cane-rod, as generally used, that it has only to be tried to be appreciated.

A rod, similar to the above, originated, in Milwaukee, in 1874, in this way: At that time I was the only one, of a large number of anglers, who frequented the lakes in the vicinity of Oconomowoc, Wisconsin, who used a *short* and light Black Bass minnow rod, and which was often the subject of many jokes on the part of my fellow-anglers. But, as it was not *always* "the longest pole that got the persimmons," some of them, at length, became convinced of the superiority of the short rod in casting and general convenience, though they were loath to alter their handsome ten and twelve feet rods.

I suggested to several to have short rods made of native cane, in the manner above described, and which I had formerly experimented with. I referred them to John C. Welles, of Milwaukee, as the proper person to make them. Accordingly, he got up several, and, for convenience, made them in three pieces—two cane-joints, of about three feet each, and a short wooden butt or handle. The result was, that the owners used them afterward in prefer-

ence to all other rods, and a demand at once sprang up for
the "Welles' rod," and they are still made and used to
some extent. Other Western manufacturers afterward
adopted the idea, and offered them to anglers in lengths
of from seven to ten feet.

But while such a rod is cheap, light, and eminently
serviceable, it has, to my mind, some very serious objections. In the first place, it is very homely and unsym-
metrical in form ; the short, stubby butt tapering so suddenly and abruptly to the cane-joint, gives the rod a very
awkward and unfinished appearance, and entirely destroys
the *balance* of the rod. Now, as remarked at the beginning of this article, "a thing of beauty is a joy forever,"
and one can appreciate this quality in a fishing-rod, as well
as in a horse, a yacht, or a gun. In the next place, it is
too stiff and unyielding, except at the extreme tip ; the
bend not being equally distributed along the entire rod, as
it should be ; and this fault, from the nature of the rod,
can not well be obviated. This I consider an insuperable
objection, for it precludes that nice discrimination in *feeling* your fish when he is taking the bait, and that delicate
manipulation of him after he is hooked. The owners of
this rod, however, are very enthusiastic in its praise, and it
is, at least, a step in the right direction for a more perfect
Black Bass rod.

THE CUVIER BLACK BASS ROD.

The most complete rod of this character which I have
seen, is made by Mr. George B. Ellard, of Cincinnati. It
is made in two pieces of choice, short-jointed Japanese
bamboo, with an adjustable handle, which can be detached

at pleasure. It is light, well balanced, honestly made, and can be handled all day without fatigue. The arrangement of the handle is a special feature; it can, with little trouble, be adjusted to any other rod. With it and a reel in his satchel, a dozen hooks, half a dozen guides, a solid metal tip, and a piece of wound silk thread in his pocket, an angler is never at a loss for the materials to enjoy a day's sport at any little fishing town, where he may by accident find himself, during the season, and where he can buy a bamboo or other cane for fifty cents.

Mr. Ellard calls his rod the "Cuvier Bass Rod," after the well-known club of that name in Cincinnati. It has been thoroughly tested during the past season on Lake Erie, and in the smaller waters of Wisconsin, Minnesota, and Michigan, and has given universal satisfaction. Its moderate price is not the least of its merits.

Section Bamboo Minnow Rod.

While, in my opinion, ash and lancewood, or some such suitable woods are to be preferred for a Black Bass minnow rod—the desired action of such a rod being more easily obtained from these materials—there are some anglers who prefer a rod of split bamboo to any other material, and for any kind of rod. And while it is possible to make as good a rod for action, and a superior one for strength and beauty from this material, the cost is necessarily very much greater—at least three times as great—for a perfect minnow rod of split bamboo.

For those who desire the *best*, at whatever cost, I can recommend a rod of this material when made by a first-class workman. But, at the same time, I would caution the angler to take the most jealous and unceasing care of such a rod, for it is not so serviceable as a wooden rod when subject to the same conditions of usage.

In order to give the reader an idea of the construction of a split bamboo rod, I can not do better than to reproduce here the following extract from a letter, written to me on this subject by Mr. T. S. Morrell, an accomplished and finished angler, of Newark, New Jersey—relating to the construction of a split bamboo Black Bass minnow rod, as made by himself:—

I have just finished a rod patterned after that described by you in "Hallock's Sportsman's Gazetteer"—a one-hand bait-rod for Black Bass. I will briefly describe my method of manufacture, as I learned it from Mr. E. A. Green :

The rod is eight and a half feet long, in three joints, of six-strip bamboo. The ferrules, reel-bands, butt-cap, and guides, I had made to order, not being an expert in working metals. The bamboo I got from Mr. C. F. Murphy, and is as tough as bone.

I first sawed the piece in two strips with a fine, sharp hand-saw; then I took a board with a perfectly straight slit sawed the length of a joint of the proposed rod. Laying the flat part of one of the strips (I had just sawn asunder) on this board over the slit, I carefully placed it sò as to get the requisite taper, and then tacked it at the edges firmly to the board.

Then, with rule and pencil I drew on the bamboo a straight line, being careful to taper it right, and sawed it out—six pieces exactly alike in size and taper—for a joint. The manner of getting the size correctly, is to take the male ferrule for the thick end of the joint, and the female ferrule for the small end ; stand each on end on a piece of paper, and mark a circle outside; then, with a pair of small compasses measure the circle into six parts, and draw a line from point to point across the circle, so that all the lines meet in the center. This will show the size and taper of each piece, and the exact shape.

The board on which I sawed out my strips has grooves cut, so that I easily plane the inside of the strips for each joint; any inequality I finish off with a file. I now place my six strips together, winding twine around tightly, but some distance apart, so that I can get my thumb and finger between, so that I can see the joints, and how they come together. If they appear loose, and I can not get them together with thumb and finger, I mark the spots with a pencil, and unwinding, file away until they come well together.

For the butt, I draw a plan on paper, that is, enough of it to represent the hand-hold, measure with compasses the distance across each strip, or cut a pattern of paper, lay it on the bamboo and mark it out. For the tip and middle joint, when I glue the strips together, I wind hard and tight and closely with twine; now I straighten them carefully (as the hot glue has made them pliant), and lay away for twenty-four hours on a shelf. I never stand them on end, as they are likely to warp out of shape.

For the butt, I have iron rings of many sizes; when the strips are glued together, I force on these rings, driving on hard, and close together. This brings the glued strips so tightly together that the joints can not be seen. Twenty-four hours after gluing, I take off the rings and wrappings of twine, and finish off with a file and sand-paper; then fit on the ferrules, which I fasten on with cement.

Before putting on the guides and metal tip, I joint the rod together, and turn it in the ferrules until I get it perfectly straight; then mark the places for the guides and tip, so that they are all in a straight line, so that the fishing-line may have as little friction as possible. I now cement on the metal tip, and lash on the guides with a string, simply to hold them in place for the silk lashings.

The rod is now ready for the silk lashings, for which I use fine red spool-silk. I wind the guides first; winding on smoothly and closely. When one side of the guide is wound, I cut off the silk, leaving half a yard, which I thread in a needle, and, pushing the latter under the lashings, draw it through tightly and cut off close. Then finish the other side of the guide in the same way.

I now, with a pencil, mark the places for the lashings the whole length of the joint, tip, or butt, on which I am working. I draw off from the spool about four feet of silk, cut it off and thread the needle; this is enough for several lashings of the tip. I make not more than a half-dozen turns on the end of the tip, and place the lashings about a half-inch apart, increasing the number of turns and the distance apart, so that at the butt of the rod the lashings are an eighth of an inch wide and one inch apart.

When the lashings, guides, reel-bands, butt-cap, etc., are all on, I give the rod its first coat of varnish, putting it on very thin and evenly; it is quite an art to varnish well. I give the rod at least four coats, each as thin as I can spread it, and each well dried before the next is put on. I do not use shellac, but varnish of the best gum.

I have, at some length, thus described my method of making a split bamboo rod, as taught me by Mr. Green. There are several other ways of doing it, and it must be understood that this is amateur work. A circular saw is a great help, and indispensable to those who make rods to sell.

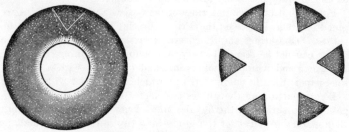

Details of Split Bamboo Rod.
(Conroy, Bissett & Malleson.)

Cut No. 1 shows a transverse section of the cane, and the dotted lines where a piece is split out. It is then planed down to the white line, leaving only the hard enamel.

No. 2 shows the strips ready for cementing.

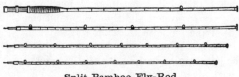

Split Bamboo Fly-Rod.
(Conroy, Bissett & Malleson.)

THE BLACK BASS FLY-ROD.

A few pages back, I made the statement that the American Trout fly-rod was the very perfection of fishing-rods, and that all other rods should conform as nearly as possible to said model or typical rod, commensurate with the manner of service required of them. Upon this principle, an honest and well-made Trout fly-rod, about eleven feet in length, and weighing from eight to nine ounces, answers admirably for Black Bass fly-fishing; and, fortunately, a suitable rod of this character can be procured from any first-class maker; but I would caution the new hand against the many *cheap* rods now in the market. A good rod can only be obtained at a fair price.

At the same time, I would here enter my protest against the lightest, and " withiest," Trout fly-rods, weighing from six to seven ounces, being used or recommended for Black Bass fishing. Such rods are but toys at the best, and only admissible for fingerlings, or Trout weighing from a half-pound downwards. I know that some anglers make a boast of using such rods, but it is on a par with some gunners who rush to the extreme in light shot-guns, and claim that a sixteen or twenty-bore is capable of as good general execution as the larger gauges. Now these are both palpable fallacies, as great as that of " sending a boy to mill " in the " History of the Four Kings," as many have found to their cost.

I am a great stickler for extreme lightness in rods when compatible with strength and action, but there is a certain limit in weight that must be observed, so as to conform to and preserve other and equally essential qualities in a good working rod. Now, while I will guaranty, in open water,

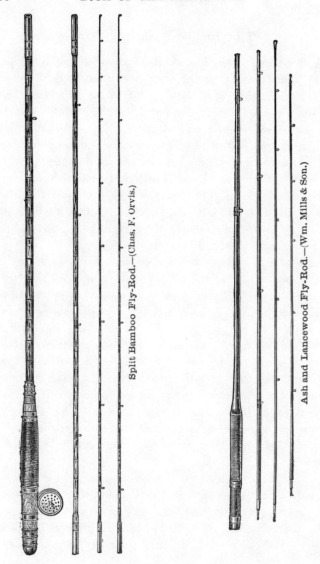

Split Bamboo Fly-Rod.—(Chas. F. Orvis.)

Ash and Lancewood Fly-Rod.—(Wm. Mills & Son.)

to land any Black Bass that swims with a well-made six
ounce split bamboo fly-rod, I will not undertake to say
how much time would be consumed in the operation; nor
do I envy the general demoralization and used-up condition of the flexors and extensors of my arms that would
ensue at the close of the contest. With a rod of suitable
weight, the largest Bass can be safely and pleasantly handled, and it is worse than useless to make a toil of a pleasure by using inadequate means.

I have an H. L. Leonard split bamboo fly-rod, weighing eight ounces, which I find " fills the bill " exactly in
all ordinary Black Bass fly-fishing; but, two years since,
in Florida, I used a twelve feet, twelve ounce ash and
lancewood fly-rod, made by Abbey & Imbrie, or at least
by their predecessors, Andrew Clerk & Co., ten years ago,
which I found none too heavy for the large Bass of the
waters of that State, and, in fact, there were times when
I wished for an additional ounce or two in weight.

A Trout fly-rod, then, weighing eight or nine ounces,
and not more than eleven feet long, is just about right for
ordinary Black Bass fly-fishing; but where the Bass run
large, averaging nearly or quite three pounds, a somewhat
heavier rod, say ten ounces, will be found a more suitable
and pleasanter rod to handle, though the eight ounce rod
will do even here, for one who is an expert fly-fisher, and
who does not mind a little extra straining of the brachial
muscles.

But while an ounce, more or less, hardly seems an appreciable quantity in the abstract, yet when added to or
taken from a fly-rod, like the fraction of an inch as applied
to a man's nose, it makes a very great difference in practice and reality ; and in the former case, it is better to have

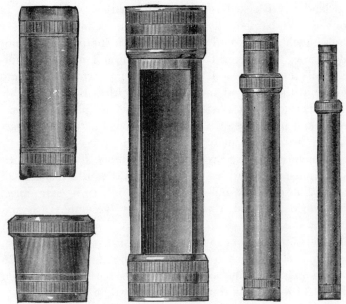

Reel Plate, Ferrules, and Butt-Cap.
(A. B. Shipley & Son.)

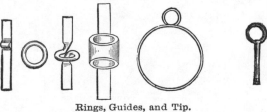

Rings, Guides, and Tip.
(A. B. Shipley & Son.)

an ounce too much, than a half ounce too little; for, like the Winchester repeating rifle when tackling a grizzly, it gives one a confidence in his resources which adds materially to the zest of his sport.

In the construction of a Black Bass fly-rod various materials are employed; the best and handsomest is, of course, section bamboo, but as I have before remarked, it is imperative to take the greatest care of such rods to preserve their usefulness. By rough usage or careless handling, the lashings are apt to become loosened, the varnish worn off, and the strips to become eventually separated; in which event the rod is worthless, for it soon goes to pieces. With proper care, however, and a due attention to the lashings, and a frequent varnishing of the rod, it will last a prudent angler his life-time. It is a tool, believe me, only to be used by an artiste.

But for every day fishing, on all sorts of waters, and under all circumstances, in the hands of a careful angler or a rough-and-tumble fisher, a good wooden rod is the best for service and wear, day in and day out; and, if made of good stuff, its action is not excelled, even by the graceful section bamboo.

My choice of materials for such a rod is ash and lancewood, which can not, I think, be excelled for a prime rod. But others may think differently, and prefer greenheart, mahoe, or bethabara, all of which woods are said to produce most satisfactory rods; and far be it from me to dissent from, or acquiesce in, their opinions, without a practical knowledge of the working of such rods, for, as I have before remarked, I have had no personal experience with these woods.

The fly-rod has the reel-seat at the extreme end of the

20

butt, and the hand piece, or grip, of course, above it; for the click-reel, which is used for fly-fishing, is a reel that is intended to "take care of itself" in the rendering of the line, and, therefore, is very properly placed where it is out of the way, and where it adds very much to the balance and general working of the rod.

The reel-seat in fly-rods is often made entirely of metal and called a "reel-plate," and which, while much admired by many, only adds to the weight of the rod, without being of material service. For myself, I prefer a plain reel-seat, simply a depression, or groove, cut in the butt of the rod, with reel-bands, as in the minnow rod. This answers every purpose, and to my mind there is nothing that can improve the beauty of a handsomely finished wooden butt; and on this account, I am also prejudiced against the hand-piece, or grip, being wound with cord, or ratan. The self-wood, of which the butt is composed, seems to me to be the best and most appropriate finish for the grip, both as regards utility and beauty; for the cord, or ratan, with which the grip is usually wound, in fine rods, is extremely liable to become loosened and worn off.

The wound hand-piece and the metal reel-plate look very attractive, but are not proof against wear and tear; and for my own use, and in accordance with my idea of the fitness of things, I think the less a rod is encumbered with fanciful and ornamental appendages, the better. We should ever bear in mind the original primitive cane fishing-pole, upon which model all rods are founded, more or less, and remember that simplicity and utility usually go hand in hand.

A very good friend of mine, with whom I have spent many pleasant angling days, once owned a very handsome

minnow rod, gotten up to his order in Boston, which was
to eclipse all other rods for style and stunning appearance.
Each piece, from butt to tip, was spirally wound with
ratan strips and silk, while the ferrules, reel-bands, reel-
plate, and guides were marvels of brightness and finish;
but in its action, the rod, of course, was a complete failure.

My friend always carried with him an extra rod, to be
used " in case of an accident " to his nobby rod.   This
extra rod was a short and common, jointed, natural cane
rod, made after the plan of the " Home-made rod," described
on a previous page.   And I noticed that the emergency
for using the common rod, always arose very soon after
making a few casts, with a great display and flourish with
the fine rod, or so soon as we were out of sight of other
anglers; for, as my friend often remarked, the flashy rod
was all very well for " dress-parade," but for real work it
" wasn't there; " and the homely, but serviceable cane-rod,
or, as he termed it, " old business," was invariably substituted.

While asking the reader's pardon for this digression,
which, however, was made more to point a moral than to
adorn a tale, I will simply add that a fishing-rod should
be made for " business," and not for display.

A Black Bass fly-rod should be made in three pieces;
the butt, we will say, of ash, and the second piece and tip
of lancewood, or if the reader please, of greenheart, mahoe,
or bethabara.   The ferrules, reel-bands and butt-cap are
of the same pattern as those used in the minnow-rod, and
should be either solid brass, or German silver, without
plating of any kind; let us have the *real* thing at all
events, for I despise affectation, or deception, in any matter
or thing whatever.   Brass is a good, honest, and bright

metal; will not rust or tarnish, and if it is used at all, let us use it on its merits; and for decency's sake, avoid the common practice of plating it with nickel, or, what is worse, silver—for the plating soon wears off and exposes the cheat.

Rings, instead of standing guides, are used, as they are lighter, and on the fly-rod answer just as well; they are lashed on with spool-silk by means of small metal strips, known as "keepers." The rings should graduate in size from the butt to the tip, and should be of the same metal as the ferrules. The metal tip of the fly-rod is a single ring, which is preferable to a solid tip, or the three-ring style, on account of its extreme lightness, for it will be remembered that the tip, or top, of a fly-rod is of very small caliber.

CHAPTER X.

FISHING-REELS.

And to that end, some use a wheel about the middle of the rod, or near their hand; which is to be observed better by seeing one of them, than by a large demonstration of words."—IZAAK WALTON.

A FISHING-REEL is made in accordance with the special service required of it, the objects of said service being twofold. The first and most important is the proper delivery of the bait in a manner and at a distance commensurate with the mode of fishing; and the second is to play and land the fish after he is hooked, or to reel the line for another cast. The reel which practically fulfills these conditions with the greatest ease and facility—in the method of fishing practiced—is the best reel to use.

The two modes of angling in which the reel is employed are bait-fishing and fly-fishing, and as the two methods differ so essentially, they require reels of widely different functions. Thus in bait-fishing the multiplying reel is used, while in fly-fishing the click-reel is indispensable.

The multiplying reel must be very rapid in its action so as to deliver the bait as far as possible at a single cast, the thumb, meanwhile, controlling the rapid rendering of the line, so as to prevent back-lashing of the spool; but in fly-fishing the line is lengthened gradually, a few feet

(237)

being taken from the reel by the hand before each subsequent cast, while the click offers the necessary resistance to the rendering of the line to permit this to be done without overrunning.

As the multiplying reel is made wide, so as to allow for the thumbing of the spool, and as this necessity is not required in the click-reel, the latter is made quite narrow, thus permitting the line to be reeled without bunching, and, at the same time, allow of its being reeled rapidly enough for all practical purposes, without a multiplying action; for the main object of a multiplying-reel, is for rapidity of action in casting, and not in retrieving the line, as is often erroneously supposed.

After a fish is hooked, a click-reel answers the purpose of playing, and landing it, as well as the best triple or quadruple multiplier made—if not better; for often a fish is reeled in by main strength with a rapid multiplier, and an attempt made to land it before it has been killed on the rod, thus curtailing the real sport of angling, and at a great risk to the angler's tackle. I speak of this now, for I have heard anglers praising a rapid-working quadruple multiplying-reel, because they could reel in a fish "so fast," basing all of its merits upon this one quality; the desire to get possession of the fish seeming to be paramount to the real sport of hooking and playing it.

THE CLICK-REEL.

The click-reel is a single-action reel, and, consequently, is the simplest form of reel, from the fact that the service required of it is simply a slow and gradual lengthening of the line with each subsequent cast; the delivery of the fly

being accomplished by pulling off from the reel a few
additional feet of the line after each cast, until the desired
or maximum distance is reached, while the click offers just
enough resistance to the rendering of the line to allow this
to be done without confusion or overrunning. The handle, or crank, is connected directly with the axle, or shaft,
and, consequently, "reeling in" the line would be slow
work were it not obviated by the reel being made very
narrow, so that the coil of line upon the shaft enlarges
rapidly, and the reeling is thus accomplished with greater
facility.

The click-reel is placed at the extreme butt of the fly-
rod, below the hand-grip, where it adds much to the
balance and general working of the rod. As the click
regulates the rendering of the line, and as the narrowness
of the reel obviates the necessity for guiding the line in
reeling, it is placed out of the way, at the extreme butt,
and "where it will do the most good." A reel should
always be placed underneath the rod, and not on top, as
is often done.

Click-reels are all constructed upon the same general
principle, but are of various patterns and composed of
various materials, being made of hard rubber, celluloid,
brass, bronze, and German silver; their weight depends on
the material used, and the angler has a large assortment
of styles and prices to select from. Any good Trout click-
reel is suitable for Black Bass fly-fishing, and can be
furnished by any of the first-class dealers.

In the choice of a click-reel, the angler should select
the lightest, when it is compatible with strength, and one
in which there is the least probability of fouling the line
on any prominent points, as projecting screws and caps,

The "Abbey" Click-Reel.—No. 4.
(Abbey & Imbrie.)

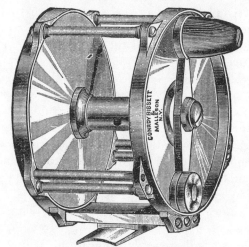

German Silver Click-Reel.
(Conroy, Bissett & Malleson.)

unprotected handles, etc. Metal reels are the strongest, and not so liable to injury as rubber or celluloid, in case of accidentally dropping, or striking them against rocks, etc.; though the latter are much lighter, and with ordinary care are just as serviceable.

There has been a very marked improvement in click-reels during the past few years, the manufacturers seeming to vie with each other to produce the lightest, neatest, comeliest, and most serviceable reel.

Abbey & Imbrie make a superb reel, the "Abbey," composed of hard rubber, with German silver spool, rim and fittings; it is extremely light and has a protected handle to prevent fouling of the line in casting, and is first-class in every respect. Nos. 3 and 4, the latter being the smaller, are the proper sizes. The "Imbrie" reel, also made by this firm, although a multiplier—and a most excellent one, by the way—has an adjustable click which allows of its being used also for fly-fishing. And the angler who is the fortunate possessor of one of these reels, Nos. 4 or 5, can use it in Black Bass fishing for either his minnow-rod or fly-rod.

Mr. C. F. Orvis, of Manchester, Vermont, has patented, and manufactures, a simple, durable, and inexpensive click-reel. It is very narrow, consequently takes up line quite rapidly, while the frame and disks of the spool are freely perforated, which renders it quite light, and assists very much in drying the line, and in keeping it free from sand and grit. Its low price, brings a good reel within the reach of the most impecunious angler.

Wm. Mills & Son's (7 Warren Street, New York) reels are unexcelled, either brass, German silver or rubber; they are fitted with protecting bands to prevent the line from

21

German Silver Click-Reel.—40 yards.
(Wm. Mills & Son.)

Pat. June 12, 1877.

The Leonard Click-Reel.
(Wm. Mills & Son.)

The Orvis Click-Reel.
(Charles F. Orvis.)

catching on the handle. Their thirty or forty yards reels are the correct sizes for Black Bass fly-fishing.

The "Leonard reel," sold by this firm, is probably the lightest metal click-reel manufactured, and holds a great deal of line for its size, being of good width. It also has a flush handle to prevent fouling of the line; two and a half inch diameter is the preferred size for Black Bass angling.

Conroy, Bissett & Malleson, of New York, A. B. Shipley & Son, of Philadelphia, and Bradford & Anthony, of Boston, also furnish the best reels and other tackle for fly-fishing. I think it but simple justice that all of these houses, who are by an honorable competition doing so much for the angler in the way of producing the most elegant and suitable tackle, should be brought to the notice of the angling fraternity.

On this point a veteran angler, the editor of the Richmond (Va.) *Whig*, becoming "impressed with the vast amount of industry, skill, talent, enterprise and genius, and philanthropy (emphatically) devoted to this task of supplying the needs and luxuries, and augmenting the pleasures of the sporting community," further says: "We say philanthropy, with emphasis—for those who thus toil for the enjoyment and happiness of their fellow-beings can not be enemies of their kind. But admit that self enters as an element of the motive, in an enlarged sense, it may be truly affirmed that self, if not a virtue in itself, is next kin to it, and is the basis and prompter of all the virtues."

Multiplying Reels.

The multiplying reel is a decided improvement on the

old single-action English reel or winch. It is made of metal or hard rubber, and of various styles or sizes, from a Striped Bass-reel to a Perch-reel. In shape and construction it differs necessarily from the click-reel, having a different office to perform, or rather the same object—the delivery of the bait—to perform in a different manner. Being intended for natural bait-fishing, it requires an easy-running and freely-rendering action in order to deliver the bait as far as possible at a single cast. As there is no click to control the running off of the line, the thumb must be used for this purpose, by effecting a gentle and uniform pressure upon the spool, and for this reason the multiplier is made much wider than the click-reel, or of the barrel or drum shape.

In its construction, a small cog or spur wheel is placed at one extremity of the axis or shaft, into which a larger cog-wheel is fitted, and to the latter is attached the handle or crank. One revolution of the handle produces two or more revolutions of the central shaft. The reel most generally known and used is the " New York Multiplier," which is manufactured for the trade in large quantities, with the retailer's name stamped on one end. It is called, by some, the " balance reel," from the fact, I presume, that it has a balanced handle, which, by some, is thought to add to the rapid working of the reel; but this fancied advantage exists in the imagination only—a simple crank handle is better.

As with the click-reel, there has been great improvements made in the multiplying reel within a few years past. Most of the manufacturers have given special attention to reels of this character, more especially for Black Bass fishing, and the result has been most grati-

fying to the angling fraternity. It is now an easy matter
to procure a first-class reel at a moderate price, considering the admirable manner in which they are gotten up;
for, by comparison with the click-reel, the former is about
double in price, and this is necessarily so, on account of
the great difference in construction of the two reels.

Among the many excellent multiplying reels now manufactured, the "Frankfort Reel" still takes the lead, and
is the reel *par excellence* for Black Bass angling. It is
known among expert anglers, in various portions of the
country, as the "Meek," "Meek & Milam," "Frankfort,"
and "Kentucky" reel. It is now made exclusively by
B. C. Milam, of Frankfort, Kentucky; and, as it is not
so universally known as its merits deserve, I will give a
brief history of it:

Some thirty years ago, there being a demand among the
anglers of Kentucky and Ohio for a better reel than was
furnished by the trade, Mr. Meek, a watchmaker, of
Frankfort, Kentucky—to whom Mr. Milam was then an
apprentice—determined to produce a reel which would
meet the requirements and solicitations of his fishing
friends; so, after considerable study and many experiments, the "Frankfort Reel" was produced, as perfect
then as it is to-day. Mr. Milam was soon afterward taken
into partnership by Mr. Meek, and the firm of Meek &
Milam soon became famous throughout the West for their
excellent reel. The demand continued to increase, until
they found a ready sale for all they could manufacture.

The reel is made by hand, from the finest materials, and
as carefully and correctly in its fittings as the movement
of a watch. The bearings and pivots are of the finest
temper, and the entire reel is as perfect in workmanship,

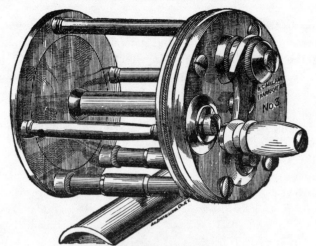

The Frankfort Reel.—No. 3.
(B. C. Milam, Frankfort, Ky.)

The "Imbrie" Black Bass Reel—No. 3.
(Abbey & Imbrie.)

and as finely adjusted, as is possible for skill to render it. Contrary to a current opinion, this reel is not more complicated than the ordinary multiplying reel, and contains but the same number of wheels, viz: two; but, by a peculiar construction of the two wheels, it multiplies four times, while the ordinary reel multiplies but twice. It runs so perfectly and smoothly that a smart stroke of the finger upon the handle will cause it to make about fifty revolutions, and this without a balance handle.

It is made with or without an alarm or click, and a drag or rubber; and, where one or both of these adjuncts are used, it does not at all complicate the working of the reel, as they are operated by small sliding disks on the side of the reel, and are not in the way in the least. The reel is, in fact, so simple and perfect in its details, that it has not been improved upon since it was first invented. They are made of German silver or brass, in six sizes, No. 6 being the largest. The best sizes for Black Bass fishing are Nos. 2 and 3.

The cost of this reel is necessarily high—in comparison with ordinary reels—from its mode of construction and materials employed, but it will last a life-time with ordinary care. There are reels that have been in use for thirty years—among the first ones made—which are as good as new to-day. I can not express my admiration for this reel more strongly, or truly, than by affirming that its invention has been as great a boon to the angler as the split bamboo rod; in fact, they are "boon" companions.

It is as great an improvement on all other multiplying reels, as they are on the old single-action English winch. With it, an angler can cast a minnow from thirty to forty yards with the greatest ease, though it is necessary that he

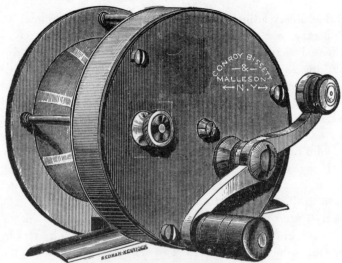

The "Conroy" Multiplying Reel.—No. 3½.
(Conroy, Bissett & Malleson.)

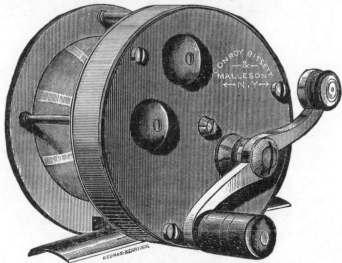

The "Conroy" Black Bass Reel.—No. 3½.
Combined Multiplying and Click-Reel.
(Conroy, Bissett & Malleson.)

should be quite dextrous in the art of using a multiplier, and *au fait* in the matter of controlling the rendering of the line with the thumb, otherwise the extreme rapidity of this reel's action will get him into trouble by its over-running or back-lashing, and the consequent tangling of the line upon the spool.

But, in justice to the reel, I will say to those who can not cast without tangling or snarling the line, or who can not reel the line evenly upon the spool, that they must look for the fault in themselves, and not in the reel. *Me judice*, I consider it the best reel in the world. The "alarm" is intended for an alarm only, and should not be used as a click to retard the rapidity of the reel's action, for this it can do to a very limited extent only, and that to the eventual detriment of the reel.

As these reels are mostly made to order, I would advise the angler who designs procuring one to order it made with the spring of the alarm stiff enough to act as a "click," in which case the reel will answer for either bait or fly-fishing; and, in my opinion, they should all be made so, considering their high price. The "alarm" originated in the days of heavy rods and lazy anglers, when, by stick-ing the butt of the rod in the bank (there often being a spike in it for this purpose), the angler could lie under the shade of a tree until the singing of the alarm gave notice of the biting of a Bass. It has outlived its usefulness, and should either be dispensed with entirely, or changed to a click. I would further advise the placing of the handle of the reel next to the reel-plate, instead of opposite to it (as Mr. Milam usually affixes it), for obvious reasons.

Abbey & Imbrie make a remarkably fine reel especially for Black Bass angling, and which they style the "Imbrie" reel. It is constructed with a hard rubber frame, German-silver spool and fittings, steel pivot and cap, center action, and with an adjustable click. It is very light and of a graceful and practicable shape, and multiplies three times. By using the click it answers well for fly-fishing.

It is a very easy-running and rapid-working reel, being second, only, in this respect to the famous Frankfort reel, though unlike the latter, is not so likely to overrun, and, on this account, is to be preferred by many anglers, who find it difficult to control, with the thumb, the very free action of that reel. Besides it is furnished at about half the price of the Frankfort reel, and is, withal, lighter. Nos. 3 and 4 are the best sizes for the Black Bass angler.

No Reel.

Those who, from any cause, can not manage a multiply-ing reel, might adopt the "Nottingham" style of angling, which is much in vogue in England, in which the reel is dispensed with. The line is made fast to the butt of the rod, and carried through the guides or rings. When ready for a cast, the line is pulled back through the guides, and laid in coils at the feet of the angler, leaving twelve or fifteen feet of line hanging from the tip of the rod. Our angler then grasps the line a few feet from the sinker and bait, gives it a few rapid whirls around his head, and casts it as far as he can, the rod in the meantime being held firmly in the left hand, and pointing toward the water. Long casts can be made in this manner, and the line re-trieved more rapidly than by the aid of any reel, but to the expert reel angler the game would not be worth the candle.

Position of the Reel on the Rod.

In order to allow the thumb to be used in controlling the cast, a multiplying reel should never be placed less than six inches from the extreme butt of the rod, and should be so placed as to be underneath when reeling up the line. I am aware that some prefer it on top, but the former mode is preferable for the following reasons: The weight of the reel naturally takes it under the rod, enabling the rod to be held steadier when reeling the line, or playing the fish; the strain of the line falls upon the guides, causing a uniform working of the rod; the line is more easily reeled up, and it was intended to be used in this manner.

The left hand should grasp the rod immediately over the reel, the thumb and forefinger embracing the rod above the reel and as close to it as possible, the ring and little fingers clasping the under surface of the reel, while the middle finger is left free to guide the line on the spool, and prevent bunching. I have noticed that all anglers who prefer to have the butt of the rod extending a foot or more below the reel, always use the reel on top, and when reeling in a fish, they invariably rest the butt against the stomach.

CHAPTER XI.

FISHING-LINES.

"I will lose no time, but give you a little direction how to make and order your lines, and to color the hair of which you make your lines, for that is very needful to be known of an angler."—IZAAK WALTON.

No doubt but many of my readers have often wondered, as I have done, where all the fine fishing-lines were made. Inquiries of the dealers failed to elicit any definite information, only such answers being obtained, as "We make them ourselves," or, "They are manufactured expressly for us," or, "They are imported for our trade."

There has ever seemed to be some mystery connected with it, though why, I can not imagine. The real manufacturers are certainly not generally known outside of the trade, and their goods are seldom marked with their own names. I do not remember ever to have seen an advertisement of a fish-line manufacturer. Perhaps it is not necessary, as the angler is supplied through the dealer, and the wholesale dealers are comparatively few.

Thinking that an account of one of the best manufactories of fishing-lines in this country, if not in the world, would not prove uninteresting, I reproduce the following description of the factory of Henry Hall & Sons, at Highland Mills, Orange County, New York, from the *New York Times* of June 6, 1880:—

(252)

How Fish-Lines are Made.

American fish-lines are the best in the world, because we use the most perfect machinery and materials in their manufacture. There are in this country five or six large establishments devoted exclusively to this production. They represent a capital of about $250,000, and produce about $100,000 worth of lines per year. The fish-line is an object of contempt to a certain class of closet philosophers, but its production at least employs money and brains with the same earnestness that marks our manufacture of more weighty objects. The largest fish-line factory in the world is the Highland Mills, Orange County, in this State, and if our anglers were only capable of boasting a little they might brag of our beating the world in the quality as well as in the quantity of our lines. In visiting this establishment I learned many interesting facts about the materials and the processes of making fish-lines. We all feel a certain awe and curiosity about the slender, tapered line that flies through the air so gracefully, yet has the amazing strength to hold a Salmon, a Trout, or a Bass in his most frantic efforts to escape. And the feeling is well justified, for not only is a fine line a proper object for respect and interest, but many of the processes of its creation are secrets veiled from the eye of even the elect. Lines are made of three substances, either cotton, linen, or silk, and they are either twisted or braided. The twisted lines may be made by hand, but braided lines are always made by machines devised especially for the purpose. For fine lines, only the finest, strongest, and longest fibers can be used. The selection of the material is, therefore, made with great care. It is spun to order in sizes to suit different kinds of lines. The bleaching of the yarn has to be very carefully done to prevent any loss of strength by chemical action on the fiber, and only vegetable dyes are used in coloring.

In the storeroom are piles of flax in skeins, which has been spun to order in Ireland, France, Belgium, and Germany. A variety of flax is needed, because that of one country is most desirable for its durability and that of another for its strength, so that the union of several kinds of thread in a line gives it greater general excellence. The exact size must be maintained throughout the thread. And the exact amount of twist, varying from two to nine turns to the inch, must be given; for if the threads be either too loosely or too tightly twisted the strength of the line is impaired. The cotton is spun expressly from selected stock in this country, and the silk, also, is spun here. The best silk is Tsatlee machine twist; the genuineness of the stock can not be doubted, if judged by the foreign character of its tickets:

"Hung yu Silk Hong. Yuekee chop. By selecting No. 1, Fine re-reeled Tsatlee silk. When obliged to Merchants best owing their regards, please to notice carefully of our sign, are without mistaken. This chop is myself reeled true Tsatlee Thown Silks."

More can not be asked. This silk is spun at silk factories and delivered on bobbins. The fineness of some of it may be judged by the fact that 3,200 yards of a thread weighs only one ounce, and yet the threads run sometimes 2,000 yards without a break. The grass lines, sold under the names of Japanese grass, sea grass, and catty grass, are all made of raw silk. The yarns of flax are wound on bobbins, and those of cotton are "beamed" or wound on a cylinder in such a way that they can be run off it without tangling.

The twisted lines are made in a "walk," a narrow shed about 400 feet long. At the head of the walk are two machines, driven by steam. They consist of pulleys, with long ropes for belts running off to the foot of the shed; also of a lot of spindles, turning very rapidly, and lines running overhead along the walk enable men at any point to move levers or stop and start the machinery at will. Two cars run on tracks down the walk; they carry the beams or cylinders of thread or the bobbins. The operator places the bobbins on pins on the cars, so that the threads may unwind; the car is brought up to the machine; he gathers up the threads in groups of three, and ties each group to a spindle in the machine. When all the 24 spindles are furnished with threads, he starts the machine, the spindles turn and twist each group of three threads into a strand; at the same time the car moves slowly along to unwind the threads from the bobbins as fast as the twist takes them up. The operator walks behind or beside the car to watch the yarns, remove lumps, and impurities from them, or to break off defective portions of a thread. The car at intervals passes under a frame hanging over the track; this frame is provided with wire hoops or fingers that descend automatically and hook under the strands after the car has passed. to sustain them, so that the weight of the long strings may not interfere with their twisting evenly in all parts. By the time the car has reached the foot of the walk each of the 24 strands has received the proper twist, so many turns to the inch. The strands are then gathered up in groups of three and tied to spindles on a tender or second car at the foot of the walk. This tender is operated by rope-belts from the machine at the head of the walk. When the strands are secured to the eight spindles of the tender the car starts back to the head of the walk, leaving the tender to twist the strands into cords. It follows them up, very slowly, to allow the cords to contract in length as they are twisted.

If this twisting of the cord as a whole were all the twist given, the cord would only be a string, the strands would be simply collected in a round form, and would have but little power to resist an untwisting tendency when wet or cut into pieces. But after a strand is formed, if some additional twist be given it, the fibers are bent and stretched until they acquire a strong reactionary force. They seek continually to straighten and contract themselves, and if the ends of the strand be kept from untwisting while it is given some slack, the strand will double up on itself, and then twist in the opposite direction from that of the first twist. In the cords thus formed the strands have lost as much of their twist as was required to form the cord; hence, they have lost the most of their reactionary, spiral tendency. But if the strands be given some additional twist to compensate for this loss, while the whole line is given its twist, the reactionary force of each strand will make it intertwine closely with the others, and hold them together in a compact, permanent twist.

A fish-line differs from a string in having just this additional twist of the strands. For this object, the machine at the head of the walk continues to twist the strands, while the tender twists the line. The line is given a little superfluous twist merely for the sake of forcing the strands to assume a smooth, compact service; some of this superfluous twist comes out when the line is wet, but the line can not be opened or untwisted without removing and untwisting each strand. It is readily seen that the amount of twist has a great effect on the strength of a line, for too little twist fails to bind the fibers together, and too much subjects them to uneven and destructive strain. Hence, machinery, by securing the utmost accuracy, makes the most perfect lines in this respect. And it also makes them rapidly and cheaply. If the threads were perfectly even and clean the lines would be perfect. But impurities and irregularities are unavoidable in even the best yarns, and the operator can not always see these nor take the time to remove all he perceives. Formerly, lines of 600 feet were twisted all in one piece, but in so long a line the amount of twist was necessarily uneven in different parts. Hence, it is now considered a better method to make long lines by joining 300-feet lengths by what is known among sailors as the "long splice."

Hand-made lines are still more perfect than those twisted by any machine. The machine, of course, secures the utmost accuracy in the twist; but the hand, through the delicate sense of the touch, detects imperfections in the thread that are invisible to the operator of the machine. The man who makes the Cuttyhunk and other hand-made lines carries nine bobbins of silk or linen on a frame hanging in front of him. Having fastened the threads in threes to spindles at the head of the walk, he walks slowly backward while the threads pass between his fingers and are twisted into a strand. He feels every thread as it goes, and detects with surprising certainty every bunch, knot, or weak place ; he picks or bites off the bunches, or stops the spindles by pulling a cord at his side, and takes out any defective part of the thread, and joins the ends again by twisting, not by tying them. When the three strands are sufficiently twisted, he ties them together to a little swivel on a string drawing a drag-weight, to allow for the contraction of the line. He passes the three strands through grooves on opposite sides of a cone called the "top," and as he walks back to the head of the walk and moves the top along the strands, the grooves allow the continued twisting of the strands to pass by the "top" and unite them at its apex, while the swivel allows the line to be twisted up by the strands. Thus, although the twist of hand-made lines is not quite so uniform as that of machine-made lines, yet the former are the better in having more perfect threads.

The braided line is the most perfect of all. No inferior threads are used in its manufacture, and the machines secure a very uniform tension of the strands. The cotton, linen, or silk threads are wound on bobbins that are mounted on a small table. The table is furnished with serpentine slots, through which the bobbins travel, and cross one another's course in such a way as to pass now outside, now inside, of one another, and thus weave or braid the strands in a regular manner. If a strand break, the bobbins all stop, and delicate weights, sustained by the strands as they are braided, give them a uniform tension. From eight to sixteen strands are put in a line, each strand being composed of three threads. As the line is formed it, is reeled up, so that the braiding is not done in a long walk, but in a room filled with compact machines clicking like looms. One girl tends several lines, picking off with nippers any lint or bunch, and removing poor strands. It is real satisfaction to an angler to see such beautiful silks going into a line. It looks like braiding cobwebs; but these fine threads, evenly and compactly braided, make a fine line of amazing strength. The tapered lines are all braided, because if one part of a twisted line be smaller than the rest, that part yields to the twisting force and gets too much twist. The tapering is done by simply dropping out a strand at regular intervals; but the machine has to be readjusted each time to secure a regular braid. Fine braided lines hitherto have often been weak, from defective manufacture; but recent improvements in the Highland Mills in the methods of working up the fiber have produced a line of wonderful strength for its size. Thus, I found that although one of the threads of a line would lift but 14 ounces, yet the line of 8 threads, braided to a diameter of 1-40 of an inch, would lift $9\frac{1}{2}$ to 10 pounds. The union of the threads in a twist or braid seems to augment their strength about 30 per cent. This fine line, 100 yards long, weighs but 150 grains; it requires 934 yards of prepared twist to make it, and as each thread or twist contains three strands, the lines contains 2,802 yards of strands.

The celebrated Cuttyhunk line is made of four different kinds of flax, Irish, French, Belgian, and German, spun to order for this purpose. Line No. 9, having 12 threads in a diameter of about 1-30 of an inch, lifts 25 pounds. They are all hand-made twisted lines, so are the various grass lines and the relaid grass lines.

The finishing of lines is generally done by some secret process that each house wishes to monopolize. The fine lines are soaked in various compounds of oils and gums to fill them with a preservative water-proof substance. The well-known enamel finish gives the line a glossy surface that excludes the water and keeps the line of a uniform weight and stiffness in casting, and also makes it run very smoothly through the rings or guides of a rod. Of course, there are many
22

inferior lines made up by second-rate factories; but it is difficult to imagine that cotton, linen, or silk can be better put together than they are now by our first-class establishments. Perhaps some better fiber will be discovered. The inner bark of the alloa tree was made into lines many years ago; and they were found to be almost imperishable even under the most unreasonable neglect. But the material is too costly for general use.

The *Forest and Stream* has this to say concerning this manufactory:

> This establishment, since its introduction of machinery, and its transfer to more commodious quarters at "Highland Mills," possibly turns out more goods than all others of a like business in the State combined, and of such superior excellence as to defy competition.
>
> The Henry Hall goods are made the standard by the trade. Every sort, kind and description of fish-line is made at this now world-wide renowned factory, as the Hall goods swept the deck at the Centennial Show, and wherever they have come in competition with foreign goods of decided reputation, the Henry Hall goods—cotton, linen and silk—have at all times asserted their distinct superiority.

REEL LINES FOR BAIT-FISHING.

The perfect line for Black Bass bait-fishing is yet in the future. The best manufactured at present is the smallest size—letter G, or No. 5—hard-braided raw silk line; and if it were made, say, of just one-half the caliber, and as tightly and closely braided, and as firm and hard as the twisted, or laid Japanese grass line, it would be all that could de desired for a bait line. I have great hopes that a line of this description will soon be made, as I have invited the attention of Henry Hall & Sons to this subject.

A bait line for casting a minnow should, in the first

place, be composed of the very best material, which, in this case, is raw silk. It should be of very small caliber, the smallest that can be made consistent with strength, and raw silk fulfills this condition better than any other material. It should be very hard, compact, and closely braided. These conditions secure a line that renders freely and easily, is quite elastic, and at the same time absorbs but little water, and will not kink or snarl in casting. The line should, moreover, be tinted some suitable color, to render it as nearly invisible as possible, for it must be remembered that we can not use a gut leader in casting the minnow.

The braided or plaited raw-silk line, as now made, fulfills all of the above conditions, except in caliber, and the manufacturers above referred to assured me that it could be made one-half less in size, were there a demand for such a line. There has been no inquiry for such a line, because it is known that there is none to be had; but the Black Bass anglers, who fish the streams of the South and West, almost universally use the relaid Japanese grass-line (which is made of raw silk), notwithstanding its kinking propensities, for in every other particular it is a good line. For lake-fishing, where the Bass are larger, the braided silk and linen lines are used almost exclusively.

The best line, then, we will say, is the braided, or plaited raw-silk line—letter G, or No. 5—for ordinary fishing; but where the Bass average fully three pounds, the next largest size—letter F, or No. 4—may be used, though I would advise the smaller line even here to be employed in preference. Raw silk lines require the greatest care to preserve their usefulness. They should be carefully dried after use, as soon thereafter as possible, for without this caution they soon become weak and rotten. And, moreover, a

SIZES OF LINES.

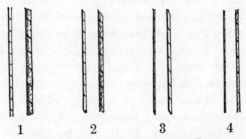

Taper Waterproof Braided Silk Lines.

☞The smaller illustration of each Cut represents the "Taper" point; the larger, the body of the Line.

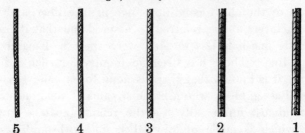

Braided Linen and Hard Braided Linen and Braided Cotton.

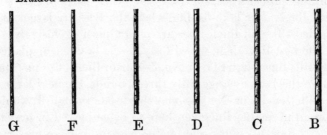

Oiled Silk, Braided Silk.

☞The above cuts are the *exact sizes* of the lines they represent. They appear, on paper, somewhat larger, as the cuts are "flat," while the Lines, from being "round," appear smaller to the eye.

(Conroy, Bissett & Malleson.)

reel-line, for bait-fishing, should never be waterproofed with any preparation, or by any means whatever, for this can only be done with great detriment to the line, as regards casting, besides increasing its caliber.

Next best to the raw silk-line is the braided boiled silk-line, or, as sometimes called, the dressed silk-line. This is a good line when plaited hard and closely, but most of them are too loosely braided; in which case they absorb water quite freely, which develops an annoying propensity of clinging to the rod in casting, and interferes somewhat with the free rendering of the line. They are made of good stock, however, and are quite strong, and nicely tinted. Sizes F and G, or Nos. 4 and 5, are the only ones to be used; and, for ordinary Bass-fishing, the latter, or smallest—letter G, or No. 5—is the proper size. The boiled silk-line should be as well cared for, and as carefully dried, after use, as the raw silk-line, and for the same reasons.

The braided linen-line is a very good one, in one respect better than the silk, being quite hard and closely plaited, but the caliber is too large. The smallest size now made is too great for a reel-line for Black Bass bait-fishing. Where the Bass run very large, however, as in lake-fishing, or in the extreme South, the smallest size may be employed with satisfaction. It will last longer than the silk-line, and will bear rougher and more careless usage. It is much heavier, however, and is not so elastic; and, therefore, not so desirable a line, in these respects, as the silk-line. The only size to use is G, or 5.

The above are the only lines that I can recommend for bait-fishing for Black Bass, where much casting is practiced, for braided lines are the only lines that will not

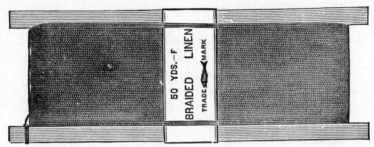

Braided Linen Reel-Line.
(A. B. Shipley & Son.)

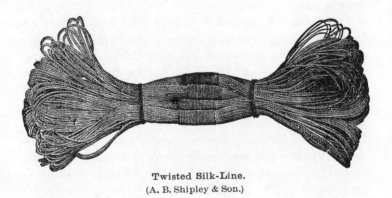

Twisted Silk-Line.
(A. B. Shipley & Son.)

kink and curl. No twisted or cable-laid line can be profit-
ably employed for this purpose, on account of this kinking propensity, which, to the angler, is a source of great
trouble, vexation and perplexity; and there is no method
by which the kink can be entirely removed or eradicated
from twisted lines. Some anglers maintain that this kinking quality can be taken out of a line by trailing it in the
water behind a boat, without sinker or hook; but this is a
delusion and a snare, for after casting a line a few times
in succession that has been treated in this manner for
hours, it will kink and snarl as badly as ever, and this is
to be naturally expected, from the mode of manufacturing
such lines. It is unreasonable, moreover, to expect a
twisted line to perform the functions of a braided line, for
this it can not do.

Use small-sized lines; they are strong enough with a
pliant rod. A line that will hold up two pounds, dead
weight, will land the largest Black Bass that swims, when
used with a proper rod. Indeed, I have often used a line,
which, toward the end of the season, when tested, would
scarcely hold a pound dead weight, but which would safely
land the largest Bass, or even Pickerel of fifteen pounds
or more.

Rod-Lines.

The twisted line has its proper place in fishing, and
sometimes answers a good purpose, as I will now explain.
There are many anglers who, from choice or necessity,
dispense with the reel in Black Bass fishing. Oftentimes
the character of the stream is such that a reel can not be
used to advantage; for instance, on streams that are narrow, and much choked with snags, roots, and other obstruc-

tions, that preclude the playing of a fish, a reel is not necessary, for the fish must be killed within a few feet of where hooked, and must, of a necessity, be landed as soon as possible.

In this case, a long, light, and pliable—but not too limber—rod must be used, say a natural cane-pole, twelve or even fifteen feet long, with the finest and smallest line that can be procured, which, in this case, is the twisted silk-line. This line is made of very small caliber, nicely tinted, of a suitable color, and is quite strong. It is manufactured by Henry Hall & Sons, in connected lengths of fifteen feet, which is about the right length of line for this kind of angling. The sizes run from No. 1, the smallest, up to No. 5, the largest. The smallest, or No. 1, is the size to use, always, when fishing on streams; but for pond or lake fishing, where Pickerel abound, No. 2 or 3 may be substituted.

Next to the silk-line, in order of merit, comes the twisted or relaid sea-grass line, domestic or Japanese, the latter being the best. They are numbered in the same way as the silk-line, No. 1 being the smallest size, and the preferable size to use. Many anglers, notably in the border and Southern States, use the sea-grass line for a reel-line, in preference to all others, because it is strong, of small caliber, quite hard and elastic; and, as they do not cast very frequently, it answers pretty well, but, as stated before, will kink when much casting is practiced. The sea-grass line is both twisted and relaid, the latter being the best, as it does not kink quite so badly as the twisted line. In relaid lines, the strands are three in number, each strand being twisted from left to right, and the strands twisted together in the opposite direction, or from right to left.

On the score of economy, twisted flax and cotton lines are sometimes used for rod-lines; but they are beneath the notice of the Black Bass angler, as the sizes are too large to be used for this purpose.

REEL-LINES FOR FLY-FISHING.

The reel-line for fly-fishing must necessarily be heavier than the line used in bait-fishing, the greater weight of the former being required to cast objects so light and delicate as artificial flies; while in the case of the small and light bait-line, the minnow, swivel and sinker give the required weight for casting. Increased weight is obtained by increase of the caliber of the line, so a fly-line is consequently of a larger size than a bait-line.

Formerly the twisted or plaited hair, and hair and silk-lines were employed altogether by the best anglers for fly-lines, but they have been almost entirely superseded by the really elegant tapered and enameled waterproof braided silk-line. The latter is the line *par excellence* for all kinds of fly-fishing, being smooth, round, polished and perfectly waterproof, and is just stiff and heavy enough to favor a perfectly straight cast, without looping or kinking, qualities that are peculiarly essential to this mode of angling. Those who have used the old-fashioned fly-lines, are prepared to speak feelingly and appreciatively concerning the great superiority and excellence of this line.

They are made in several sizes for Salmon, Black Bass and Trout fishing; are very strong and serviceable, and, for Black Bass angling, can be purchased in lengths of from twenty-five to thirty yards. They are usually fashioned with a regular and gradual taper for several yards to

23

the fly-end, the fly-end being only about one-half the caliber of the reel-end. Hall & Son's lines, which is the best
way, taper both ways from the middle. They are usually
stained of a greenish-olive hue, which harmonizes well
with the tints of the water, sky and foliage. From
twenty-five to thirty yards is the right length, and the
size should be either E or F, which corresponds with Nos.
3 and 4, some dealers designating the sizes by letters,
others by numerals.

The silk and hair-line is still used to some extent, but
it is open to many objections. At best, it is a weak line,
and soon rots and becomes worthless by use, even with
good care. The ends of the hairs become frayed, and
separate after a time, and are a constant source of annoyance, by sticking out at various places on the line, pre-
venting it from working smoothly and freely through the
rings of the rod. When used for Black Bass angling, the
size suitable for Trout fishing will answer, and the length
should be about thirty yards.

Next best to the tapered enameled silk-line is the oiled
braided silk-line; though this is not tapered, it is a good,
strong and useful line, and is used by many anglers in
preference to all others. It is tinted of a similar shade to
the enameled line, and altogether is a very satisfactory fly-
line, being heavy enough, and, withal, cheaper than the
tapered line. Letters E and F, or Nos. 3 and 4, are suitable sizes.

Next in order is the braided linen-line, either waterproof or plain. Where economy in price is the necessary
object, this is the best line to select, though the angler
should bear in mind that the best is the cheapest, for he
knows full well that to no other class of goods does this

maxim apply with more force than to fishing-tackle. This line is strong, firm and round, and is capable of long and hard service, if proper care is taken to dry it thoroughly always after using. It is well adapted for making a nice, straight cast, and will not curl or kink. It is usually stained a light shade of slate, or a grayish drab. Letter F, or No. 4, is about the right size.

Some fly-fishers use the ordinary braided raw or boiled silk-lines, which, while being the very best lines for bait-fishing, are not so well adapted for fly-lines, on account of their light weight; the medium sizes, however, answer tolerably well. Letter E, or No. 3, is the correct size, when used for Black Bass fly-fishing.

All fishing-lines that are not absolutely waterproof should be carefully dried after use; and even waterproof lines would be much benefited by an airing previous to putting away. Even the best lines become weak and worthless through want of proper and judicious treatment. It is impossible to make a line that is indestructible, or proof against mildew or rot, though many anglers seem to think to the contrary, judging from the shiftless and reprehensible manner in which they use them; then, when the line fails, they blame the manufacturer.

HAND-LINES FOR TROLLING.

There are many persons who can not, or will not, use a fishing-rod, but who greatly enjoy trolling with the hand-line and spoon-bait for Black Bass. For the benefit of these unfortunates, I will describe the proper line to be employed for this mode of fishing.

The only line that is suitable for the purpose is a braided

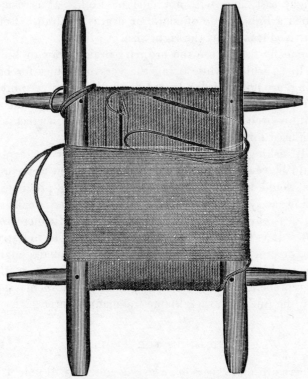

Braided Linen Trolling-Line.
(A. B. Shipley & Son.)

or plaited linen or cotton line, size C or D (1 or 2). Such lines are large enough to preclude cutting the hands, and they will not kink or twist, qualities that are peculiarly essential for this kind of fishing. A twisted line, of any material, is inadmissible here, for the revolving of the spoon, if a swivel is not used, will cause even a braided line to twist on itself and kink; therefore, one, or even two, swivels should always be attached to, and near the spinning-bait. A trolling hand-line should be from seventy-five to a hundred yards long.

CHAPTER XII.

SILK-WORM GUT.

"But if you can attain to angle with one hair,—you shall have more rises, and catch more fish."—IZAAK WALTON.

THE material of which leaders and snells are composed is a mystery to many anglers. It is eminently fitted for the purposes mentioned, being as nearly invisible as any substance can well be, and at the same time is quite strong and impermeable to water.

It is really the "fluid silk" of the silk-worm, drawn out into a continuous length. This fluid silk, which in its natural state resembles colorless varnish, is contained in long cylindrical sacks, many times the length of the worm, and which are capable of being unfolded by immersion in water, and the fluid silk can be drawn out into threads, longer or shorter, coarse or fine, as may be desired.

Mr. Wm. Gray, of Davenport, Iowa, in an article in the *Forest and Stream*, gives some very interesting information concerning the process of drawing out the threads, which, to many anglers, will be new. He says:—

In all my reading I have never seen a sentence in reference to that most essential article to the sportsman angler, viz.: silk-worm gut; what it was and how prepared. I know that many skillful fishers know nothing about where it comes from. Others think that because it is called silk-worm gut, therefore it is the intestines of the silk-worm, just as catgut (violin strings) are made from the

(270)

intestines of a cat (?) or a sheep, after the mucous membrane has been removed from it. But such is not the case. It is true that it comes from the inside of the silk-worm, but it is not what we would call the gut.

More than forty years ago I was curious to know what this article was, but not until within four years ago did I ascertain. Inside of the silk-worm there are two lobes or sacs lying together, somewhat like the two lobes of eggs in a fish. When these lobes are fully developed they consist of a viscid fluid, and if the worm were allowed to live this would all be spun out of its mouth as a cocoon of silk. But if silk-worm gut is wanted, the worms are taken when the lobes are mature (or ripe, as they term it,) and thrown into strong vinegar for about two hours. The effect of this immersion in vinegar kills the worms, makes the external part of their bodies very tender, and thickens the fluid in the lobes into a soft, tough pulp.

The next process is to remove it from the vinegar and remove the outer part carefully, and one at a time, these lobes are caught by the thumb and finger by the ends, with each hand, and stretched apart to the length required, and given two or three twists around a small pin placed in each end of a frame, where they remain till dry enough to be bunched up ready for market. That this is the way that gut is finished we have some evidence by examining a thread of it in the bunch as commonly sold. At each end you will see where it has been twisted around the pin, and beyond that, where the piece held in the fingers has been stripped out, which is usually flat.

That there are other insects than the common silk-worm (how many I do not know) who have this lobe of fluid matter that is utilized into fishing gut I am satisfied. More than forty years ago I got a quantity of gut (how or from whom I do not remember), but it was different from any I had ever seen before or since. It was heavy and long. Some of the threads were nearly three feet, perfect in smoothness and equal in thickness, and as thick as good salmon gut. The color, however, differed from the ordinary gut, being brown-colored, as if soaked in tea, but I am satisfied it was the natural color. I still have a few threads of it in my tackle-book, which have been there about forty-five years. I have just looked at them, and find that the longest yet remaining is twenty-three and a half inches; a good, clear thread; one of the lightest of the lot.

About as long ago as I can remember there was an article sold called sea-weed, which was used by fly-fishers. It was from three to four feet in length, round, smooth, and tapered from the root to the point, but was not reliable as to its strength. I have not seen any of it for nearly fifty years past.

The long and heavy gut to which Mr. Gray alludes, is, possibly, the product of one of our native silk-worms, as Dr. T. Garlick, of Bedford, Ohio, one of the fathers of pisciculture in the United States, states that he has drawn silk gut from four to six feet long, sufficiently strong for Salmon fishing, from the larva of the *Atticus œcropia*, the largest of our native silk-worms.

Dr. Garlick describes the process, in the *Forest and Stream*, as follows:—

I have drawn silk gut not only from the *Atticus œcropia* and *A. prometheus*, but also from the Italian silk-worm. I have never killed the worm, nor put it in vinegar for this purpose, which may be the best method. Soon after the larva ceases to feed he begins to spin his cocoon, which is the right time to draw the silk gut. I pin the worm to a board, putting one pin in his caudal extremity, and another pin about one-third of his length back from his head. I then, with a sharp knife, cut off the forepart of the worm far enough back to cut off a very little of the sac containing the silk, which is a fluid of about the consistency of the white of an egg. I then take a large pin, and dipping it into the fluid silk, which adheres to the pin, I draw out the silk slowly (the more slowly the larger will be the gut), until I have drawn out all, or nearly all, of the silk contained in the sacs. I then take another pin, and attach it to the other extremity of the gut, at the point where I divided the worm. The two pins are then stuck into a board, drawing the gut taut, which soon becomes hard and fit for use. The fluid silk hardens to some extent immediately on coming in contact with the air.

LEADERS, OR CASTING LINES.

The silk-worm gut imported into the United States, and used for leaders and snells, is usually in short lengths of from twelve to fifteen inches. In forming leaders, these are knotted together to the desired length. There are many grades of gut, and the angler will do well to remember that the best is the cheapest.

Black Bass leaders should be from six to nine feet long, and composed of the best single Spanish silk-worm gut, heavy and strong, hard and round. The gut lengths should be perfectly clear and sound, quite smooth, and without inequalities or rough places. The rod-end of the leader should be composed of a large-sized gut, the next length a trifle smaller, and so diminish by a gradual taper to the fly-end. The several lengths should be neatly and firmly knotted together by what is technically known as the double water-knot. The ends should be cut off closely; or, if the single water-knot is used, the ends should be first wrapped with silk, waxed and varnished, and then cut off neatly and closely.

It should be remembered that it is necessary to soak and soften the ends of the gut-lengths previous to tying. The water-knot, if correctly tied, can be easily slipped apart and the snell of a fly inserted, when it is to be securely drawn together again, the snell having a knot tied on the end to prevent its pulling out; but more of this anon.

Some leaders are now made with loops for attaching the

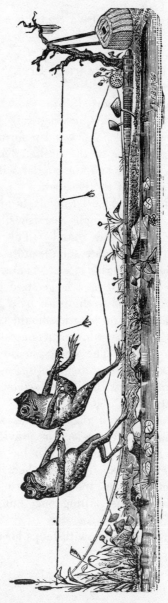

Testing the Leader.
(Chas. F. Orvis.)

flies, which is a very convenient and expeditious way, but the old method is still much in vogue, and both plans have their advocates.

Too much care can not be exercised in selecting the leader, for upon its soundness and excellence depend much of the pleasure and success of fly-fishing. It should be carefully examined in every inch of its length, and the knots closely inspected. The leader should always be stained some suitable neutral tint; either a slightly greenish, grayish, or smoky hue will answer. Strong green tea, diluted black ink, or a weak solution of indigo, make good stains. The leader should have a loop at each end, for attaching the reel-line and stretcher-fly.

I will not enter into the details of making leaders, as they can now be purchased so cheaply, and of such superior excellence, that the amateur can hardly hope to equal them, even were it necessary. The leaders known as "mist-colored" are all that can be desired, and the angler can have them sent by mail from any first-class dealer, who will select them "upon honor." I will only add, beware of double or twisted-leaders; they are an abomination to the Black Bass fly-fisher.

SNELLS, OR SNOODS.

For utility and convenience, hooks are tied on short pieces of gut, gimp, or sea-grass, called snells, or snoods. The best material for snells is silk-worm gut, as it is light, strong, and nearly invisible. It should be stained of a similar color, and in the same manner as the leader.

The length of snells for Black Bass angling should be from six to eight inches; and they should be composed of

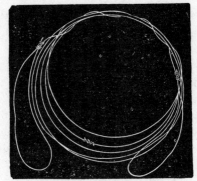

Leader, or Casting Line.
(A. B. Shipley & Son.)

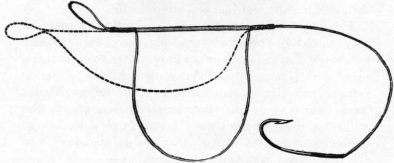

Shipley's Self-hooking Elastic Snood.
(A. B. Shipley & Son.)

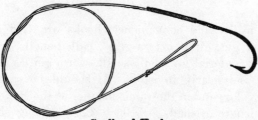

Snell and Hook.
(A. B. Shipley & Son.)

single, heavy gut, though they may be made double if the gut is very light or fine.

The hooks should be neatly, carefully, and securely tied on with waxed silk, and varnished; and a strong and firm loop must be formed on the other end of the snell, for attaching to the reel line. The ends of the gut should be softened by soaking in warm water before tying on the hook and forming the loop.

Gut snells, or loops, are always used for artificial flies; when snells are used, they should be from three to six inches in length, and should always be formed of single gut, with, or without loops in the ends, according to the style of leader used, whether with loops for the attachment of the fly-snells, or not.

Messrs. A. B. Shipley & Son, of Philadelphia, manufacture a patent, self-hooking, elastic snell, formed by tying a short piece of silk rubber cord across a bight of the gut-snell, giving it a spring or play of two inches or more. Messrs. Shipley say that it has proved very successful, and describe its *modus operandi* as follows :—

"The fish, on biting and attempting to let go the bait, is at once caught; as when the tension of its biting or pulling at the bait ceases, the snood flies, or springs immediately, and fastens the hook, itself, thus saving the setting of the wrist, or loosing the fish by inattention."

In fishing for Black Bass in waters where Pickerel or Pike-Perch abound, it becomes necessary to substitute gimp, for the gut of the snell, as the sharp, long, and numerous teeth of these species would make short work of the delicate gut, by fraying it or cutting it in two, and thus subject the angler to the great annoyance and aggravation of often loosing both hook and fish.

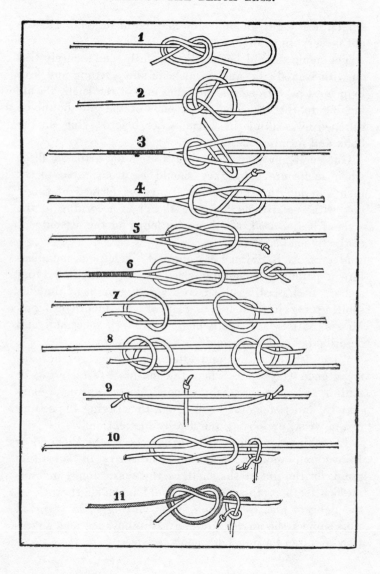

KNOTS.

In angling, as in sailing, there is no accomplishment so necessary, or that proclaims the finished angler or sailor so well, as his ability to tie a good knot. The beginner should study the plate of "knots" thoroughly, and by practice learn to tie each and all of them readily and properly. I have seen otherwise good anglers who could not tie a correct or graceful knot, and the knife was always brought into requisition to "untie" their clumsy efforts; in this way their lines become shorter daily, and "beautifully less."

There is always a right way and a wrong way to do every thing; and though a knot may seem an unimportant thing, it is really often a most vital one, many times causing the angler to lose a good fish, and might result in the loss of his life to the sailor. The new hand will please remember that whatever is worth doing at all, is worth doing well.

Fig. 1 is the "common" knot for forming a loop at the end of a line, or snell. It has its uses.

Fig. 2 is the *best* knot for tying such a loop; it looks a little intricate, but can be learned by practice, and once learned, will be a "well-spring of pleasure."

Fig. 3 is a good and simple method of attaching the reel-line to the loop of the leader, or snell. It is the "tiller-hitch," or "helm-knot," so-called because it can be instantly cast off by a jerk on the end; being thus the safest hitch for the main-sheet in sailing.

Fig. 4 is a more secure knot for attaching the end of the line to loop of leader, or snell; it makes a small and neat knot, and is easily untied. It is the "becket-hitch," with a small round knot in the end of the line to prevent its working loose.

Fig. 5 is another method of fastening reel-line to loop of leader, or snell; it is a very safe and secure knot, and is a modification of the "reef-knot," (fig. 10).

Fig. 6 is similar to fig. 5, with the end of line fastened on itself by a half-hitch; it is very secure, but a little more difficult to untie than fig. 5. Figs. 3, 4, 5, and 6 are all good knots for bending the line to loop of leader, or snell; they draw up close and snug, will not slip, and are easily loosened. The angler can take his choice, but he should never tie his line and leader together by the common knot (similar to fig. 1), or the square knot (fig. 10). The leader should always be provided with a loop in each end, neatly seized with good sewing silk, and varnished. In bait-fishing, a loop may be formed on the end of the reel-line, by which it may be fastened to one ring of the swivel, when it is desired to pass the loop of the snell through the opposite ring.

Fig. 7 is the "single water-knot," for tying lengths of gut together to form the leader; it consists in half-hitches at the ends of the gut-lengths, which are formed around the opposing gut-lengths, as shown in the figure; this forms a sliding knot for securing the end of the snell of a drop-fly.

Fig. 8 is the "double water-knot" for the same purpose as fig. 7; it is more secure, but not so neat, as double hitches are used in its construction, as plainly shown in the figure.

Fig. 9, shows the method of fastening the snell of a dropper by the single or double water-knots. After the two parts of the water-knot are drawn tight, as shown in the figure, a round knot is made in the end of the snell of the fly, and is put through the open loop between the two halves of the water-knot, which latter are then drawn together close and snug, holding the snell tightly and securely. By using this mode of attaching droppers to the leader, they stand at right angles to it, and may be changed as often as desired, and with but little trouble, by simply sliding the water-knots apart, taking out the snell of one fly and inserting another. The flies can not pull out, as might be supposed, for the strain and struggles of a fish only serve to make the knot draw more closely together.

Fig. 10 is the " reef-knot," or common square knot, and is a very safe and strong knot for many purposes ; it never slips or jams, when properly tied, and is easily loosened; but in tying this knot, if the second turn or hitch is not made exactly right, it forms a "granny-knot," than which there is no worse or more uncertain knot made, and yet nine persons out of ten tie a "granny-knot." The novice will do well to study this common knot, and learn to tie it correctly. It is sometimes used for tying the lengths of a leader, in which case, as also with the single water-knot, the ends should be cut off closely, and neatly whipped with fine sewing silk and varnished.

Fig. 11 is the form of knot generally used by manufacturers of leaders, or casting lines, for tying together the gut-lengths ; it is a very simple knot to tie, though it looks somewhat difficult in the figure, and in the way that I have seen some attempt it, *is* a difficult knot. I have drawn the two lengths of different colors, one white, the other dark, so that the construction of the knot can be more easily seen. The ends of two gut-lengths are passed by one another, or in other words lapped, sufficiently to

24

allow of their being tied by a single hitch and drawn
tightly, just like tying a single knot in a double string
(as in fig. 1).   Usually the knot is made double by passing the ends of the gut through twice, instead of but once,
in tying ; that is by simply tying what is known as a
"surgeon's knot" (for ligating arteries) with a double
thread.   The short ends are then trimmed off closely.   If
a leader is made with loops for attaching drop-flies, this is
the best knot to use in making the leader itself, being,
like fig. 10, secure and unyielding.

Where knots like figs. 10 and 11 are used in constructing the leader, and no loops are provided for attaching
droppers, the latter must be secured by a half-hitch, just
above a knot in the leader, as shown in figs. 10 and 11,
which is a very good plan.   It must be borne in mind,
that in tying lengths of gut together, or in tying loops or
knots in gut-snells, the ends must first be soaked in water
until quite soft and pliable ; this must also be observed in
bending or tying a hook on a gut-snell.

CHAPTER XIII.

HOOKS.

" For in the Prophet Amos, mention is made of fish-hooks; and in the book
of Job, which was long before the days of Amos, for that book is said to have
been written by Moses, mention is made also of fish-hooks, which must imply
anglers in those times."—IZAAK WALTON.

THE best fish-hooks are made in England, that country
supplying the world with hooks of all sizes and styles, for
all kinds of fishing. The town of Redditch has been
famous for its fish-hooks for at least two centuries. There,
are located the celebrated makers, Harrison, Hemming,
Alcock, and others, whose familiar names are almost synonymous with hooks and needles, both articles being
usually made by the manufacturers mentioned.

The following brief account of the process of making
fish-hooks will doubtless prove interesting to most of my
readers. It is an extract from a letter in the *Forest and
Stream*, written by Miss Sara J. McBride, of Oswego, New
York, the well-known, skillful tyer of artificial flies; and
whose writings are as charming and attractive as her
artistic imitations of the insect world. The letter is one
descriptive of a recent visit to the celebrated factory of
Alcock, at Redditch, England:—

And this is Alcock's! How familiar the name! What a host of
reminiscences rise as we enter the doors—"Round Bend Kendall,"
"Kirby," "Sneck Bend," "Alcock's Best;" all spring up like phantom forms. Through the kindly courtesy of Mr. Alcock we were

(283)

shown through the different apartments and saw the various manipulations the wire taken from the coil undergoes, until the delicately
pointed, japanned hook is ready for the market. In one corner of a
room there was a large pair of upright scissors; with a quick snap
two hundred or more pieces of the required length were cut from a
bundle of wire; six to ten of these pieces are taken, held firmly
against an iron bar, and an incision made with a sharp knife, for the
barb. Next the filer takes each one separately with a pair of pliers,
holds it in a vise, and with a few deft movements of a file, the
embryo hook is pointed.   Now they are bent on different forms.
This is the christening period. They come forth, Sproat, Limerick,
O'Shaughnessy, Kirby, Kendall, Sneck Bend, Hollow Points, and
Round Points. The hardening process is the next in order. As we enter
this department our nostrils are assailed by a fearful stench of burning fish-oil. We would like to retreat—an instant's consideration—
we decide to ignore the olfactory nerves and keep on. Here we are
shown rows of ovens, all filled with pans of burning, blazing hooks.
They are kept in this fiery furnace from fifteen to twenty-five minutes,
then taken and thrown into the bath of oil. We were informed they
formerly used water for cooling, but now they considered oil the best.
True to Yankee instinct, I queried why. The workman did not
enter into a learned discussion on the molecular construction, or
atomic properties of steel, and the consequent differentiation of the
particles in cooling, as a Boston girl might have done, but with a
wise nod and a firm pressure of the lips said, "The oil is the best."
I thought the oil was used to keep visitors from intruding. The
hooks taken from the oil are quite brittle. To remedy this they are
reheated. During this process, which lasts but a few minutes, they
are stirred briskly in sand.

We next visited the scouring room. Here were eight small barrels,
all filled with hooks and fine sand, revolving and turning round and
round with a deafening clash and clang. In this room the workmen
escaped quizzing. The noise was too much for me. Now for the
finishing touches—the japanning. The japan is a black, tarry liquid
made in Birmingham, the composition of which seems to be a trade
secret, as I failed to learn it. Two coats of japan are applied; they
are heated moderately in an oven and thoroughly mixed after each
heating.

In the wareroom we are shown immense quantities of hooks, all sizes, done up in packages of thousands and tens of thousands, ready to be shipped to all parts of the world. Here is the small delicate hook for France, so diminutive that the rude scale of inches has to be laid aside and only the French milimeter can do it justice; hooks for Canada, United States, Australia, and New Zealand; triple hooks, double hooks, hooks flattened, hooks ringed, hooks headed, and hooks eyed. All kinds of hooks for all kinds of fish.

The most approved hooks for Black Bass, are the Sproat, O'Shaughnessy, Dublin Limerick, Cork Shape Limerick, Round Bend Carlisle, or Aberdeen, and Hollow Point Limerick; they are best in the order named, and those made by Harrison & Son, and T. Hemming & Son, excel all others.

There are fish-hooks and fish-hooks, and to the uninitiated one hook is as good as another; all they can see in a hook, is the fact that it has a shank, a bend, and a bearded point.   But to the angler this contracted view is not sufficient.   There are many styles of shank, numerous forms of bend, and various ways of fashioning the barb and point, all of which are of the highest practical importance.   Some hooks are made for general service, while others are formed exclusively for particular kinds of fish, or for special methods of angling.   The fish-hook of to-day is not essentially different from that used by the ancient Greeks and Romans, to the casual observer; but to the practiced eye, the hooks now produced, for form, temper, and strength have never been equaled in the history of the world.

The form, quality, and general excellence of hooks, as now made, is the result of the competitive skill and great experience of the manufacturers of Redditch, England, whose energies and resources have been directed in this peculiar channel for nearly two hundred years; and, as might be inferred, as between the hooks of the first-class makers, there is but little choice, so far as quality and workmanship are concerned.

There is no implement of the craft that is so universally kept in stock at the small stores and shops throughout the country as the fish-hook; and these hooks, as a rule, are of very inferior quality, as might be inferred when we take into consideration their cheapness, notwithstanding the fact that they must net the dealer at least fifty per cent. profit, or he would not sell them.

While the average angler is inclined to use heavier rods, and stronger lines, than are actually necessary, he does not seem to be so much impressed with the importance of strength in a fish-hook, but accepts those of the small dealers mentioned, with a blind faith that a hook is a hook, and that one is as strong as another, if of the same sized wire; and, morover, he recognizes but two forms of hooks, the Kirby, or side-bend, and the straight, or more or less rounding-bend.

Now there are no fallacies so great as these, for the hook is of the most vital importance to the angler, and he should obtain the very best to be had, both in form and quality. Fish-hooks, in themselves, being of so comparatively small a price, it is the most insane idea of economy to purchase any but those of the very best quality. The most approved form of bend and barb, should also be taken into serious consideration.

The highest grades of English hooks, like English gun-barrels, are thoroughly tested by causing them to sustain a strain, twice or thrice as great as they are usually put to in actual service, and the extra care and manipulation, and the superior stock used in the construction of such hooks, make their cost somewhat higher; but this extra amount is money well expended, for the angler can rely upon them with the utmost confidence, provided they are the product of the best makers; there is but one thing left to decide his choice among such hooks, viz., the peculiar bend or form given to the hook, of which there are several that are good enough. I might add, that all first-class hooks are japanned, or black, and that a blued hook is always of an inferior quality.

As regards the shape and bend of a hook, my first choice for Black Bass angling is the " Sproat Bend," and the next best form, in my opinion, is the "O'Shaughnessy." In general form and bend the two hooks are identical, but their difference consists in the form of barb, and direction of the point. In the latter peculiarities, the Sproat is fashioned after true scientific principles, being a central-draught hook; that is, the short, squarish, or somewhat angular barb, terminates in an abrupt point, which, if continued upward, would intersect a line drawn from the extremity of the shank and continuous with it. In other words, the direction of the point of the hook is towards the end of the shank.

When the Sproat hook is tied on a snell, and the point of the hook is held against the ball of the thumb, and traction made on the snell, the direction of the point of the hook is on the same plane, or in the same direction or axis as the line of the snell, thus constituting what is termed a central-draught fish-hook. The wire of the Sproat is a trifle smaller than the O'Shaughnessy, which

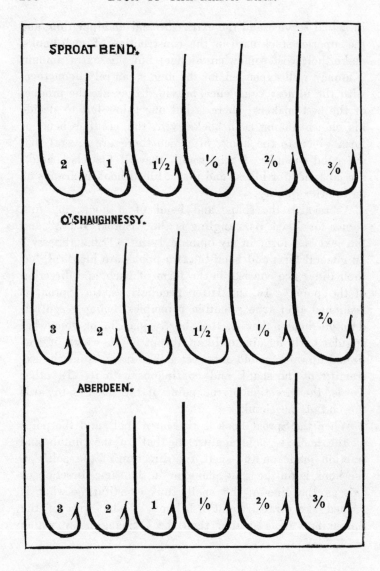

is another advantage. The latter hook has a long and somewhat hollow point, which is curved outward.

The Sproat Bend I regard as the very best hook manufactured. I first commenced its use ten or twelve years ago, and have since used no other. Its appearance is somewhat against it, but it is like "a singed cat." By the side of a delicate, blued, gracefully-shaped Aberdeen, it looks black, and rather clumsy, with its short barb and peculiar bend, but it means "business." Its temper is just right, and when you strike a fish it goes right through any part of the mouth, never springing out, and never disappointing you. I have had the Aberdeen so soft as to completely straighten and pull out, and so brittle as to break like a pipe stem, but the Sproat Bend has yet to fail me. For staying qualities it is perfection itself.

The "Dublin Bend," or Dublin Limerick, as it is sometimes called, and the "Dublin Limerick Forged," are excellent hooks, and are identical in form and bend with the O'Shaughnessy hook, the only difference consisting in the caliber of the wire, which, in the latter, is a trifle heavier. The Forged Dublin Limerick has the wire flattened by hammering or forging; it is a remarkably strong hook.

The "Cork-Shape Limerick," has an almost round bend, with a straight shank, and a long straight point, which is parallel with the shank in its direction, and a very good hook, being of rather smaller wire than the Sproat.

The "Carlisle" hooks are made of very small wire, and are very delicate and attractive to the eye, but for Black Bass fishing I do not admire them, though, until I came across the Sproat hook, I used the round bend Carlisle (Aberdeen) altogether. Still, many anglers prefer them

25

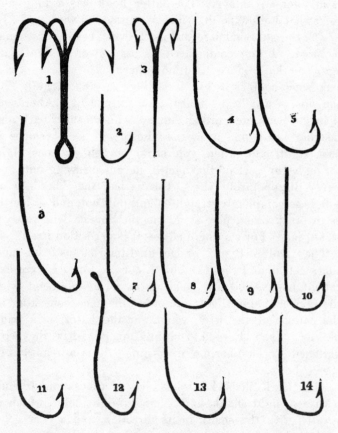

1. Tripie hook.   2. Lip hook.   3. Double fly-hook.
4. Dublin Bend   5. O'Shaughnessy.   6. Chestertown.
7. Limerick.   8. Cork Shape.   9. Sproat.
10. Aberdeen.   11. Kirby Carlisle.   12. Gravitation.
13. Kinsey.   14. Sneck Bend.

on account of the small wire, which is not so apt to injure the minnow, but I might say here, that if a minnow is put on with care, it need not be injured to a greater extent, even with the Forged Dublin Bend hook, than with the Carlisle. The round-bend Carlisle, or Aberdeen hook, has a perfectly round bend, and a long straight shank; the barb is long, with the point curving outward.

The "Hollow Point Limerick" is the last hook that I will mention, favorably; it is a very old form of hook, and is still a great favorite with many, notably the veterans of the angle, whose experience with this hook dates back to the heyday of youth. The form of the Limerick is well known; it has a straight shank, and a very abrupt bend, with a long, straight, and hollow point.

The Kirby Carlisle, the Kirby Limerick, and, in fact, all hooks with the "Kirby" or side-bend I can not recommend for any kind of angling. It is the worst possible crook that can be given to a fish-hook, being both unscientific and impracticable.

The needle-pointed, or hook without a beard or barb, has been recommended for fly-fishing, but it will not answer for the Black Bass. So long as the fish remains in the water, and a proper tension of line is maintained by the angler, it holds as well as any other hook, but when the fish leaps from the water in its struggles to free itself, like the Black Bass, there is a great liability of its shaking out such a hook.

Artificial flies, tied on extremely small barbless and needle-pointed hooks with a circular bend, have been used in Japan for centuries, and while such hooks may do for the Brook Trout, and fishes closely allied to it in habits, they are totally unsuitable for the Black Bass, or any fish

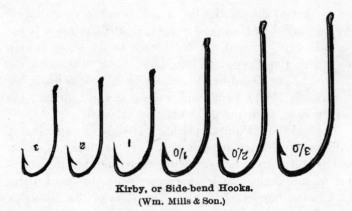

Kirby, or Side-bend Hooks.
(Wm. Mills & Son.)

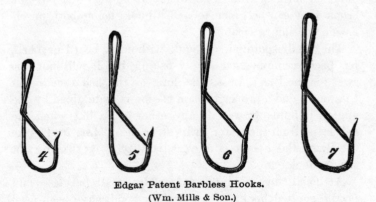

Edgar Patent Barbless Hooks.
(Wm. Mills & Son.)

that makes such desperate efforts to get away, when hooked.

The Edgar patent barbless hook, manufactured by William Mills & Son, is made upon a very different principle, and is all that the inventor claims for it. This hook, while having no barb, has a "keeper" which securely holds the fish after it is hooked, rendering it impossible for it to escape, even with a slack line. It is the only "patent" fish-hook that has any real merit, though it seems to me like taking too much advantage of a fish, and is likely to foster and encourage a careless and shiftless style of angling. Still it will no doubt become quite a favorite hook with many. To my mind the great charm of angling consists in using a proper judgment (born of a thorough knowledge of the fish and its habits) in presenting the bait, and the exercise of skill and science in hooking, playing, and landing it.

The Edgar hook is hand-made, composed of good and reliable wire, and for fresh water fishing is made in several sizes, and numbered from 1 to 10, No. 1 being the smallest. For Black Bass, the proper sizes are Nos. 4, 5, and 6 for bait-fishing, and Nos. 2 and 3, for fly-fishing.

CHAPTER XIV.

ARTIFICIAL FLIES.

" To frame the little animal, provide
All the gay hues that wait on female pride;
Let nature guide thee. Sometimes golden wire
The shining bellies of the fly require;
The peacock's plumes thy tackle must not fail,
Nor the dear purchase of the sable's tail.
Each gaudy bird some slender tribute brings,
And lends the growing insect proper wings:
Silks of all colors must their aid impart,
And every fur promote the fisher's art."—GAY.

FLY-FISHING and the art of making artificial flies
dates back at least to the ancient Greeks and Romans.
During the palmy days of the Roman Empire, the rod,
line, hook, and artificial fly were well known. Noël de la
Moriniére tells us that the lines were generally made of
horsehair, single, double, and plaited; and according to
Ælianus the hair was colored in different ways. The
fishing-rod was chosen with reference to the supposed weight
of the fish to be caught, and the resistance it could offer.
The hooks were of copper or iron, and coated with tin.
The art of making flies of feathers and other materials has,
perhaps, never been carried further in our own time, even
in England itself. It is possible that the national love
for fly-fishing was introduced into Britain by the Romans.

It is with some degree of trepidation that I approach the
subject of artificial flies, for I am afraid that I hold some

very heretical notions on the subject. But of one fact I am positively convinced, and that is, that there is a good deal of humbug in this matter, as evidenced in the many fine-spun theories and hair-splitting arguments that are advocated and advanced (pertaining to the construction and use of artificial flies) by some anglers, but which theories do not hold good in practice,

In England, more especially, do anglers proceed to extremes as theorists in the matter of artificial flies for Trout fishing. They seem to be divided, principally, into "colorists," or those who think color of paramount importance to form, and "formalists," or "entomologists," who maintain that form is every thing, and profess to imitate the natural fly, in its proper season, in every particular of form and tinting. But there is no evidence that one class is more successful than the other, as anglers. On the other hand are the followers of Mr. Pennell's system, or plan, who confine themselves to, and advocate the employment of, but three "typical" flies—green, brown, and yellow palmers, or "hackles"—and claim that they are sufficient for all practical purposes, and can be made available for different waters and seasons, by increasing or diminishing the size of the flies, as circumstances seem to demand. While the adherents to this latter theory are fully as successful, from all accounts, as those who have a list of nearly a thousand named flies to choose from, and enjoy the satisfaction of having reduced the perplexing matter to a delightful simplicity, and of obviating the troubles of a repeated changing of the cast of flies as practiced by others —they must sometimes feel a regret deep in their hearts for casting down and sweeping away their idols and cherished traditions, and to a certain extent the poetry of fly-fishing, by their iconoclastic though sensible opinions and practices.

Where fish are plentiful and in a " biting mood," almost any fly, be it never so rudely tied, and of the least possible resemblance to any thing in the insect creation, will be successful, even if clumsily cast; on the contrary, there are times when the best made flies, cast by the most skillful artists, are necessary to induce a rise. Between these extremes must we look for rules for our general guidance, and without occupying further space with arguments, pro and con, it will be sufficient to say that there are certain general rules which apply to the character of the fly to be used at certain times, and which rules are the result of, and founded upon, the experience and observations of fly-fishers for many generations past.

These rules, so far as they apply to Black Bass fly-fishing, are few and simple :—

1. Flies should be small, rather than large, the average Trout-fly being usually large enough.

2. On bright days, and with clear, low, or fine water, flies should be quite small, and of subdued, dark, or neutral tints.

3. For cloudy days, and high, turbid, or rough water, larger and brighter flies should be used.

4. For very dark days, or from sunset until dark, or on moonlight evenings, gray or whitish flies, of good size, should be employed.

I shall not go into an entomological description of flies and their counterfeits, for it is neither requisite nor advisable, so far as Bass flies are concerned.. For those who feel an interest in this subject, however, I can recommend, cheerfully, the several fine works published in England on

the construction of Trout and Salmon flies; among the best
of which are Ronald's "Fly-Fisher's Entomology," and
Pennell's "Modern Practical Angler."

I will merely state that the majority of artificial flies
are of two kinds, and are intended to represent the perfect
winged insects of certain orders, and the larvæ of others;
thus, most Trout-flies are the pretended imitations of some
of the species of the orders *Diptera* and *Neuroptera*, the
former comprising the two-winged insects, as the gnats,
mosquitoes, midges, etc., and the latter the four-winged
insects, as the May-flies, dragon-flies, etc. The larval
form of fly is supposed to represent a caterpillar, and is
called a "hackle," or, more correctly a "palmer." It must
be borne in mind in this connection that an artificial fly,
when wet, presents a much different appearance from the
same fly when dry, and our flies should be tied with reference to this contingency.

The term "hackle" is likely to cause some confusion in
the mind of the new hand, if not explained; for it is susceptible of several meanings, as used by anglers and fly-
tyers. The proper meaning of the word is a "feather"
from the neck or saddle of the cock, and known as a
"neck-hackle," or a "saddle-hackle," as the case may be.
These hackle-feathers are used to imitate the legs or feet
of an artificial fly; and as one variety of fly consists only
of a body with a hackle wound spirally around this body,
from one end to the other, this form of fly has come to be
known, in this country, at least, as "a hackle," though, as
stated before, the proper name is "palmer," and it is designed to imitate a caterpillar, for it is only a body bristling
with "legs."

Then there is the "hackle-fly," which is a fly with body,

wings, and, perhaps, a tail, and, in addition, a hackle-feather tied on at the shoulder, to represent the legs; and most flies are made in this way, though a few, notably, some salmon-flies, have, in addition to wings, tail and feelers—the entire body wound with a hackle, like a palmer. This is known as a "combination-fly," and, like all salmon-flies, does not pretend to imitate any thing in nature.

It is not my intention to give any instruction in the art of fly-tying, nor do I deem it at all expedient, for it is an art that can not be taught by written directions, without the aid of explanatory cuts and diagrams, and even then in but a moderate degree. The best way for one to obtain an insight into the mysteries of the art, is to carefully dissect and take apart the flies of the best makers, for in the taking apart one can acquire more or less of the *modus operandi* of the putting together.

The most approved hooks for bass-flies are the Sproat, O'Shaughnessy, Dublin Limerick, Cork Shape Limerick, and Hollow Point Limerick. I consider them best in the order named, though the O'Shaughnessy is thought by many to be the best. It is the same in all respects as the Dublin Limerick, except that it is a little heavier in wire, and it differs from the Sproat only in the barb, the latter having a shorter barb, with the point straight, or pointing toward the extreme end of the shank, forming a true center-draught hook. The barb of the O'Shaughnessy is a little longer, and the point is turned slightly outward. But any of these hooks will give good satisfaction. They are made in the best manner, and of the best material, by R. Harrison Bartleet & Co., successors to Richard Harrison & Co., and T. Hemming & Son, of Redditch, England.

The most suitable sizes, for bass-flies, are Nos. 2, 3, 4 and 5, the last being the smallest that should be used under ordinary circumstances, though, for the smallest flies, Nos. 6 and 7 may be employed. These numbers apply to all of the hooks named above.

Flies may be tied on a silk-worm gut-snell several inches in length, or may have simply a small, short gut-loop. Those with loops can be used as "stretchers" or tail-flies; but when used as "droppers" or bob-flies, they must be attached to the leader by a half length of gut, say four inches long.

Many "trout-flies" are used, and with good effect in Black Bass fishing, for really the form and color of the fly does not seem to make much difference with the Bass; he does not seem so "fastidious," as it is termed, in his choice of flies. Most of the "general" trout-flies are taken as patterns for bass-flies, as the Coachman, Professor, Soldier, Grizzly King, Queen of the Water, King of the Water, Ibis, Kingdom, Quaker, etc., and all of the palmers or "hackles."

As every angler will become partial, sooner or later, to certain flies, and adopt them as favorites to the exclusion of others, I deem it unnecessary to allude to but few, except in a general way ; and those that I shall particularize are such as I have used many times with most gratifying results.

I have had more uniform success, day in and day out, with the black, brown, red, yellow, and gray hackles (palmers), than with the winged-flies; though some of the latter I have employed with excellent success for high or rough waters, and those with light-colored or white

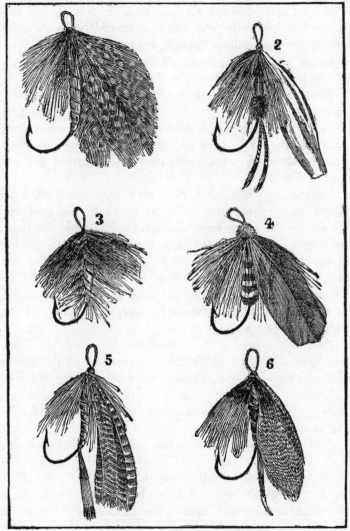

No. 1. Polka.   No. 2. Coachman.   No 3. Hackle.
No. 4. Bumble Bee. No. 5. Abbey.   No. 6. Grizzly King.

wings can not be surpassed for twilight-fishing, or for very gloomy days.

The following flies, tied for me by C. F. Orvis, of Manchester, Vermont, expressly for Florida waters, I found very taking at suitable times:

McLeod.—Body, emerald green, with gold twist; tag, yellow and red floss; wings, dark mottled brown; tail, green drake, with red ibis and mottled yellow; hackle, yellow; antennæ or feelers, scarlet.

Imperial.—Body, red, with silver twist; tag, silver; tail (whisk), red and white; hackle, black and white; wings, large, grayish white, bordered with black; feelers, scarlet.

Green and Gold.—Body, emerald green, gold twist; tag, scarlet; tail, white and red; hackle, yellow; wings, olive green.

La Belle.—Body, pearly blue, silver twist; tag, red and gold; hackle, blue; wings, pure white; tail, red and white.

White and Ibis.—Body, pearl, gold tinsel; tag, peacock herl; tail, red and white; wings, white and scarlet; tag, red; hackle, white and scarlet.

Royal Coachman.—Body, scarlet, and peacock herl; tail, pin-tail duck; hackle, brown; wings, white.

Mr. Orvis also tied the next two flies, from patterns furnished by myself, and which have for years been favorite flies with me, when winged flies are at all admissible. As I am the originator of them, I have named them Oriole and Polka. They are totally unlike any thing in nature or art, but the Bass seem fond of them, nevertheless. The Polka has some general resemblance to the Abbey.

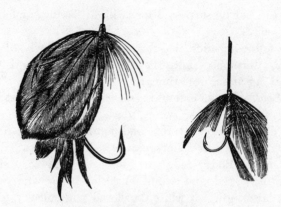

Large and Small Bass Flies.
(A. B. Shipley & Son.)

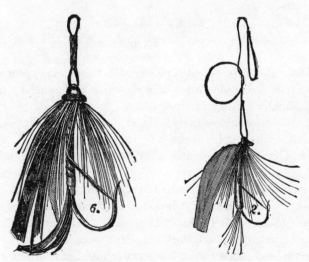

Bass Flies on Edgar's Barbless Hooks.
(Wm. Mills & Son.)

Oriole.—Body, black, with gold tinsel; hackle, large, and black; wings, bright yellow; tail, mixed black, and white.

Polka.—Body, scarlet, gold twist; hackle, red; wings, black with white spots (guinea hen or woodpecker); tail, brown and white, mixed.

The flies which follow are part of an assortment tied by Abbey & Imbrie, and have been remarkably and unusually successful with me, whenever winged flies were called for:

Professor.—Body, yellow; hackle (legs), golden brown; tail, scarlet ibis; wings, yellow, mottled.

Queen of the Water.—Body, dark yellow, gold tinsel; hackle, red; wings, mallard, mottled.

Grizzly King.—Body, green; hackle, gray; tail, red; wings, pin-tail duck or mallard.

Soldier.—Body, scarlet; hackle, red; wings, gray.

Montreal.—Body, red; hackle, scarlet; wings, wild turkey.

Governor Alvord.—Body, peacock herl; hackle, red; tail, red ibis; under wings, brown, upper wings, drab.

Seth Green.—Body, green, with yellow stripe; hackle, red; wings, brown (woodcock).

Abbey.—Body, scarlet, gold twist; hackle, red; tail, golden pheasant; wings, pin-tail duck.

Ferguson.—Body, yellow, gold twist; hackle, green; tail, peacock, yellow and scarlet; wings, yellow and scarlet, and wild turkey.

Kingdom.—Body, white, striped with green; hackle, red; wings, woodcock (brown).

Gold Spinner.—Body, orange, gold tinsel; hackle, light red; wings, gray.

Captain.—Body, gray, and peacock herl; hackle, red; tail, scarlet, green and wood-duck; wings, gray.

Ibis.—Body, scarlet mohair, silver twist; tail, hackle, and wings of the red ibis.

The following flies are also good ones, some being great favorites with certain anglers:

Reuben Wood.—Body, white, with red head; hackle, brown; wings and tail, rayed feathers of mallard.

Dr. Fowler.—Body, white; tail, scarlet; hackle, scarlet and white; wings, red ibis and white.

Green Drake.—Body, white, ribbed with black; hackle, ginger; tail, dark; wings, mottled green and yellow.

Gray Drake.—Body, dark gray; hackle, gray; tail, dark; wings, gray (mallard).

Brown Drake.—Body, golden brown; hackle, brown; tail, dark brown; wings, golden brown.

Holberton.—Body, orange, gold tinsel; hackle, peacock herl and scarlet; tail, wood-duck and scarlet; under wings, red ibis and yellow; upper wings, peacock and wood-duck.

Shoemaker. — Body, alternate rings of salmon and gray; hackle, light red; tail, wood-duck; wings, mallard (gray).

Superior.—Body, dark claret; hackle, brown; tail, blue macaw; wings, wild turkey.

General Hooker.—Body, alternate yellow and green rings; hackle, red; tail, wood-duck; wings, tail feathers of ruffed grouse.

Quaker.—Body, gray; hackle, yellow; wings, horned owl's wing.

King of the Water.—Body, scarlet, gold tinsel; hackle, red; wings, bright mottled, mallard.

Green Mantle.—Body and hackle, bright green; wings and tail, mottled, mallard.

Henshall.—Body, peacock herl; hackle, white hairs from deer's tail; tail, two or three long fibers of peacock-tail feathers; wings, light drab (dove).

Oconomowoc.—Body, creamy yellow; hackle, white and dun (deer's tail); tail, ginger; wings, cinnamon (woodcock).

The *White Moths,* or *Millers,* are excellent flies for moonlight evenings, or at dusk. They may be pure white, or all white with yellow body, or all white with gray wings. The bodies should be made full and fluffy.

The *hackles,* or *palmers,* are made with various-hued bodies, as black, green, red, or yellow, or peacock herl, with either black, red, brown, yellow or gray legs. A pure white hackle is very killing about dark. A most excellent hackle is made from the hairs of a deer's tail, somewhat in the fashion of the "bob," so extensively used in Florida and Texas.

The three "typical" hackles of Mr. H. Cholmondely-Pennell, and which he uses to the exclusion of all other flies, are described as follows:

Green.—Dark-green body; very dark-green hackle for both legs and whisk.

Brown.—Body, dark orange; fiery or cinnamon-brown hackle for legs and whisk.

Yellow.—Body, golden yellow; darkish golden-olive hackle for legs and whisk.

These flies are admirable for Black Bass, however they may be for Trout, and the angler who carries but a limited assortment in his fly-hook should include these "hackles," in various sizes; they will not disappoint him.

26

As I have described quite enough for the beginner, and, perhaps, too many, I will only allude to some by name, which will often be found equal to the above, and, for some waters, superior :

Bumble Bee, Jungle Cock, Hoskins, California, Moosehead, Widow, Academy, Blue Jay, Page, Yellow Sally, Blue and Drab, Pheasant, Raven, Claret, Tippulium, Davis, Tanner, White and Green, Motley, Premier, Black and Tan, Black and Gold, Purple Bass, Fire Fly, Little Egg, Gray Coflin, Brown Coflin, Sand Fly, Stone Fly, Hawthorn, Dark Mackerel, etc., etc.

It will be seen that the angler has quite an extensive list to choose from, for most of the flies named are kept in stock by our best dealers. As a rule, the smallest bass-flies should be selected for general fishing; and those of subdued tints will be found the most successful, saving on the exceptional occasions already referred to. As has been already mentioned, most of the flies named are patterned after trout-flies of the same names; and, while some of the latter are large enough, quite a number are too small, and must be enlarged somewhat for bass-flies.

But there are flies, and enough, to suit those of every taste, even should the angler be so fastidious and dainty as "Ye Sunberry Fisher," as described by *Punch :*

> "Ye Sunberrye fysher has flies of all feathers,
> For all sorts of seasons, in all sorts of weathers.
> Flies when ye Springtide is blustrie and showerie,
> Flies when ye Summer is grassie and bowerie,
> Flies when ye Autumn is golden and grainie,
> For hot weather, cold weather, mistie, or rainie.
> Red-spinner, palmer, black peacock and gray,
> Yellow dun, golden dun, March brown, and May,
> Sand-fly and stone-fly, and alder and gnat,
> Black midge and marlow bug—all round his hat."

CHAPTER XV

ARTIFICIAL BAITS.

"And therefore I have, which I will show to you, an artificial minnow that will catch Trout as well as an artificial fly ; and it was made by a handsome woman that had a fine hand, and a live minnow lying by her."—IZAAK WALTON.

TROLLING-BAITS—SPOON-BAITS.

THE most commonly-used trolling-bait for Black Bass is the spoon-bait or trolling-spoon. It is now made of all shapes, and many sizes ; but all are made upon the same general principle, and are merely variations of the original trolling-spoon, which was fashioned like the bowl of a spoon, a single hook being soldered to one end, and a hole drilled in the other end for attaching the line.

By trailing or trolling such a spoon at the end of a line from a moving boat, it revolves gracefully beneath the surface of the water, the burnished surfaces flashing at each revolution, and proves quite an effective lure.

Manufacturers vie with each other in producing novel shapes and so-called improvements, but there is nothing better than the original spoon-bowl with a single hook. The double and triple hooks, usually attached to the modern spoons, are liable to be crushed and broken by the jaws of a large fish, if hooked in a position favorable to this contingency.

Trolling-spoons are all made with a concave and a convex surface ; the latter surface being brightly polished or

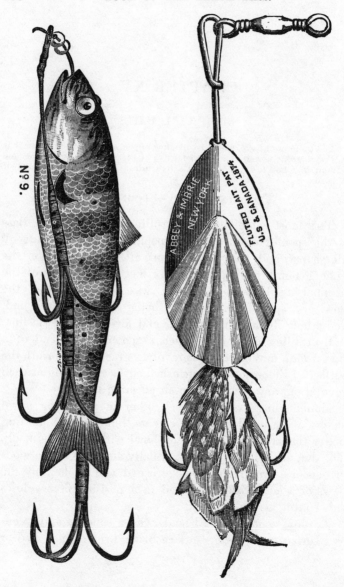

burnished, while the former is generally painted, and usually of a red color. They are made of tin or brass, and often plated with nickel, silver or gold; but so long as spoon-baits are brightly burnished, it matters not what the material is, for the Black Bass is not a judge of metals, but will grab at any thing bright and in motion.

The depending hook or hooks may be plain, or dressed with a tuft of feathers or braid, called, by courtesy, a "fly;" but these fanciful additions, while pleasing to the angler's eye, do not enhance the "taking" qualities of the lure, for it is the flashing and glancing of the revolving spoon that attracts the fish; and it can not be made more effective by these ornamental appendages, or, as I have sometimes seen, by the addition of a live minnow, or a strip of fat pork!

One or two brass swivels should always be attached to the spoon-bait or line, to prevent twisting or kinking. Particular attention should be paid to the hooks of trolling-spoons, for many of them are of inferior quality, though the American spoons are, as a rule, furnished with better hooks than the English baits of the same grades.

As a rule, most persons use too large spoons for Black Bass, using generally Pickerel baits. For the Black Bass, the spoon should be no larger than the bowl of an ordinary sized tea-spoon, for trolling with the hand-line; and when trolling with the rod, they should be still smaller.

Abbey & Imbrie's new Fluted Spoon-Bait is a very finely finished and attractive bait; it is of the same shape as the original spoon, but with a fluted section, which adds very much to its attractiveness when spinning; the hooks

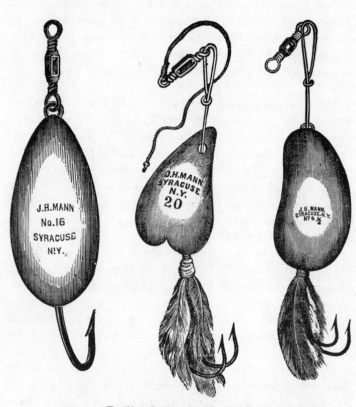

Trolling-Spoons for Hand-line.
(J. H. Mann.)

1. Oval.   2. Perfect Revolving.   3. Kidney.

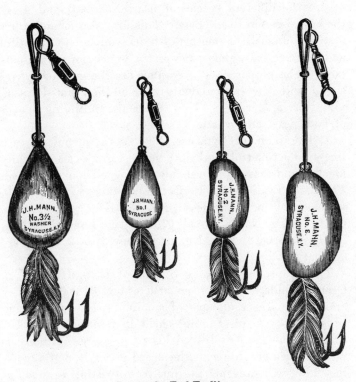

Spoons for Rod Trolling.

(J. H. Mann.)

1 and 2. Egg.　　　3 and 4. Kidney.

are of good quality and reliable. It is made in a number of sizes for different species of fish ; Nos. 2, 3, and 4 are the best sizes for Black Bass. This firm also manufactures a spoon of shell or mother-of-pearl, which is a beautiful and effective bait, almost too pretty to use for such a purpose. The proper sizes to employ are those which correspond with the sizes above given, of their fluted spoon, viz: Nos. 2, 3, and 4. They also make Skittering Spoons of both pearl and metal.

J. H. Mann, of Syracuse, New York, manufactures a line of superior trolling baits ; the best grades are carefully finished and thoroughly reliable, with good hooks attached. For hand trolling, his Perfect Revolving Spoon, No. 20, with controlling link ; Oval, No. 16 ; Kidney Shape, No. $6\frac{1}{2}$; and Egg, No. $3\frac{1}{2}$, are all good baits. For rod trolling, his Trout Spoons, Egg, No. 1 ; Kidney, Nos. 2 and 3, are all that can be desired.

The Improved Trolling Spoons of L. S. Hill & Co., Grand Rapids, Michigan, are articles of real merit. They are made in the semblance of a minnow, the spoon being supported by a spiral spring, held in position by a "U" shaped guide, and readily yields to pressure. It finds its proper circle according to the speed given it, and revolving either way prevents the line from twisting so much as with some other spoons. Nos. 1 and $1\frac{1}{2}$ are the proper sizes for Black Bass.

Other trolling-spoons or baits are made in fanciful shapes, and variously styled minnows, propellers, spinners, etc., but are no better, and many of them not so good as those above mentioned ; for the nearer a spinning spoon-bait approaches the original spoon, already referred to, the more practical and useful it becomes.

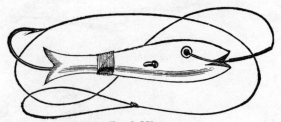

Pearl Minnow.
(A. B. Shipley & Son.)

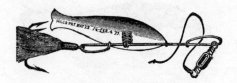

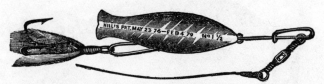

Hill's Improved Trolling Baits.
(L. S. Hill & Co.)

27

Flexible Protean Minnow.
(A. B. Shipley & Son.)

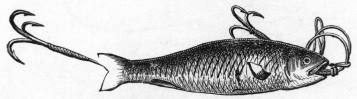

Artificial Flexible Minnow.
(Conroy, Bissett & Malleson.)

Nº I.
Caledonian Minnow.
(Chas. F. Orvis.)

Jointed Metal Minnow.
(Abbey & Imbrie.)

ARTIFICIAL MINNOWS.

Artificial minnows for trolling, spinning, or casting, are made of metal, glass, and rubber, large and small, and gilded, silvered, or painted in attractive ways. Some of them are quite successful as baits, while others are comparatively worthless. They are made both in our own country and in England, and as their numbers, and styles, and forms are constantly increasing, I do not deem it advisable to particularize or give special descriptions. While I have experimented with many of them, I do not employ them in angling for the Black Bass.

For trolling or spinning, none of them are so effective as the spoon-baits; while for casting, they are not to be compared with the natural minnow, alive or dead. I will merely name some of those that are best known, and more generally used: Caledonian, Phantom, Flexible, Jointed, Devon, Protean, Shadow, Pectoral, Unique, Professor, Metal, Glass, Pearl, Silver, and Gilt minnows, and the Dace, Gudgeon, Trout, and Kill Devil.

ARTIFICIAL INSECTS, ETC.

Artificial insects, as bees, grasshoppers, crickets, beetles, May-flies, dragon-flies, and likewise artificial frogs, crawfish, hegramites, shrimps, worms, etc., are now made which resemble the original creatures very closely. They are to be used in surface fishing, in the same way as artificial flies, and must be kept in constant motion, otherwise the Bass soon discover the deception; but if skillfully used, they are often quite successful baits. They certainly have the recommendation of cleanliness and general convenience as compared with their original prototypes.

Artificial Helgramite.
(Conroy, Bissett & Malleson.)

Artificial Insects.
(A. B. Shipley & Son.)

Artificial Crawfish.
(Conroy, Bissett & Malleson.)

THE BOB.

Of all baits or lures used in Black Bass angling, one of the rudest in structure, the most nondescript in appearance, yet one of the most effective and killing in actual practice, is the "bob" of the extreme Southern States.

It has been in use in Florida for more than a century, and was first described by that quaint old naturalist, Bartram, in 1764. His description and method of using it, are identical with the "bob" and its use at the present day in Florida, Louisiana, and Texas.

The "bob" is composed of a triple hook, or three hooks tied back to back, and invested with a portion of a deer's tail, in the manner of a large, bushy, hackle; often intermixed with red and white feathers, or strips of scarlet cloth. It forms a tassel or tuft, somewhat similar to the so-called triple hook "fly" attached to most trolling spoons.

CHAPTER XVI.

NATURAL BAITS.

"And, good master, tell me what baits more you remember."—IZAAK WALTON.

MINNOWS.

AMONG anglers, the term minnow is used to express any small fish used for bait, whether adult fish of certain families, or the young of others. But the term properly belongs to the family CYPRINIDÆ, which comprises numerous genera, and some of the genera are composed of many species.

The most generally diffused species are *Luxilis cornutus*, the common shiner; *Semotilus corporalis*, the common chub; and *Ceratichthys biguttatis*, the horned chub. The shiner is, by all odds, the best bait for the Black Bass, being quite silvery, as its name implies, and shows well in the water. It is not so hardy, or long-lived, on the hook, as the chub; but on account of its white and silvery appearance it is especially desirable for turbid or rough water, and on cloudy or dark days, though it is, for that matter, a good bait at all times.

The chubs are good bait on bright days with clear and still water; they have rather tough mouths, endure the hook well, and are rather more lively than shiners, and on these accounts are preferred by many anglers.

The young of some of the species of *Catostomidæ* (suckers), are also very good baits on sunny days, with clear and low water; their tough, leathery, and projecting lips are well adapted for the hook. They are quite hardy and lively.

The young of *Perca americana* (yellow perch), are excellent baits on ponds and lakes, early or late in the season; especially if the spinous dorsal fin be clipped off with a sharp knife, or a pair of scissors. They show well in the water, and often prove an attractive lure during the seasons mentioned.

As a rule, good-sized minnows should be employed, say from three to five inches long. The large minnows are livelier, more hardy, and live much longer on the hook than the small ones. A half-pound Bass will take the largest minnow as easily and as readily as the smallest one, so there is no fear of using minnows too large. It is true, that at times, the largest Bass seem to take to the smallest minnows, but on these exceptional occasions, they are off their feed, to a certain extent; for, usually, the largest Bass takes the largest minnows.

In baiting with the minnow, the hook should be entered through the lower lip and out through the nostril; if this is carefully done, the minnow will live a comparatively long time. Sometimes, with small minnows, the hook is passed out through the socket of the eye, care being taken not to injure the eye-ball. Another excellent way, especially with large minnows, is to pass the hook through both lips, the lower one first, and out through the upper one. When minnows are hooked in either of these ways, a dead one is often as good as a live one, for the moving of the line causes them to move in a natural manner. Where the water is without a current, as on ponds or lakes, and

where the minnows are quite small, they may be, for still
fishing, but under no other circumstances, hooked just
back of the dorsal fin, and just above the backbone. But
in hooking a minnow in this way, the angler should bear
in mind the injunction of Father Izaak, in reference to
hooking the live frog: use him as though you loved him.
Chubs and suckers should always be hooked through the
lips, which are comparatively tough.

An excellent method for affixing the minnow to the
hook, in still-fishing—for it will not answer at all for
casting—and one that will well pay the angler for the extra
time and trouble involved, is as follows:

"Take a piece of cotton thread about a foot long, tie the
middle of it tight under the barb of the hook; now take
the minnow in the left hand, lay the hook on its side, the
barb up by the shoulder of the bait, with the shaft along
the belly; now pass the thread over the shoulder and
around under the fish, and tie the shaft of the hook, then
pass the thread along the shaft until under and behind the
back fin, then tie tightly around the shaft of the hook, then
pass the thread on each side of the fish up to the back, just
behind the back fin, and tie with a bow knot. This fastens
the bait securely without hurting it, and you will have as
lively a bait as ever used for still-fishing."

The angler can not be too careful of his minnows. The
water in the bucket should be frequently changed, without
waiting for them to appear at the surface to breathe—the
usually accepted indication to change the water—for their
vitality and strength are already impaired when this takes
place, and many of them can not be revived afterwards.
When available, especially in very hot weather, a piece of
ice should be placed on the top of the minnow pail, and

covered with a woolen cloth. A little salt, added to the water in the pail, is very beneficial and adds to the preservation of minnows.

It is a good plan, when practicable, to use two minnow-buckets, one of which, containing most of the minnows as a reserve, should be sunk in the water, and a few minnows taken out, as needed, for the bucket in use. In this way the entire stock can be utilized in good condition.

In carrying minnows to any distance, they should not be too much crowded in the pail; fifty minnows is enough for a five-gallon bucket. When more than this number is required, additional pails should be provided. A handful of water-weeds in the pail will prevent the minnows from being so much injured, as they otherwise would be, when conveyed over rough roads.

When it is not practicable to allow of a frequent changing of the water, the latter may be oxygenized or aërated by inserting a rubber, or other tube, well toward the bottom of the pail, and pumping air through it by means of a rubber bulb, such as is attached to a pump-syringe. It is worse than useless to blow through such a tube with the mouth; for the breath, being deprived of its oxygen in the lungs, carbonic acid gas takes it place, which is poisonous to the minnows; yet I have frequently seen this done by individuals, who erroneously supposed that they were freshening the water, because of the numerous bubbles produced.

THE HELGRAMITE.

The larva of the horned corydalis (*Corydalis cornuta*), an insect belonging to the order *Neuroptera*, is variously called "helgramite," "dobson," "grampus," "dobsell," "hellion," "kill-devil," "crawler," and other euphonious names. The male of the perfect, winged-insect has long antennæ, or horns, from which its specific and common names are derived.

It exists for several years in the larval state, when it is generally known as the "helgramite," being a curious, flattened, and, to most persons, a repulsive-looking worm, growing to a length of two or three inches, and about a half inch in width. It has a head and pincers resembling, somewhat, those of a beetle; has six legs along the thorax; while the body is composed of a number of rings, to which are attached fringes bearing some likeness to small legs; the body terminates in two short appendages, or tails, on each of which are two small hooks. The color is a dark, dirty, brown.

The helgramite, by means of its hooks and pincers, clings readily and tenaciously to different objects, and hides securely under rocks, bowlders, driftwood, logs, etc., even in swift-running streams. They may be found cling-ing to the decaying timbers of old dams and bridges, and in the crevices of submerged stone-work at these places. They are found on the "riffles" of streams, under the bowlders and flat stones, and may be taken in these situa-tions with the minnow-net, by stretching the latter across the foot of the riffle; when the stones above the net are turned over, the helgramite, being thus disturbed, curls himself into a ball and drifts into the net.

They can be found, in fact, hiding under almost any submerged object in the shallow portions of streams. They feed upon decaying wood and vegetation, and other substances. They can be kept alive for almost any length of time, in a vessel half filled with wet pieces of rotten wood, and damp aquatic vegetation. In this way the angler can always have a ready supply of bait on hand.

The helgramite is hooked by inserting the point of the hook under the cap or shell that covers the neck, from behind forward, and bringing it through next to the head. It is a capital bait for the Black Bass, especially when the Bass are found on the riffles or rapids, and in shallow water.

THE CRAWFISH.

The crawfish (*Cambarus*), sometimes called crayfish and crab, is, in some localities, and at certain seasons, a good bait, especially when casting its shell, when it is called a "peeler," or a "shedder." The crawfish exists wherever the Black Bass is found, in greater or less quantities. In waters where it is very abundant it forms an excellent and killing bait.

"Distinct species live in the mountain streams and in the springs at their sources. Some frequent the marshes of the lowlands (both the fresh and salt marshes), either near the streams, or adjacent to the bays, sounds, or ocean. Some occur beneath stones in rivers, creeks, or branches; in the muddy basis; beneath stones in the rapids; among grass and weeds in more quiet places, and in coves; under shelving grassy banks; in holes at the bottom of ponds, lakes, dams, and mill-races. Others bore holes in the meadows, or even in the hill-tops near water; and in bringing up the mud and clay from their tube-like holes, pile it as a chimney at the entrance. These species at particular times place a plug of clay in the orifice of the chimney and seal themselves in for a certain length of time. Still others reside in the drains and mud of the rice-fields and plantations of the South, and sometimes burrow through the embankments, allowing the water to flood the region."

The crawfish is used as a bait for the Black Bass only in still-fishing, when it serves a good purpose. In its usual state it should be hooked through the tail, but "peelers" may be hooked through the head or body. They may be kept alive a long time in damp aquatic grass, moss, or weeds.

GRASSHOPPERS AND CRICKETS.

Grasshoppers and crickets are at times very taking baits. They should be used as surface baits entirely, and should be employed only when a brisk breeze is blowing, and on the windward side of the water; for it is at such times that they are blown into the water, and the Bass are then on the look out for them. The water, also, being broken into ripples by the breeze, enhances the angler's chances of success. These insects should be hooked through the upper part of the thorax or body, small hooks being used.

FROGS.

On marshy streams and ponds, young frogs are sometimes used for baits, with good success, in still-fishing. They may be hooked through the lips, or through the skin of the back. They should be of small size, and kept in pretty constant motion, as they are inclined to bury themselves in the mud, or hide under stones, on the bottom, or crawl out upon objects on the surface, if left too long to their own devices.

Salt water shrimps, when they can be procured, are good baits for Black Bass, alive or pickled, that is, preserved in salt or strong brine.

I have seen Black Bass caught with cut bait, and even the humble " wum ;" but the angler who is reduced to such severe straits, is more to be pitied than envied. It would be in better taste to offer pork to a Mussulman, or *pâté de foie gras* to a tramp.

Holberton Fly-Book.
(Conroy, Bissett & Malleson.)

CHAPTER XVII.

MISCELLANEOUS IMPLEMENTS.

"My rod and my line, my float and my lead,
    My hook and my plummet, my whetstone and knife,
My basket, my baits, both living and dead,
    My net and my meat, for that is the chief:
Then I must have thread, and hairs green and small,
With mine angling-purse, and so you have all."
                                        —Izaak Walton.

The Fly-Book.

Among the necessary adjuncts to the fly-fisher's outfit
is the fly-book, whose pages, well-filled, are more interesting to the angler than the best written pages of classic
lore, poetry, or fiction. Fly-books are now made of many
patterns and sizes, and of various grades of quality and
material. They are constructed of calf-skin, pig-skin,
Morocco, or Russia-leather, with parchment leaves for
holding the flies. Those with the "Hyde," or metal-clip,
for keeping the flies separate and at full length, are the
best and most satisfactory, for obvious reasons. They are
made in various lengths, from five to seven inches; and
of a capacity for holding from three dozen to a gross
of flies.

There is nothing neater, better, or more substantial in
this line than Abbey & Imbrie's "Southside" fly-book.
It is made of Russia-leather, with strap and patent clasp;
has double parchment leaves, well-stitched, and is provided

(327)

Creel, or Fish-Basket.
(A. B. Shipley & Son.)

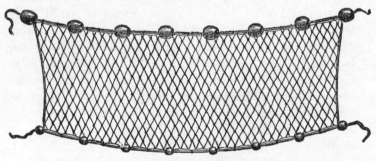

Minnow-Seine.
(A. B. Shipley & Son.)

with the metal-clip, and two leaves of heavy porous cloth for drying wet flies. It is also furnished with large pockets, and compartments for leaders, and snelled hooks. It has a capacity for one hundred flies, and is made of a uniform quality, which is of the highest grade.

The " Holberton " fly-book, of Conroy, Bissett & Malleson, is one similar in style and construction, and is a first rate article. The price of this book depends on the material used in its construction, its capacity for a greater or less number of flies, and the length of the book. One holding four dozen flies is large enough for all practical purposes in Black Bass angling.

Creel, or Fish-Basket.

For fly-fishing, or bait-fishing, when wading a stream or fishing from the bank, a creel is very useful and convenient for holding the angler's catch. Fish are preserved in much better shape, condition and appearance by its use, and it is altogether more satisfactory than the shiftless way of " stringing " the Bass, and allowing them to become water-soaked and flabby, by immersing the " string " in the warm and shallow water near the shore, or even by " towing " them after the angler, if wading.

For Black Bass, the largest Trout-creels will answer every purpose; say Nos. 3 or 4, having a capacity of twenty or twenty-five pounds. The shoulder-strap should be leather or webbing, with a shoulder-pad, to prevent cutting or bruising the shoulder.

Fish-baskets or creels should always be well washed, and carefully dried after use, to keep them clean and sweet. When washing them, a little carbonate of soda or

28

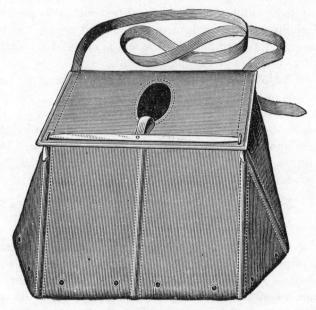

Folding Canvas Creel.
(Abbey & Imbrie.)

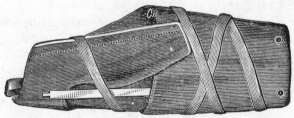

Canvas Creel, Folded.

carbolic acid should be added to the water to destroy the
"ancient and fish-like smell."

A new and very desirable article in this way is the
"Patent Folding Canvas Creel," devised and made by
Abbey & Imbrie. It is constructed of water-proof canvas,
and is capable of being folded into a small and compact
package. When in use it has flexible ribs for keeping it
in shape, which are rendered practicable by the light
metal stretcher, which also serves to fasten down the top.
Around the lower edge is a row of holes, with brass eye-
lets, for the purpose of ventilation and drainage. It
answers the purposes of its construction admirably. Size
C is best adapted for Black Bass fishing, it being esti-
mated to hold twenty pounds.

The Landing-Net.

For boat fishing, the landing-net should have a long
handle, which is best when made in two pieces, with a
strong brass ferrule joint. It should be as light as possible,
and on this account bamboo cane is the very best material
for the handle. The rim or ring should be ten or twelve
inches in diameter, of brass, solid or folding; the latter
are the most portable and convenient, and are made with
two or more hinge joints. The net should be deep, and
of a tolerably coarse mesh; linen is the most durable
material, though cotton will answer.

For fishing from the bank, or for wading the stream, a
short-handled Trout-net is to be preferred, as it is more
easily carried and answers every purpose better than the
long-handled net. Those with oval, wooden rims are the
lightest, and are as good as any. The long-handled net

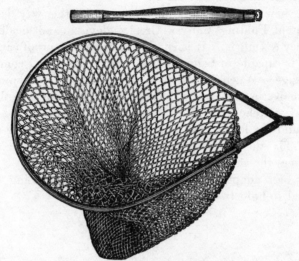

Short-Handled Landing-Net.
(A. B. Shipley & Son.)

Long-Handled Landing-Net.
(Conroy, Bissett & Malleson.)

will answer here by using but one joint of the handle.
There should be a blunt hook, or ring, at the end of the
handle for attaching to the creel-strap, so as to leave both
hands free for casting, and playing the fish.

MINNOW-SEINES AND NETS.

For catching minnows for bait-fishing, the most expeditious way is to use a linen or cotton minnow-seine, from
three to five feet wide, and from five to fifteen feet long.
These seines can be purchased mounted or unmounted.
The mountings consist of cork and lead-lines, with their
floats and sinkers, and two handles or brails. The mesh
should be quite fine.

A very simple and convenient contrivance for the same
purpose—and much similar to one used by myself—is thus
described by a gentleman of Baltimore, Maryland, in
" Forest and Stream : "

As I hear so many fishermen complaining that they can not get
a net suitable to catch minnows, that is easily carried, I thought it
might be of service to the fishing fraternity in general if I were to
describe a net of my own invention that is easily carried in the
pocket, can be adjusted in a minute, and has never failed to provide me with plenty of minnows. I take a bung or round block of
wood of two and one-half to three inches in diameter, and bore four
holes opposite to each other in the edge of it. I then insert a piece
of umbrella-rib, about twelve to fourteen inches long, in each hole.
The holes must be made deep and small enough for the wire to fit
tight. The paragon wire is the best. I leave the end of the rib
that has the little eye in it outside. I then lay the bung and wires
on a square piece of mosquito-netting, and stretch it and sew it
firmly at the four corners to the eyes in the ribs. In the center of
the bung I put a screw-eye, and in the center of the mosquito-net
sew a piece of string, leaving ends about eight inches long. Any

Patent Adjustable Float.
(Bradford & Anthony.)

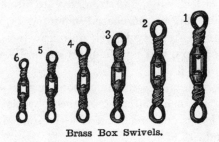

Brass Box Swivels.

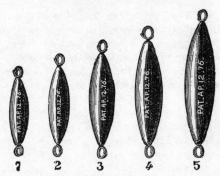

Patent Adjustable Sinkers.
(Bradford & Anthony.)

straight, stiff stick picked up on the shore serves as a handle, being made fast to the net by a strong piece of twine through the screw-eye, and with a piece of bread tied in the net with the string, and perhaps a small, flat stone to make it sink, it is ready to catch minnows. They will come over the net for the bread, and when it is raised up quickly the resistance of the water causes it to belly, and the minnows will not get out. When bait enough has been taken, I pull the wires out of the holes, drop the bung into the net, and roll it up on the wires.

Another very simple and effective device for the same purpose is thus described by a well-known angler, of Nashville, Tennessee, in the "Chicago Field:"

This simple contrivance astonishes all who see it, because they naturally ask the question, how it was that no one ever thought of it before? A globe of wire netting split in two, fastened at the bottom by hinges, and attached to a stick by strings from the top—this is the whole affair, save a small place in the center for bait. The two hemispheres are so arranged as to open partially from their own weight, if allowed to touch bottom; or they can be separated by pulling one of the strings above mentioned. As minnows are generally found in shallow, clear water, it is easy to see when enough have entered the trap, to close and draw it out. This invention does away entirely with seining, and the disagreeable necessity of wading in the water. The pole or stick upon which the trap is hung may be made of any desired length, and jointed, thus permitting the entire apparatus to be packed in a small space. Those of our Nashville anglers who have seen it are of the opinion that nothing else will be used for catching minnows, once they become known.

FLOATS, OR CORKS.

The float should never be used when it can be dispensed with, as it is detrimental to good casting, and is always in the way. It becomes necessary, however, in shallow streams, where the bottom is covered with snags, roots, weeds and other obstacles, and may be used in still-fishing, where crawfish, frogs or helgramites are used as bait; but, when used, it should be as small as possible, consistent with the weight of the sinker required, and should be employed for the sole purpose of keeping the hook away from the bottom, and not as an object of intense and constant observation to indicate a bite.

An egg-shaped, oval, long or barrel-shaped cork-float may be used; or, still better, perhaps, a swan-quill or porcupine-quill float may be employed with advantage, in situations referred to above.

The best of all, however, and the only real improvement ever made in fishing-floats, is the "Patent Adjustable Enameled Float." This handy article, instead of the usual ring and quill slide, has spiral rings of wire at each end of the float, for ready attachment or detachment to or from the line without removing the bait or hook. The attachment is made in a moment to any portion of the line; and, when attached, can be moved up or down the line at will, and will remain stationary wherever placed. These floats are hollow, quite light, and well finished. To those anglers who are partial to the use of a float, it is an invention of great merit and advantage.

THE SWIVEL.

A brass box-swivel should always be employed in bait-fishing for Black Bass. It prevents, in a great measure, the twisting, kinking and snarling of the line, so annoying to the angler. In rod-fishing, the smallest sizes—Nos. 5 or 6—are large enough; and, usually, no additional weight or sinker will be required. The line should be made fast to one ring, and the snell of the hook attached to the other. In trolling, two swivels can be used with advantage—one attached to the snell of the hook or spinner, and the other attached to the line some two or three feet above. In trolling with the hand-line, larger swivels may be used—as Nos. 2 or 3. Brass swivels should always be used, as they do not rust, a strong objection to steel swivels. When sinkers are used in addition, they should be attached about a foot above the swivel.

SINKERS.

Generally, in Black Bass angling, no sinker, in addition to the swivel, is necessary, the latter being heavy enough to keep the live bait beneath the surface. But there are cases and times when the sinker is brought in requisition; for example, when the minnows used for bait are large and strong and keep on the surface, or where the stream is quite rapid or current swift.

When the ordinary ringed-sinker is used without a swivel, the line should be tied in one ring, and the snell of the hook looped in the other. The smallest-sized sinker is usually heavy enough, though sometimes a larger size is necessary. Buckshot or small bullets should not be used when the oval sinker can be had, as they offer too much resistance to the water, and often cause the line to twist or kink.

The " Patent Adjustable Sinker," with spiral rings like the adjustable float, is the best form of sinker to use, and should take the place of the old-fashioned ringed leads. The simplicity and effectiveness of the device by which they can be put on and taken off the line, without dis-

29

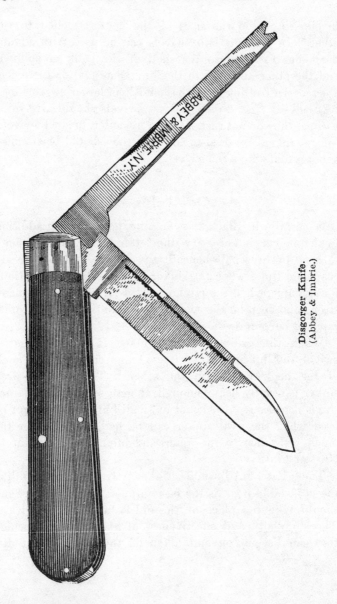

Disgorger Knife.
(Abbey & Imbrie.)

turbing hook or bait, should receive the approval of all anglers, and render their adoption universal. They insure neatness and dispatch, qualities not to be despised in angling.

CLEARING-RING.

The hook, in angling, often becomes fast or foul in snags, roots, rocks or grass, and frequently is thereby lost or broken, to the disgust of the angler. By the employment of a clearing-ring the hook can almost invariably be easily detached from these obstructions without damage. These are rings made expressly for the purpose, composed of brass or iron, with a hinge to admit of their being readily adjusted to the line. The method of using them is as follows:

The ring is opened at the hinge and the line encircled, when the ring is again closed, and allowed to run down the line to the point of obstruction; the weight of the ring detaches the hook, when it is drawn up, a hand-line being attached to the ring for this purpose. If the hook is very firmly fastened to the root or snag, the ring is raised a few feet by its cord and allowed to drop suddenly, when its weight will usually clear the hook. A very good substitute for the clearing-ring, and one easily obtained, is the ordinary bar of lead, used for making bullets. A hole is bored in the flat bar, through which the hand-cord is fastened. When used, the bar is bent around the fishing-line, forming a ring, and is very easily attached or detached.

DISGORGERS.

Very often a Bass is hooked in the gullet, and sometimes in the stomach, though the angler should never allow him to gorge the bait to this extent. It is best to strike quickly, so as to hook him in the mouth. In the event of the Bass swallowing the hook, is is necessary to cut out or tear out the hook, and often at the cost of scratching or lacerating the angler's fingers; and especially is this apt to be the case when a Pickerel or Pike-perch is thus hooked, their long and sharp teeth being as sharp as needles.

To avoid this unpleasant feature, a disgorger is very handy and efficacious. It consists of a stout piece of wire, six or eight inches in length, with one end flattened; in this flat end a notch is filed, with cutting or sharp edges, when, by pushing this sharp notch along the hook, the latter is easily detached or cut out.

A very convenient tool is made by Abbey & Imbrie, No. 48 Maiden Lane, New York City, and designed especially for this purpose, a cut of which is here presented, which explains itself. In addition to the disgorger, it has a strong, sharp blade, which can be made available for many purposes, not the least of which is to kill the fish as soon as caught, by severing the spinal cord at the junction of the head and body. This should always be done by the humane angler, for two good and sufficient reasons: It immediately puts an end to the suffering of the fish, and keeps the flesh firm and in good condition.

MINNOW-PAILS.

To the bait-fisher for Black Bass, the proper form of bait-can is quite an important item. There are two general styles, one for boat-fishing, and one for stream-fishing.

The best plan for a minnow-bucket for boat-fishing, and

where a large pail can be utilized, is to have two pails, one fitting within the other.   This form of pail is generally and conveniently made as follows:

The outer bucket is of heavy tin, and made round, with a capacity of from two to five gallons; a stout wire bail or handle is attached, with a wooden or tin hand-piece.   The inner bucket is also made of tin, to fit somewhat loosely in the outer one; but the top of this bucket should be an inch below the top of the outer pail.   It has an opening, fitted with a lid on top, through which the hand can be readily inserted; and has a tin-hasp and loop for fastening securely.   In addition, there is a flat tin-handle, in the form of an arch, on the top of the lid, by which the inner pail can be easily lifted out.

The inner pail is freely perforated on the top, bottom and sides, so that, upon raising it, the water leaves it rapidly, and a minnow can thus be readily selected. Whenever necessary, the inner pail can be taken out, the top securely fastened by the hasp and loop, and the pail sunk in the water to revive the minnows, while the angler is taking his lunch or *siesta*.   Both pails should be well painted, inside and out.   Sometimes the lower half of the inner pail is formed of copper or galvanized iron wire-gauze.

For fishing in a stream, where the angler is a-foot, a much smaller and lighter bucket must be used, on the score of portability and general convenience.   In this case, the bucket is made single, usually, and of an oblong or oval shape, to admit of its being more readily carried.   It is fitted with a handle or bail, and the top is soldered in, an inch or two below the rim of the bucket; and this top only is perforated.   There is also a lid in the top, which is usually

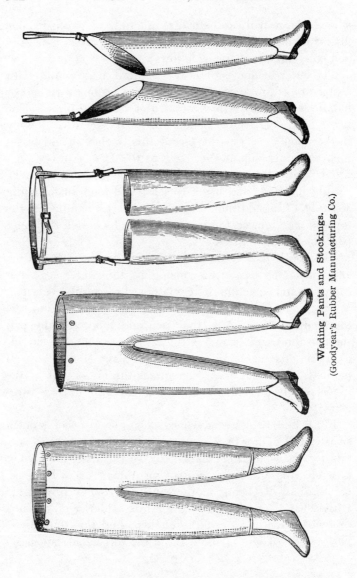

Wading Pants and Stockings.
(Goodyear's Rubber Manufacturing Co.)

secured by a bolt of stout wire. A double pail, the inner one being made principally of copper or galvanized iron wire-cloth, would be vastly more convenient, without adding much to the weight.

The English style of bait-kettle is made single, with perforated top, and is formed round but tapering, being broad at the bottom, and narrow at the top. Sometimes they are made square, with the top formed of woven wire-cloth.

Mr. J. C. Hitchcock, of Oconomowoc, Wisconsin, has patented and manufactures a very convenient minnow-bucket for boat-fishing. The outside bucket is of heavy tin, oval in shape, and is divided into two compartments by a central partition. One of these compartments is a double-walled refrigerator for holding ice and the angler's luncheon, while the other contains an inner minnow-bucket composed principally of heavy copper wire gauze; there is an attachment for aërating the water, which, with the coldness imparted to it by the ice chamber, keeps the minnows lively and strong.

WADING PANTS AND STOCKINGS.

Wading pants or stockings, rubber boots or leggins, are indispensable to the angler's comfort and well-being in stream-fishing, either for fly-fishing or bait-fishing. Rubber hip-boots have been much used for this purpose, but they do not wear well, and are heavy and clumsy. Mackintosh and luster wading-pants and leggins are now furnished at a moderate price, and are much to be preferred, being light and very serviceable. They are made with stocking feet, in which case a pair of brogans, or old shoes, must be worn, and this is much the best plan for wading.

Bass Rod Case with Handle.

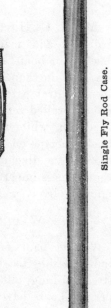

Single Fly Rod Case.

Leather Rod and Reel Cases.

(Thomson & Són.)

They are also furnished with boots attached, with cork or rubber soles, and are very durable.

No stream-fisher's outfit is complete without these conveniences, which are now made by the Goodyear Rubber Manufacturing Company, perfectly reliable, waterproof, and fully equal to the best English goods. The Mackintosh goods of this Company are formed with a layer of solid rubber between two outer layers of stockinet, or other light and porous cloth, rendering them light, pliable, proof against cracking or breaking, and thoroughly waterproof.

ROD AND REEL CASES.

Leather cases for the rod and reel are very convenient and desirable articles, especially for the angling tourist. A good and highly-prized rod or reel should have the best care; and a rod, especially, is liable to serious injury when protected only by a common canvas cover.

Thompson & Son, 301 Broadway, New York City, the well known manufacturers of sportsmen's goods, make a specialty of leather rod and reel cases. They are made of heavy bridle leather, with handle, and if required, a padlock. The rod cases are made to hold one or more rods. To the angler who delights in completeness of outfit, I can cheerfully recommend these useful articles. They will be duly appreciated by any angler who has ever made an extended trip to the woods, lakes, or streams by the usual modes of conveyance.

PART THIRD

ANGLING AND FLY-FISHING.

CHAPTER XVIII.

THE PHILOSOPHY OF ANGLING.

"You are assured, though there be ignorant men of another belief, that angling is an art, and you know that art better than others; and that this truth is demonstrated by the fruits of that pleasant labor which you enjoy,—when you purpose to give rest to your mind, and divest yourself of your more serious business, and (which is often) dedicate a day or two to this recreation."—IZAAK WALTON.

In the days of good old Father Izaak Walton, angling was, as stated by him in the title of his famous book, the "contemplative man's recreation." While this is no less true in our own day, the art of angling has extended its sphere of usefulness by becoming, not only the recreation of the contemplative man, but of the active, stirring, over-worked business and professional man, as well. While in the comparatively slow-coach days of the quaint Walton it was rather a recreation of choice, it has, in this age of steam become, in a measure, one of necessity.

The American idea of rest and recreation seems to have been based upon the Mosaic law of resting on the seventh, or last day of the week. A man must first gain a competency, and rest afterwards, even if it took seven times seven years to gain the first condition—wealth—for then, only, would he be entitled, or in a proper condition to enjoy his *otium cum dignitate.*

In the rapid race for wealth and distinction, men labor, night and day, with mind and muscle, especially during the seasons of business activity. But too often, alas, they labor in vain, and find that the "bubble reputation," or the "wealth that sinews bought," has in a moment been swept away, after years of toil and anxiety. Or, if they make their footing sure, they find, too often, that the result has only been attained at the expense of a permanent impairment of health, for which the dearly bought treasure is but a sorry recompense; and the oft-imagined and fondly looked for goal, of a life of peace and quiet and the enjoyment of the hard-earned competency, has been realized to be one of short continuance, or of long bodily suffering.

To keep pace with the rapid strides of trade and traffic, as much labor is now performed in one day, as was formerly done in a week. Consequently, between the busy seasons, or "heats," in this race for wealth and place, men find it absolutely necessary—not so much from choice, as necessity—to rest and recuperate, and build up the exhausted energies, the tired brain and relaxed muscles, and to gird up the loins for renewed efforts.

The necessity being acknowledged, the question then arises: in what way can this rest and recreation of the muscular and nervous tissues of the body be best attained? When men think of rest and relaxation, their thoughts turn naturally to the woods, to the fields, to running streams and quiet lakes, or the sea-shore. If it is simply a Sunday stroll, their steps naturally and irresistibly lead them to green fields, or the river side; or a drive along the country road with its hedges, and birds, and crossing brooks. If it is a day's holiday, it must be a picnic in the grand old woods, and near a lake, or stream, or at least a babbling rill. The very idea of perfect rest is associated with mossy banks and cool sparkling waters. It is doubtful if there is a sweeter line in human language, or one more expressive of perfect bliss, of lasting peace, of complete rest, of true happiness, of quiet contentment, than that of the Psalmist: "He maketh me to lie down in green pastures : he leadeth me beside the still waters."

But the question : where can rest be found ? has already been answered in the crowds of tired pilgrims—they are called pleasure-seekers, but they are looking for rest—who are seen each summer-time wending their ways by rail and steamer, to the mountains, to the sea-shore, to the Adirondacks, to the Great Lake region, to the wilds of Maine and Canada, to the charming streams and lakelets of Wisconsin, Michigan, and Minnesota, or simply to "the country"—any place, in fact, is their Mecca, where may be found rest and quiet, green fields, green hills, green trees, and clear, cool water.

Then, the season for angling, coming as it does during the midsummer vacation, in the pleasantest weather and during the lull in active business matters, presents at once the means and the opportunity for enjoyment and rest, for recreation and peace. Horace Greeley once said to the writer, that he had been for years eagerly looking forward to the time when he could lay down his pen, for a few days, and "go a fishing;" but that time never came during his busy life. His dreams of a brief season of what he considered the very essence of rest and contentment, were never realized—he died a martyr to an overworked brain.

Rest and recreation to the active mind does not mean mere idleness, or as it is more poetically expressed : *dolce far niente;* this, to many, would be more irksome than the hardest work. Many men have a horror of going into the woods, to the wilderness, to the lakes, or the sea-shore, because there is nothing to do, nothing to occupy their minds, nothing to save them from *ennui* after the novelty wears off. The busy, active man can secure rest only by diverting the muscular and nervous energies in new and unaccustomed channels. This may be accomplished, in a measure, by cards, chess, music, reading, etc., as purely intellectual recreations; while riding, driving, boating, yacthing, archery, shooting, etc., furnish ample means for muscular skill and exercise ; but *angling* brings into play both the mental and physical capacities. To be a good angler requires good judgment, much patience, rare skill, a full share of endurance, and a lively imagination; the latter quality is not absolutely essential, but it helps mightily when " luck" is bad, and on it depends the æsthetic and poetical features of the art.

But the persons who are disposed to "take time " to indulge in these or similar recreations, in our country, are quite limited. In England, it is considered part of a gentleman's education to know how to ride, to row, to shoot, to sail, and to cast a fly, and he is the better for it, morally, physically, and intellectually. In our own country it is too often considered " a waste of time" to acquire or practice these manly and healthful accomplishments. Our girls may learn music, and dancing, and painting, as means and acquirements necessary to the securing of a husband, but any attempt on the part of our boys to learn any of the manly sports, in a regular and systematic way, must be frowned down as opposed to all our ideas of thrift and economy, and a gross misuse of " time." What we need is more muscular Christianity ; we would then have sounder minds in sounder bodies.

A few weeks taken from the fifty-two composing the

year, and devoted to angling, shooting, boating, or "camping out," would not be missed in the long run from the business man's calender, but, on the contrary, would return an interest, which, though it could not be computed by any rate of per centage, would be sensibly felt and realized in a clearer brain, a stronger body, and a better aptitude for business. The clergyman would acquire broader views of humanity, and preach better sermons. The physician would better appreciate, and oftener prescribe, Nature's great remedies, air, sunshine, exercise, and temperance. The lawyer's conscience would be enlarged, and his fees possibly contracted. The poet's imagination - would be more vivid; the artist's skill more pronounced. Nerve would keep pace with muscle, and brawn with brain.

I have purposely avoided any allusion to the Gipsy blood inherent in our veins, or the savage traits yet manifest in our flesh, and their liability to crop out, as evidenced in our love for Nature and Nature's arts. I do not look at it in that light. I claim that the more enlightened and civilized a nation becomes, the more it is interested in the works of Nature and her laws; that the more progress we make in the arts and sciences, and all the achievements of a high state of civilization, and the more artificial and advanced we become in our ideas of living— the more readily we turn for rest and enjoyment, for recreation and real pleasure, to the simplicity of Nature's resources,

> "Knowing that Nature never did betray
> The heart that loved her."

Angling is an art, and it is not beneath the dignity of any one to engage in it, as a recreation. It is hallowed by "Meek Walton's heavenly memory," and has been

30

practiced and commended by some of the best and truest
and wisest men that ever lived; for, as Father Izaak says:
" It is an art, and an art worthy the knowledge and practice of a wise man." Did the art of angling require an
apologist, I could here produce evidence, in precept and
example, of good and wise men of all ages, from the days
of the Fishers of Galilee down to the present time, up-
holding and commending the moral tendencies and the
healthful influences of the art of angling, and its virtue
of making men better physically, intellectually, and spirit-
ually.

"O, sir, doubt not but that angling is an art," says
Piscator to Venator, " is it not an art to deceive a Trout
with an artificial fly? A Trout that is more sharp-sighted
than any hawk you have named, and more watchful and
timorous than your high-mettled merlin is bold?"

Is it not an art to glide stealthily and softly along the
bank of a stream to just where the wary Bass or timid
Trout is watching and waiting, ever on the alert for the
slightest movement, and keenly alive to each passing
shadow; to approach him unawares; to cast the feathery
imitation of an insect lightly and naturally upon the surface of the water, without a suspicious splash, and without
disclosing to his observant eyes the shadow of the rod or
line; to strike the hook into his jaws the instant he un-
suspectingly takes the clever ruse into his mouth; to play
him, and subdue him, and land him successfully and artis-
tically with a willowy rod and silken line that would not
sustain half his weight out of the water? Is not this an
art? Let the doubter try it.

"Doubt not, therefore, sir, but that angling is an art,"
says Walton, "and an art worth your learning. The

question is, rather, whether you be capable of learning
it?"

Exactly so, Father Izaak; the question is, not merely
"to be or not to be," but whether one is "capable" of
learning it; for though any one may become a bait-fisher,
it is not every one that can learn the fly-fisher's art; for,
continues Walton, "he that hopes to be a good angler,
must not only bring an inquiring, searching, observing
wit, but he must bring a large measure of hope and
patience, and a love and propensity to the art itself; but
having once got and practiced it, then doubt not but
angling will prove to be so pleasant, that it will prove to
be, like virtue, a reward to itself."

CHAPTER XIX.

CONDITIONS WHICH GOVERN THE BITING OF FISH.

"So I have observed, that if it be a cloudy day, and not extreme cold, let the wind sit in what quarter it will, and do its worst, I heed it not."—IZAAK WALTON.

To seek to know all the conditions, positive and hypothetical, qualifying and exceptional, which govern the "biting" of fish, is about as vain and discouraging a pursuit as the search for the philosopher's stone.

To know, positively, before leaving one's office, counting-house, or workshop for a day's outing, that it is the day of all others of the season, and that the phase of the moon, the conditions of sky and atmosphere, the direction and force of the wind, and the temperature and condition of the water are just right to insure success, and to know just what bait or fly to use, and in what portion of the stream to fish, under these conditions, implies a state of knowledge that can never be attained by ordinary mortals; and though we are created, "little lower than the angels," it involves a pursuit of knowledge under such extreme difficulties, that even prescience and omniscience are but ciphers in the total sum, for it leaves out the most important factor in the calculation—the fish itself.

Yet it is in just this hope of reducing the matter to the certainty of a mathematical proposition, that some anglers are continually puzzling their own brains, and taxing the patience of their angling friends.

(356)

They imagine that fish, somehow, form an exception to the rest of the animal creation, and are governed in their feeding, or "biting," by certain laws, as unchanging as those of the Medes and Persians; and that these immutable laws have an outward expression in certain states and conditions of weather and water; and that it is only necessary to ascertain the peculiar combination of wind, weather and water, under which fish feed, *nolens volens*, to be able to effect their capture easily.

The glorious uncertainty attending the "biting" of fish, even at apparently favorable times, has been observed for ages, and has invested the gentle art with a glamour, and an air of mystery, in which the element of chance, or luck, is a prominent feature. The angler wending his way homeward is accosted at every turn with the interrogatory of, "What luck?" while "fisherman's luck" has become an universal synonym of failure.

Many anglers, in lieu of more cogent reasons, have conveniently relegated this whole question to "luck," and have ceased to trouble themselves much about it, taking the good with the bad, in a spirit of calm philosophy or in meek submission to the inevitable.

Even while engaged in solitary angling, so conducive to quiet meditation, the habits and idiosyncrasies of fish do not often occupy our thoughts, but other and wholly irrelevant themes. And even with all the information that can be obtained, by close and careful observation of the habits of fishes, and the nature of their surroundings, there is still left much to be explained, and some things that seem to be beyond our comprehension, which we might safely leave to chance or luck, until we understand them better.

And perhaps it is best so, for there has ever been a delightful uncertainty attending the angler's art, and therein lies one of its chiefest charms; for while it stimulates the angler to renewed effort, it consoles him in defeat. The pleasures of anticipation have ever exceeded those of fruition, and ever will while "hope springs eternal in the human breast."

The angler spends the evening before his "day's fishing" in overhauling his tackle; polishing the ferrules of his trusty rod; oiling his reel; looking for weak places in his line; arranging, lovingly, his leader, hooks and flies; and finds enthusiastic enjoyment in the examination of his treasures, and in pleasant retrospective and prospective reveries in connection therewith.

He retires with contented mind, and an innate consciousness of unbounded success on the morrow, and dreams of arching rod and leaping fish, of mossy banks and murmuring streams, of cool shadows and spicy breezes; and when morn hath "with rosy hand unbarr'd the gates of light," he sallies forth with buoyant footsteps, his breast swelling with fond anticipation, and in that happy and expectant state of mind known only to lovers of the angle.

Perhaps he returns at close of day, weary and footsore, and with an almost empty creel; what matter? All through the lovely day his spirits have never flagged; his last cast was made with even more hope and confidence than the first. And even though his creel be empty, his heart is filled with the music of the birds, the purling of the stream, the fragrance of the flowers, and, above all, with love for his Creator; and it has set him thinking of that eternal stream of time clothed with everlasting groves of never-changing green.

And, then, the day has simply been an "unlucky" one for fishing; yesterday was no doubt a "good day," and to-morrow will be better.   He finds consolation in accounting for his "ill-luck," and can easily see a reason for it in some peculiar phase of the water, the wind, or the weather.

Now, while it is not wholly a matter of luck, on one hand; and while, on the other, it is useless to expect to obtain an invariable law in respect to the "biting" of fish, there are many things that we can learn by intelligent observation.

It involves no great comprehension of the sciences of ichthyology, meteorology, hydrography, entomology and botany, as professed by some, nor of the mysteries and hocus-pocus of the art as practiced by others; for there is often as little reason in the repeated change of a cast of flies by the scientific fly-fisher, as in spitting on the bait by his humbler brother; yet both have unbounded faith in their respective methods, and probably faith has as much to do with successful angling as any one attribute.

But why do fish eagerly take the bait one day, and utterly refuse it the next, when, apparently, all other conditions are equal?   This is a poser, and has baffled observant anglers for ages, and will, in all probability, never be solved satisfactorily.   As a short cut to its solution, it might be said, that they were hungry one day, but not so the next.   Certainly a very reasonable conclusion if it were sustained by fact, which it is not, if we judge hunger by its usual manifestations; for fish seem to bite best on a full stomach, and often refuse the proffered bait on an empty one; this fact is patent to all observant anglers, and I have proved it in many instances.

But let us begin at the beginning.

The great problem of life with fishes seems to be to eat and avoid being eaten. Very well. Now, which is the controlling influence in a fish's mind—if he has any, perhaps, in deference to authority, we had better call it instinct—his desire to eat, or his desire of self-preservation? Now, right here, may be involved the fundamental principle governing this whole question of a fish's "biting."

Let us see. That fish can abstain from solid food for an indefinite period, procuring some nourishment from the water they breathe, as in confinement, during hibernation, and during the breeding season, is well known, and needs no corroborative evidence here.

That, when they do feed, and the supply of food is abundant, they completely gorge themselves—some even ejecting the contents of their stomachs to enjoy the gratification of refilling them—is also an authenticated fact.

When their stomachs are thus filled and gorged with food, it is reasonable to suppose that, like other predacious animals, they remain listlessly about their haunts, or retire to some secluded retreat, to digest it at their leisure; and, during the process of digestion, refuse to notice their usual food; for I have frequently observed Black Bass remain motionless for hours, except a slight movement of the fins, utterly regardless of the schools of minnows that were swarming about them, and this at a season when they usually "bite" the best.

Now, this alternate feasting and fasting may be a necessary habit, to enable fish to meet the exigencies of spawning, hibernation (in some), and the vicissitudes of the element in which they live, and the abundance or lack of food at certain times.

Streams are often rendered turbid by heavy rains, and lakes and ponds by what is termed "working" or "blossoming." At such times fish can not see well enough to find their food or discern their enemies, and consequently lie secure in their hiding-places. When the water becomes clear, they again venture forth to eat and be eaten.

Then, heavy and continued rains, violent winds, and the change of season, affect the food-supply of fishes, and, consequently, the fishes themselves. These various causes make fish seem capricious in their time and manner of feeding.

Then, again, while all the conditions may be favorable for their feeding, they may be deterred from seeking their food by a fear of enemies; and only venture forth when the cause of such fear has disappeared, or their qualms of stomach overcome their prudence.

But little can be learned in this respect from fishes that are confined in aquaria, or from those that are artificially cultivated, for these unnatural conditions presuppose a change in their habits.

We know that fish, in their native waters, are quite timid, and ever on the alert for danger—a footstep on the bank, or a shadow cast suddenly on the water, will cause them to hastily skurry away.

No food, however tempting, can entice them so long as there is an appearance of danger, and their caution is then set down as eccentricity.

Now, all this may, or may not, be; but it is as reasonable as any other theory; and this habit of alternate feasting and fasting, for a longer or a shorter time, will explain, in some measure, many of the features in regard to the uncertainty of "biting" in fishes of inland waters.

As before stated, there is much that can be learned by
31

closely observing the habits of fish, the character of their haunts, and the nature and variety of their food; so as to enable the angler to know, so far as can be known, when and where to find the fish at certain seasons, or at different stages of the water; when they are most inclined to "bite;" and to know, approximately, what bait to use.

This information can be acquired in no other way but by patient and continued observation; and, without it, all is guess-work. It is just as essential to the angler to know where to fish, as to know how. If he has a fair knowledge of the habits of game-fish, he can at once seek out the most likely places, on lake or stream, by seeming intuition.

Black Bass are found at different localities in the same waters, at different seasons, and frequently shift their quarters many times during the same season, depending on the nature and locality of their food; the influences of wind and weather, condition of the water, etc.

Thus, early in the season, they will be found on streams in shallow water, just below the rapids, or "riffles," where the water is warmest, feeding on helgramites and other larvæ, crustacea, minnows, etc. As the water gets warmer, they resort to stiller water, under overhanging trees, and feed upon the surface when the insects and flies appear. Still later, they seek greater depths, adjacent to shelving banks, gravelly shoals and rocky ledges, seeking minnows, mollusks, etc.

They may be found one day in water, say ten feet deep, and the very next day be seen in the shallowest water near shore. I will mention a striking instance of this kind:

On one occasion, I went in company with a party of

expert anglers to Upper Nemahbin Lake, near Delafield, Wisconsin.   My companion was Captain B., Chief of Police of Milwaukee City; and he exhibited considerable impatience and concern because of the other boats starting ahead of us over the favorite fishing-ground; but I saw that the three other boats were proceeding over this ground—where, on the preceding day, I had taken a fine lot of Bass—without getting so much as "a bite."

We followed in their wake, casting right and left along the edge of the bulrushes, but in vain; until, finally, we reached the end of the line of rushes, at the inlet of the lake.   Mr. B was discouraged, but I, on the contrary, was elated—for I had observed the dorsal fins of numerous Bass in the shallow water between the rushes and the shore; and I had observed, further, that the Bass were feeding on insects and flies which were being blown into the water by a brisk wind.

I proposed fishing back over the same ground to the evident disgust of the Captain.   But I began casting between the bulrushes and the shore, in the shallow water under the lee of the bank, and fastened to a large Bass at almost the first cast.   The Captain followed my lead; and, on arriving at our original starting-point, a few hundred yards distant, we had taken fifteen fine Bass.   The three boats had made the entire circuit of the lake, and the six anglers in them, fishing on the usual grounds, had not, altogether, taken half as many fish, when they joined us for luncheon.

In lacustrine waters, Black Bass first appear in the shallowest portions, where the water is warm, and feed upon crustacea, mollusks, etc., retiring to deeper water as the season advances.   When the patches of rushes and other aquatic plants are well grown, they will be found near them, feeding on the minnows and small fry which congregate there. When the ephemeral flies of early summer appear, the Bass will then be found where these are most numerous; and they, at this time, feed at the surface.

I was once fly-fishing for Bass in the Neenah Channel, at the outlet of Lake Winnebago, Wisconsin. The stream was quite swift, with a rocky bottom, and the surface was covered with May-flies, upon which the Bass were feeding. I was enjoying royal sport, using a cast of two brown hackles, and frequently fastened a fish to each fly.

A boat-load of rustic anglers, with tamarack-poles and short lines, seeing my success, dropped down abreast of me, and anchored within fifty feet of my boat. They were using small minnows for bait, with heavy sinkers on their lines, which, of course, carried the bait to the bottom, where were feeding schools of White Bass (*Roccus chrysops*). As I took only Black Bass from the surface, they caught nothing but White Bass at the bottom. They could not understand it, and I did not enlighten them, for I had no desire to see my pet fish "yanked out" by tamarack-poles and tow-strings. I left them, shortly, in the glory of "snaking out"—as they called it—the unfortunate White Bass, wondering, meanwhile, why they could not catch Black Bass like "that other fellow."

But do we really know any of the conditions favorable or unfavorable for angling? We are told that fish will not bite when the water is rendered high and turbid by freshets; during a thunder-storm, with heavy rain; on dark, cold days, with a blustering East wind; and on bright, still and hot days, when the water lies unruffled, like a burnished mirror. If this be so, it is extremely fortunate, and we can apply the rule of exclusion here, and at once dismiss all such occasions from further consideration; for I take it for granted that the reader has no desire to "go a-fishing" at such times.

Fortunately, again, the season for angling is during pleasant weather, in Spring, Summer and Autumn; and I have always observed that the pleasantest days for the angler's comfort, were usually the most propitious and successful days for angling.

It matters little, for bait-fishing, whether the day be bright or cloudy, or whether the wind is in the East, West, North, or South, so long as it is a pleasant wind, and is not too raw and chilly. I have had "good luck" with the wind in either quarter, and from a gentle breeze to half a gale; on days that were hot, bright, and cloudless, as well as on those that were cloudy and rather cool.

To be sure, it makes some difference as to the character of the waters; the pleasantest days are best for small streams and shallow waters, while the more unlikely days would better suit lakes and deep waters; though in either case, the pleasantest days, in all respects, are the best.

The fish in deep waters are not so easily affected by the vicissitudes of weather, as those in waters of shallow depth. As exceptional cases I might add that I have had as good success with a reefing east wind, or a half-gale from the north-west, on lakes of good depth, as at, seemingly, the most favorable times.

Once, on La Belle Lake, at Oconomowoc, Wisconsin, I went fishing when the wind was blowing quite fresh from the West. I proceeded to the lower end of the lake, some three miles, when the wind suddenly hauled around to the north-west, blowing great guns, and causing the "white-caps" to roll furiously. It was impossible to make head-way against it, so I was compelled to anchor, which I did in a bight of bulrushes, in water from ten to twelve feet deep, but near a gravelly bar. Here I took, in a little more than two hours, twenty-five Black Bass, which after-wards turned the scales° at seventy-five pounds. I have always considered this catch as being one of the best I ever made. On my return, owing to the high wind and heavy sea, it was all I could do to keep my boat from swamping.

On another occasion, on Oconomowoc Lake, I fished at a rocky bar, which divided the lake into two portions. The wind was blowing a half-gale from the East, and quite cool; the shallow water on the bar was churned and tossed into billows of seething foam by the high wind, enabling me to fish in water but a foot or two in depth ; and in a short time I took nine Bass, the smallest of which weighed four pounds. I was then forced to relinquish my sport, as I had "run out" of minnows.

Again, on Genesee Lake, in the same locality, I once made a good catch under peculiar circumstances. On this occasion I was "frogging," as this lake, at that time, was famous for the quantity and quality of its bull-frogs. After spearing a "good mess" of greenbacks, I was stand-ing on a sand-bar, which divides the lake into two parts during low water, and was idly watching the waves rolling up on the bar, which were being driven with great fury by a strong south-west wind. I chanced to see several Black Bass, evidently feeding in the surf; and I then be-gan devising ways and means for their capture.

Near by, was a water-logged boat, in which I saw a

tamarack pole, and, upon investigation, I found that there was a short line and hook attached. My plans were soon formed. I went to a small hole of water, that I had previously observed, which was left after the drying up of the outlet of a marsh at the lower end of the lake, and in which I had seen a great many small minnows, an inch or two long. Dipping up a lot in my handkerchief, I took it by the corners and proceeded along the shore, dipping up water occasionally to keep the bait alive. On the bar I scooped a hole in the sand for the bait, filled it with water and went to fishing. The novelty of the situation, and my curiosity as to the result of the experiment, quieted my conscience and justified the employment of such primitive measures. Baiting the hook, I waded into the surf as far as I could with ordinary boots—for, being early in the season, the water was quite cold—I was soon pulling out the Bass, and took in this manner, with a short pole and six feet of line, fifteen splendid Bass.

In angling, it may be safely accepted as a truism, that *any* wind is better than *no* wind ; a gale being better than a perfectly still day, especially when the water is clear. The reason for this is, that the surface of the water being agitated and ruffled by the breeze, the fish are not so apt to see the angler.

An east wind is popularly regarded as an unfavorable wind for fishing, but it is not necessarily so. The opinion is of English origin, for in the humid climate of Great Britain an east wind is exceedingly raw, chilly, and disagreeable, and is held to be productive of all manner of evils, being particularly dreaded by sufferers from rheumatism, neuralgia, or gout. The anglers of England, of course, share in this common detestation of an east wind, and this prejudice is clearly shown by British writers on angling, from whom most of our ideas on fishing were formerly derived.

But it is only after such a wind has prevailed for several days, so as to lower the temperature of inland waters, that it, in any way, affects the "biting" of fish. This, no doubt, is often the case in Great Britain, and has led to the erroneous supposition that an east wind, under any and all circumstances, is most unfavorable for the angler; and this idea has, to a great extent, been tacitly accepted to apply to our own country-as well.

But unless the fish have an inherited traditionary remembrance of that "remarkable east wind" which divided the waters of the Red Sea and enabled Moses and his followers to pass over dry-shod, which causes them to become suspicious of every east wind that blows, I can not conceive how it affects their feeding, except, as stated before, when it has been of sufficiently long continuance to cool the water.

Along the Atlantic coast of the United States an east wind is generally held to be unpropitious for fishing; but in this case *post hoc* is mistaken for *propter hoc;* in other words, the effect is mistaken for the cause. After an unusually long series of east winds, or easterly gales, the tides are much affected thereby, and rise much higher, and spread over more extensive surfaces. The fish, as a matter of course, take advantage of this state of affairs, and, accordingly, extend their range in quest of food, being rewarded by great quantities of crustacea, mollusks, etc., which before were inaccessible on account of the shallow water. At such times, the fish are not found on their usual feeding grounds in the tideways, and hence has arisen the erroneous idea that they do not feed during an east wind.

Many bait-fishers have an abiding faith in the signs of the Zodiac in influencing the biting of fish; believing that when the "sign" is in the feet (Pisces), and also just before and after, encroaching on the domains of the legs (Aquarius), and head (Aries), that fish feed better than at other times. They, of course, always remember the successful occasions at these periods, but soon forget, or imagine some satisfactory reason for, the failures; and thus their superstitious belief seldom weakens.

The moon, likewise, is supposed by many to influence the feeding of fish. In Florida, the opinion is very prevalent among hunters and fishermen, that deer, fish, and other animals feed principally when the moon is above the horizon, night or day, particularly at moon-rise, moon-south, and moon-set. This belief also obtains in other sections of our country, and the adherents to the theory are, withal, so consistent, that their faith can not be shaken by repeated failures, and they seldom hunt or fish except when the "moon is right."

While I am not a believer in the theory of the moon's influence over terrestrial objects, I am not prepared to say that there is nothing whatever in the moon affecting the feeding of fish; for while fish certainly feed much at night, they seem to feed more especially on moonlight nights. Still, I do not attribute this fact to any influence possessed by the moon, beyond the light it affords, to enable the fish to find their prey. I have often observed that during the season of full-moon, fish were more apt to be sluggish and off their feed during the day time; and this I have always attributed to the fact, that they did their feeding mostly at nights, at such times. Many anglers only fish from the last quarter until the new moon.

A perfect day for fishing, might be described as a warm, pleasant day, with a balmy, invigorating breeze; a mellow sunlight, not too bright, produced by a somewhat hazy atmosphere, or by drifting clouds; when the season has been neither too wet nor too dry; such a day as makes it a pleasure for one to breathe, and inhale with delight the odors and fragrance of forest, field, and stream.

Not a day that produces a feeling of exquisite languor, and disposes to delicious, dreamy reveries, like the stimulant effect of an opiate; but a day when the atmosphere seems filled with some indescribable aerial stimulant, that acts upon the brain, nerves, and circulation like sparkling wine; that rouses the energies and spurs the nerves, pulses, and muscles to action; such a day as makes one desire to laugh, to sing, to leap, to caper, to race through the meadows, to indulge in sudden impulses, in short, to make one feel a boy again.

Such a day, when the water is semi-transparent or translucent, and of such a temperature when it is most pleasant to bathe in—such a day, I say, is sure to be a satisfactory one to the angler, and the fish will be pretty sure to bite.

On a day such as I have just described, I once made my largest catch of Black Bass, though I have always been opposed to " big catches," on principle; for I hold that when the sole object in angling is to catch fish as long as they will " bite," the proceeding leaves the province of sport, and degenerates into pot-fishing, or, what is worse, useless and unjustifiable slaughter; much in the same way that, when an unprincipled merchant, during the war, took unfair advantage of certain circumstances, and sold goods at an advance of five hundred per cent., and who, when afterwards boasting of the fine *per centage* of profit realized, was told by a plain-spoken old gentleman that the transaction passed the limits of per centage, and entered the bounds of petit larceny.

But as an honest confession is good for the soul, I will relate the incident referred to : I was fishing in Okauchee Lake, Wisconsin, in company with two friends from Cincinnati, on a really perfect day in July. We had, unfortunately, a bountiful supply of fine minnows for bait, and after we had taken more than enough fish, I proposed to stop; but my friends, to whom the experience was new, could not be induced to relinquish the exciting sport, so I continued fishing, under protest, and we took during the day one hundred and fifty-three Bass, and, with shame do I confess it, more than one-half—I am afraid to say just how many more—fell to my rod.

In justice, however, but not as a redeeming feature, I will state that the fish were not wasted, but a hundred fine Bass were packed in ice and expressed to friends in Cincinnati, and the balance were distributed among the hotels of Oconomowoc.

I always look back upon this circumstance with regret, though I have done penance for the transaction, many a time and oft, since, by stopping at a dozen Bass, when I might have taken twice the number.

Some anglers tell us that fish will not bite *before* a rain ; others say they will not take a bait *during* a rain ; and still others affirm that it is useless to fish *after* a rain. Now, while there is a grain of truth in each of these opinions, yet if we blindly accept all of them and endeavor to follow them, we shall have no further use for our fishing-tackle.

I do not think that rain, *per se*, has any influence whatever upon the feeding of fish. It is, of course, impossible for us to judge in this matter by a comparison with terrestrial creatures; but, fishes being inhabitants of the watery element, it is not reasonable to suppose that a rain makes any difference with them at all—at the time—though they profit or not, by the subsequent rising and roiling of the water, more or less, according to circumstances.

The multitudes of insects which are said to be beaten down from the overhanging trees and from the air, into the water, during a shower of rain, must be taken *cum grano salis;* for insects, like most other mundane creatures, know enough to "come in out of the wet." We really find no more insects floating on the water during a rain, than at other times, though it is true that many are collected and swept by rains from the surface of the ground, and washed into the streams by swollen brooks and branches; but with the insects, go, also, the washings, debris, and particles of soil to discolor and thicken the streams, so that the fish may really fast in the midst of plenty, not being able to see the sudden influx of food by reason of the turbidity of the water: and, again, it is doubtful if fish feed much on dead insects.

The fish, however, on the other hand, are enabled to extend their range in foraging for food, during seasons of high water, when the water has cleared sufficiently to allow them to discover it.

I have noticed that fish usually bite better just before a shower; especially if the weather be murky and warm, and I think this can be accounted for in this way: It is generally quite calm, for a longer or shorter time previous to a summer shower, and the water being still, the fish do not bite, as they see the angler too distinctly—and this is why some have said that it is not a good time to fish *before* a rain—but immediately preceding the shower, a brisk breeze usually springs up, rippling the water, and it is at this time that fish seem to become possessed with a sudden impulse to feed, not on account of the impending rain, however, as many suppose, but because the angler is hid from view by the ruffling of the water. Sometimes this breeze accompanies the rain, and at other times follows the rain, and in either case the fish will bite best while the breeze continues. When a shower is followed by a calm, fish, of course, will not bite, in clear water, and as this often happens, it follows that some anglers hold to the opinion that they never bite *after* a rain.

I have tried to impress the reader, all through this chapter, with the importance of keeping out of sight of the fish as much as possible, for herein lies the greatest secret of success in angling; and fish will be found to bite better, always, when conditions are such as to favor the screening of the angler from their ever-watchful eyes, and, when, at the same time, the water is sufficiently clear to enable them to discern the bait on or beneath the surface.

In fly-fishing, especially, must this caution be exercised to its fullest extent, for the casts being necessarily much shorter than in bait-fishing, the angler is more liable to be seen; and herein lies the foundation of the opinion, entertained by many, that Black Bass are more uncertain to rise to the fly than the Brook Trout. I hold that Black Bass, during the proper season, will rise as readily to the fly, under the same conditions, as the Trout.

But the fact is, that while the Bass is as wary as the Trout, he is not so timid. The Trout darts away at the first glimpse of the angler, while the Bass will hold his ground, though ready to depart unceremoniously when occasion calls, eyeing the angler meanwhile, and entirely ignoring his best skill, though he cast his feathery lures never so lightly and naturally. The Bass is too knowing to be taken in by any such deception so long as he sees the angler at the other end of the rod; hence, more caution is really necessary in fly-fishing for Black Bass than for the Brook Trout.

In regard to the best time of day for angling, there is not much choice, and it is governed a good deal by the season of the year, the temperature of the water, and by the character of the day itself, though, as a rule, fish are sluggish and off their feed during the middle of the day, with a bright and warm sun, say from noon until three o'clock, except early and late in the season, when the water is still cold, when the middle of the day is often the best time.

For bait-fishing, on small streams, the early morning hours, about sunrise, are often the best; though on large streams and lakes there is nothing gained by early fishing, as the fish do not bite well until the sun is several hours high.

The latter part of the afternoon, until sundown, is often the best part of the day for the angler. On cloudy days, however, the middle of the day is often the most favorable, especially if the weather is rather cool.

For fly-fishing, the early morning hours succeeding sunrise, and from an hour or two before sunset until dark, or with a nearly full moon, even later, will be found the best hours for filling the creel.

Of course, all of these times must be governed by conditions of the wind, weather, and water, whether favorable or not; for no matter what the hour of the day, it will be the most successful, when other conditions are most favorable, and approach more nearly to the "typical" day for angling, as described in this chapter, the most prominent features of which are pleasant weather, translucent water, and a fresh breeze.

Thunder, and electrical conditions of the atmosphere, I leave out of the account altogether, as we have no means of judging of the influence of so subtile an agent as electricity on the finny tribe; nor have I ever observed any peculiar effect on fishes from these causes, though great stress is often laid by some anglers on the influence of an atmosphere surcharged with electricity, whatever that may mean; but it is no more reasonable to suppose that fishes would be disturbed by electrical conditions of the air, than terrestrial animals would be inconvenienced or otherwise by electric conditions of water.

But, notwithstanding all of our patient and careful observations of the habits of fish, their food and their surroundings, and our study of the various conditions of wind, weather, and water, there will be days and days in the experience of every angler, when the fish will utterly refuse to bite; and this on such days as the most finished, practiced, and observant angler would pronounce exceedingly favorable in every particular. At such times one is forcibly reminded of the analogy existing between the will of woman and the "biting" of fish, as related in the familiar lines :—

> "For if she will, she will, you may depend on 't;
> And if she won't, she won't; so there's an end on 't."

Every Black Bass angler has seen—where the water was clear enough for observation—the Bass seize his minnow through seemingly mere caprice, and, instead of attempting to gorge it, would take it gingerly by the tail, toy with it, and finally eject it, or spit it out, as it were; and this would be repeated several times in succession, or until the angler's patience became exhausted, when, while unjointing his rod, he would muse upon the waywardness of fish in general, and would be convinced that Solomon never went a-fishing, or he would have added another item to the four things too wonderful for his ken, or at least have substituted "the way of a fish with a bait," for the less puzzling proposition of "the way of a man with a maid."

CHAPTER XX.

THE BLACK BASS AS A GAME FISH.

" He is a fish that lurks close all winter; but is very pleasant and jolly after mid-April, and in May, and in the hot months."—IZAAK WALTON.

THOSE who have tasted the lotus of Salmon, or Trout fishing, in that Utopian clime of far away—while reveling in its æsthetic atmosphere, and surrounded by a misty halo of spray from the waterfall, or enveloped by the filmy gauze and iridescent haze of the cascade—have inscribed tomes, sang idyls, chanted pæans, and poured out libations in honor and praise of the silver-spangled Salmon, or the ruby-studded Trout, while it is left to the vulgar horde of Black Bass anglers to stand upon the mountain of their own doubt and presumption, and, with uplifted hands, in admiration and awe, gaze with dazed eyes from afar upon that forbidden land—that *terra incognita*—and then, having lived in vain, die and leave no sign.

It is, then, with a spirit of rank heresy in my heart; with smoked glass spectacles on my nose, to dim the glare and glamour of the transcendent shore; with the scales of justice across my shoulder—*M. salmoides* in one scoop and *M. dolomieu* in the other—I pass the barriers and confines of the enchanted land, and toss them into a stream that has been depopulated of even fingerlings, by the *dilettanti*

32   (377)

of Salmon and Trout fishers; for I would not, even here,
put Black Bass in a stream inhabited by Salmon or Brook
Trout.

While watching the plebeian interlopers sporting in an
eddy, their bristling spines and emerald sides gleaming in
the sunshine, I hear an awful voice from the adjacent
rocks exclaiming: "Fools rush in where angels fear to
tread!" Shade of Izaak Walton defend us! While ap-
pealing to Father Izaak for protection, I quote his words:
"Of which, if thou be a severe, sour complexioned man,
then I here disallow thee to be a competent judge."

Seriously, most of our notions of game fish and fishing
are derived from British writers; and as the Salmon and
the Trout are the only fishes in Great Britain worthy of
being called game, they, of course, form the themes of
British writers on game fish. Americans, following the
lead of our British cousins in this, as we were wont to do
in all sporting matters, have eulogized the Salmon and
Brook Trout as the game fish *par excellence* of America,
ignoring other fish equally worthy.

While some claim for the Striped Bass a high place in
the list of game fish, I feel free to assert, that, were the
Black Bass a native of Great Britain, he would rank fully
as high, in the estimation of British anglers, as either the
Trout or the Salmon. I am borne out in this by the
opinions of British sportsmen, whose statements have been
received without question.

W. H. Herbert (Frank Forester) writing of the Black
Bass, says: "This is one of the finest of the American
fresh water fishes; it is surpassed by none in boldness
of biting, in fierce and violent resistance when hooked, and
by a very few only in excellence upon the board."

Parker Gilmore ("Ubique") says: "I fear it will be almost deemed heresy to place this fish (Black Bass) on a par with the Trout; at least, some such idea I had when I first heard the two compared; but I am bold, and will go further. I consider he is the superior of the two, for he is equally good as an article of food, and much stronger and untiring in his efforts to escape when hooked."

In a recent issue of the London "Fishing Gazette" (England), Mr. Silk advertises: "Black Bass (*Grystes nigricans*), the gamest of American fish. 300 for sale (just arrived), length from 3 to 5 inches; 6 months old. Price, 10s. ($2.25) each."

Now, while Salmon fishing is, unquestionably, the highest branch of piscatorial sport; and while Trout fishing in Canada, Maine, and the Lake Superior region justifies all the extravagant praise bestowed upon it, I am inclined to doubt the judgment and good taste of those anglers who snap their fingers in contempt of Black Bass fishing, while they will wade a stream strewn with brush and logs, catch a few Trout weighing six or eight to the pound, and call it the only artistic angling in the world! While they are certainly welcome to their opinion, I think their zeal is worthy of a better cause.

The Black Bass is eminently an American fish, and has been said to be representative in his characteristics. He has the faculty of asserting himself and making himself completely at home wherever placed. He is plucky, game, brave and unyielding to the last when hooked. He has the arrowy rush and vigor of the Trout, the untiring strength and bold leap of the Salmon, while he has a system of fighting tactics peculiarly his own.

He will rise to the artificial fly as readily as the Salmon or the Brook Trout, under the same conditions; and will take the live minnow, or other live bait, under any and all circumstances favorable to the taking of any other fish. I consider him, *inch for inch* and *pound for pound,* the gamest fish that swims. The royal Salmon and the lordly Trout must yield the palm to a Black Bass of *equal weight.*

That he will eventually become the leading game fish of America is my oft-expressed opinion and firm belief. This result, I think, is inevitable ; if for no other reasons, from a force of circumstances occasioned by climatic conditions and the operation of immutable natural laws, such as the gradual drying up, and dwindling away of the small Trout streams, and the consequent decrease of Brook Trout, both in quality and quantity ; and by the introduction of predatory fish in waters where the Trout still exists.

Another prominent cause of the decline and fall of the Brook Trout, is the erection of dams, saw-mills and factories upon Trout streams, which, though to be deplored, can not be prevented ; the march of empire and the progress of civilization can not be stayed by the honest, though powerless, protests of anglers.

But, while the ultimate fate of the Brook Trout is sealed beyond peradventure, we have the satisfaction of knowing, that, in the Black Bass we have a fish equally worthy, both as to game and edible qualities, and which, at the same time, is able to withstand, and defy, many of the causes that will, in the end, effect the annihilation and extinction of the Brook Trout.

Mr. Charles Hallock, the well-known author, angler, and journalist, says:—

No doubt the Bass is the appointed successor of the Trout: not through heritage, nor selection, nor by interloping, but by fore-ordination. Truly, it is sad to contemplate, in the not distant future, the extinction of a beautiful race of creatures, whose attributes have been sung by all the poets; but we regard the inevitable with the same calm philosophy with which the astronomer watches the burning out of a world, knowing that it will be succeeded by a new creation.

As we mark the soft vari-tinted flush of the Trout disappear in the eventide, behold the sparkle of the coming Bass as he leaps into the morning of his glory! We hardly know which to admire the most—the velvet livery and the charming graces of the departing courtier, or the flash of the armor-plates on the advancing warrior. No doubt the Bass will prove himself a worthy substitute for his predecessor, and a candidate for a full legacy of honors.

No doubt, when every one of the older States shall become as densely settled as Great Britain itself, and all the rural aspects of the crowded domain resemble the suburban surroundings of our Boston; when every feature of the pastoral landscape shall wear the finished appearance of European lands; and every verdant field be closely cropped by lawn-mowers and guarded by hedges; and every purling stream which meanders through it has its water-bailiff, we shall still have speckled Trout from which the radiant spots have faded, and tasteless fish, to catch at a dollar per pound (as we already have on Long Island), and all the appurtenances and appointments of a genuine English Trouting privilege and a genuine English " outing."

In those future days, not long hence to come, some venerable piscator, in whose memory still lingers the joy of fishing, the brawling stream which tumbled over the rocks in the tangled wildwood, and moistened the arbutus and the bunchberries which garnished its banks, will totter forth to the velvety edge of some peacefully-flowing stream, and having seated himself on a convenient point in a revolving easy chair, placed there by his careful attendant, cast right and left for the semblance of sport long dead.

Hosts of liver-fed fish will rush to the signal for their early morning meal, and from the center of the boil which follows the fall of the handsful thrown in, my piscator of the ancient days will hook a two-pound Trout, and play him hither and yon, from surface to bottom, without disturbing the pampered gormands which are gorging themselves upon the disgusting viands; and when he has leisurely brought him to hand at last, and the gillie has scooped him with his landing-net, he will feel in his capacious pocket for his last trade dollar, and giving his friend the tip, shuffle back to his house, and lay aside his rod forever.

Rev. Myron H. Reed, an enthusiastic angler, who follows the example, in a double sense, of those disciples, who, being fishermen of the waters, became also fishers of men, ventures this prediction :—

This is probably the last generation of Trout fishers. The children will not be able to find any. Already there are well-trodden paths by every stream in Maine, in New York and in Michigan. I know of but one river in North America by the side of which you will find no paper collar or other evidences of civilization; it is the Nameless River.

Not that Trout will cease to be. They will be hatched by machinery, and raised in ponds, and fattened on chopped liver, and grow flabby and lose their spots. The Trout of the restaurant will not cease to be. He is no more like the Trout of the wild river than the fat and songless reed-bird is like the bobolink. Gross feeding and easy pond-life enervate and deprave him.

The Trout that the children will know only by legend is the gold-sprinkled, living arrow of the Whitewater—able to zig-zag up the cataract, able to loiter in the rapids—whose dainty meat is the glancing butterfly.

But is the Black Bass worthy to succeed and supersede the speckled beauty of the cool mountain streams, as the game-fish of American waters ? Let us see—

Reader, go with me
This perfect morning in the leafy June,
To yon pool at the gurgling rapid's foot—
Approach with caution; let your tread be soft;

Beware the bending bushes on the brink;
Touch no branch, nor twig, nor leaf disturb,
For the finny tribe is wary.

          Rest we here, awhile.
Behold the scene! Above—the ripple,
Sparkling and dancing in the morning sun.
At your feet—the blue-eyed violet, shedding
Sweet perfume, and nodding in the breeze.
The red-bird, ablaze, and with swelling throat
Chants loud his song, in yonder thick-set thorn.
The dreamy, droning hum of insects' wings,
Mingles with the rustling of the quivering leaves.
On the gravelly shoal, in the stream, below—
Sleek, well-fed cattle contented stand,
Beneath the spreading beech.

          Across the narrow stream,
Leans a giant sycamore, old and gray,
With scarr'd arms stretching o'er the silent pool;
And gnarl'd and twisted roots bared by the wash
And ripple, for, lo these hundred years.
The bubbles of the rapid play hide and seek
Among their arching nooks.

          Beneath those bare roots,
With watchful eye, proud monarch of the pool,
A cunning Bass doth lie, on balanced fin,
In waiting for his prey.

          Now, with supple,
Yielding rod, and taper'd line of silk;
With mist-like leader, and two small flies—
Dark, bushy hackles both—I make a cast.
With lengthen'd line I quickly cast again,
And just beneath the tree the twin-like lures
As light as snow-flakes fall, and gently linger,—
Half-submerged,—like things of life, obedient still
To slightest tension of line and rod.

          Look! Saw you that gleam
Beneath the flood? A flash—a shadow—

Then a swirl upon the surface of the pool?
My hand responsive to the sudden thrill,
Strikes in the steel; the wary Bass is hook'd.
With light'ning speed he darts away toward his
Ark of refuge—his lair beneath the roots.

The singing reel,
And hissing line, proclaim him almost there,
When I " give the butt."   The faithful rod,
In horse-shoe curve, now checks his headlong flight.
Egad! he tugs and pulls right lustily;
But still the barb is there.   The rod now bending
Like a reed, resists the tight'ning strain, and
Turns him in his course.

In curving reaches,
Back and forth, he darts in conscious strength;
Describing arcs and segments in the shadows
Of the ruffled pool.   Ha! nobly done!
With a mighty rush he cleaves the crystal flood,
And at one bound, full half a fathom in
The realm above, he takes an ærial flight;
His fins, extended with bristling points;
His armor, brightly flashing in the sun;
Shaking, in his rage, his wide-extended jaws,
To rid him of the hook.

Gracefully, now, I lower
The pliant rod, in courtesy to the brave;
The line, relieved of steady strain, baffles
The wily Bass; the hook holds fast and firm.
Back he falls with angry splash, to the depths,
For friendly aid of snag, or stone, or root
Of tree—for thus, my friend, he oft escapes,
By fouling line, or hook.   But, he never sulks!
Not he; while life remains, or strength holds good,
His efforts are unceasing.

Now up the stream—
Now down again—I have him well in hand;
Reeling in, or giving line; fast and slow,—

High and low,—the steady strain maintaining;
The good rod swaying like a rush, as he
Surges through the flood.

              Another leap!
Ye gods, how brave! Like a lion shaking
His shaggy mane, he dives below again.
Did you mark, my friend, his shrewd intent,
As he fell across the line? If he then
Had found it stretched and tense, his escape
Was surely made. But the tip was lowered;
And with yielding line, the hook still held him fast.

              Now, truly, friend, he
Makes a gallant fight! In air, or water,
All the same, his spiny crest erect,
He struggles to the last. No sulking here;
But like a mettl'd steed, he champs the bit,
And speeds the best with firm-held, tighten'd, rein.
Now down the stream, he's off again, like shaft
From long-bow swiftly sped—his last bold spurt—
The effort cost him very dear; his strength
Is ebbing fast.

              In decreasing circles
Now he swims, and labors with the tide.
As I reel the line, he slowly yields,
And now turns up his breast-plate, snowy white—
A vanquish'd, conquer'd knight.

              Now, my friend,
The landing-net; 'neath the surface hold it,
With firm and cautious hand. There, lift him
Gently out; and as gently lay him down.
His bright sides rival the velvet sward, in
Rich and glossy green.

              See the great rent
The hook hath made! How easily 'tis withdrawn!
You marvel how I held him, safe? By the
Equal and continued strain of willowy rod,
And ever faithful reel.
33

Valiant, noble Bass!
Fit denizen of the brawling stream!   Thy
Last fight is ended—thy last race is run!
Thy once lov'd pool 'neath the sycamore's shade,
Thy fancied stronghold 'neath its tangled roots,
Shall know thee no more.

Place him in thy creel;
Lay him tenderly on a bed of ferns,
Crisp, green and cool with sparkling, morning dew—
A warrior in repose!

———

[In the preface I have stated that the reader need not look for rhetorical efforts nor poetic descriptions in this book, for I make no pretense to a possession of the "divine afflatus;" it is hardly necessary, therefore, to say that the foregoing description of the "Capture of the Bass" forms no exception to that statement, for I am fully aware that it is faulty both in rhythm and measure.

The description was originally written as plain prose, but it read so much like an affectation, or an attempt to be poetical, that I considered it the least evil to put it in its present form; which I did by the changing of less than a dozen words.   The charitable reader will therefore please regard it, and read it, as plain prose, while the hypercritic will please consider the (poetical) feet developed rather (as in the case of the Bass) as fins, which will place it beyond the pale of critique.]

CHAPTER XXI.

FLY-FISHING.

" And now, scholar, my direction for fly-fishing is ended with this shower, for it has done raining."—IZAAK WALTON.

ARTIFICIAL FLY-FISHING is the most legitimate, scientific and gentlemanly mode of angling, and is to be greatly preferred to all other ways and means of capturing the finny tribe. It requires more address, more skill, and a better knowledge of the habits of the fish and his surroundings than any other method.

Fly-fishing holds the same relation to bait-fishing that poetry does to prose; and, while each method will ever have its enthusiastic admirers, only he who can skillfully handle the comely fly-rod, and deftly cast the delicate fly, can truly and fully enjoy the æsthetics of the gentle art. As the lover naturally "drops into poetry" to express the ardent feelings of his soul, "with a woful ballad made to his mistress' eyebrow," so the real lover of nature and the finny tribe as naturally takes to fly-fishing, and finds liquid poems in gurgling streams, and pastoral idyls in leafy woods.

A friend in Texas, to whom I sent a bass-fly (an Abbey), and who had never seen a " fly " before, enthusiastically declared it to be " a fish-hook poetized," and thought that a " Black Bass should take it through a`love of the beautiful, if nothing else." Not only the fly, but every implement of the fly-fisher's outfit is a materialized poem.

Fly-fishers are usually brain-workers in society. From time immemorial the fraternity has embraced many of the most honored, intellectual and cultured members of the liberal professions and arts. Along the banks of purling streams, beneath the shadows of umbrageous trees, or in the secluded nooks of charming lakes, they have ever been found, drinking deep of the invigorating forces of nature—giving rest and tone to overtaxed brains and wearied nerves—while gracefully wielding the supple rod, the invisible leader, and the fairy-like fly.

Oh! how the sluggish pulses bound, the deadened nerves thrill, and the relaxed muscles quicken, responsive to the inspiration of the electric rise of the gamey denizens of the stream; and oh, how the buried forces of life are resurrected, renewed and strengthened by the hopes, and fears, and struggles, of the contest which follows! And when at last the brave beauty has been lovingly deposited in the creel, the restored angler feels that he has won a double victory; for, in the death of the fish, he sees renewed life for himself.

But the true fly-fisher, who practices his art *con amore*, does not delight in big catches, nor revel in undue and cruel slaughter. He is ever satisfied with a moderate creel, and is content with the scientific and skillful capture of a few good fish. The beauties of nature, as revealed in his surroundings—the sparkling water, the shadow and sunshine, the rustling leaves, the song of birds and hum of insects, the health-giving breeze—make up to him a measure of true enjoyment, and peace, and thankfulness, that is totally unknown to the slaughterer of the innocents, whose sole ambition is to fill his creel and record his captures by scores; and who realizes naught in his surroundings but

the hot sun, slippery rocks, baffling winds, and the annoyance of overhanging trees and bushes. The time is coming when such an angler will receive, as well as merit, the
scorn and contempt of all good and true disciples of the
gentle art.

RIGGING THE CAST.

By a reference to the chapters devoted to the implements of angling, the reader will obtain a full description
of those used in fly-fishing, which are the fly-rod, the click-
reel, the tapered fly-line, the leader, the fly, the fly-book,
the creel, the landing-net, and the useful adjuncts, for
stream-fishing, of wading-pants or stockings; and, by
referring to the pages on knots, the following directions
for rigging the cast will be rendered more intelligible:

A few snelled Sproat or O'Shaughnessy hooks should be
carried in the fly-book, to use with such natural baits as
grasshoppers, beetles or dragon-flies, in case the artificial
fly does not prove successful. They are to be used in the
same manner as artificial flies.

The beginner being now provided with all the tools, it
is in order to put his rod together, attach reel, reel-line,
and cast of flies, and proceed to business. In rigging the
cast, if the leader is provided with loops at each end, and
also loops for drop-flies, proceed as follows: To the small
end of the leader attach the stretcher or tail-fly by passing
the loop of the leader through the loop of the snell and
over the fly, then draw together. Three or four feet from
the tail-fly attach the dropper, or bob-fly, in the same manner; that is, put the loop of the snell over the loop of the
leader, and push the fly through the latter loop and draw
tight; or, if the leader is not furnished with loops for this

purpose, slip a knot of the leader (about three or four feet from the tail-fly) apart, and, after making a round knot in the end of the snell of the fly, put it through the opened knot of the leader and draw together; this will hold firm, and the dropper-fly will stand at right angles from the leader.

If, however, the gut-lengths of the leader are tied by hard, close knots, instead of the slip-knot or double water-knot, then the snell of the dropper must be attached close to and above a knot of the leader, by a single knot or half-hitch, a round knot having previously been made in the end of the snell, to prevent the half-hitch from working loose; this is probably as good and safe a way as any.

The cast is now ready, for I do not advise the use of more than two flies. If, however, the angler wishes to employ three, the third fly, or second dropper, must be attached three feet above the first dropper, and, in this case, the leader should be nine feet long. But the beginner will have all he can attend to with a six-feet leader and two flies. The leader having been previously straightened by soaking in water, or rubbing with India-rubber (the former method is to be preferred), and attached to the reel-line, the angler is now armed and equipped as the law directs, and ready for

Casting the Fly.

Casting the artificial fly is performed by two principal motions, a backward and a forward one. The former is to throw the flies behind the angler, and the latter is to project them forward and beyond. That is all there is

in it. These are the main principles involved, and the
first or backward motion is merely preparatory to the
second or forward one, the latter being the most important.

But the style and manner of making these two motions
are all-important; for upon the correct, skillful, and, I
might say, scientific performance of them, depends the
success of the angler. The main objects of the two motions are, first, to get the line and cast behind the angler
in a straight line, without lapping or kinking; and, second, to project the line forward without snapping off the
tail-fly, casting it perfectly straight, without confusion, and
causing the flies to alight before the line, without a splash,
and as lightly as the natural insect dropping into the water.
This can only be done by the novice, with a short line,
about the length of his rod, and he should not attempt a
longer cast until he is perfect in this. When he can lay
out his short line perfectly straight before him, without a
splash, every time, he can then venture further.

But we are getting along too fast; we must go back to
first principles—the two motions.

The backward and forward movements are each made
in about the same length of time, but while the former is
a single movement, the latter is a double one; that is, it is
divided into two motions, or parts; though these two forward motions are made in the same length of time as the
backward movement.

I will now try to explain these movements more ex-
plicitly, with the aid of the annexed cuts and diagrams.

The prospective fly-fisher having his rod, reel and cast
in readiness, stands near the bank of the stream, with a
clear space of fifteen or twenty feet behind him. Having

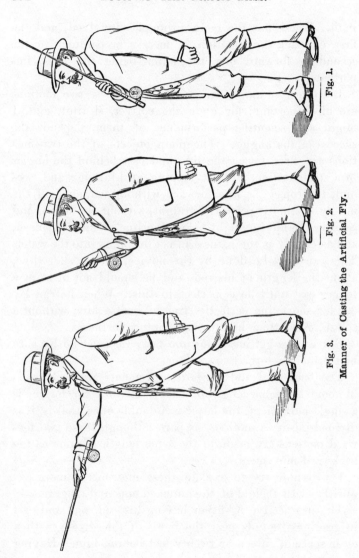

Fig. 1.

Fig. 2.

Fig. 3.

Manner of Casting the Artificial Fly.

the line about the length of his rod, to begin with, he takes the hook of the tail-fly between his left thumb and forefinger and stretches the line taut; then, by waving the rod slightly backward over the left shoulder, and at the same time releasing his hold of the tail-fly, the line straightens out behind him, the right elbow meantime being held close to the body, as the backward movement is made with the wrist and forearm entirely. The position of the right hand during this portion of the cast is with said hand grasping the rod just above the reel (the reel being at the extreme butt, and on the under side of the rod), and with the reel and palm of the hand toward the angler, the thumb looking toward his right shoulder (see figure 1).

When the line and leader are on a straight line behind him, which the beginner must learn to judge and time exactly, without looking behind him, he brings the rod forward with a gradually increasing rate of speed, until the rod is slightly in advance of him, say at an angle of fifteen degrees off the perpendicular; then, for the first time, the right elbow leaves the body, and, at the same time, the rod is turned in the hand in the opposite direction (see figure 2); that is, with the back of the hand toward the angler, so that, at the end of the cast, the reel is below the rod, while the back of the hand is upward, and, without stopping the motion of the rod, the right arm is projected forward to its full extent, and on a line with the shoulder (see figure 3). This is the second part or motion of the forward movement, and consists in merely following the direction of the flies with the tip of the rod, so as to ease their rapid flight, and allow them to descend without confusion, and to settle upon the water noiselessly, and with-

out a splash. Thus we see that the backward movement
is in one time and one motion, and the forward movement
in one time and two motions, as the military have it, or
according to the following formula of time:

$$1. \; \text{♩} = 2. \; (a) \; \text{♩} \; (b) \; \text{♩}.$$

No. 1 represents the backward throw, in one motion, in
the time of a half note. No. 2 represents the forward
cast, in one time and two motions, a and b, in the time
of two quarter notes. This is not to be understood as
fishing by note, but the relative time of making the different motions in casting the fly approaches very nearly
that of the formula given. This is better explained by a
reference to the foregoing cuts; where figure 1 represents the backward throw, and figure 2 represents the
first part or motion (a), and figure 3 the second part or motion (b), of the forward cast.

Sometimes these movements are made straight backward and forward over either shoulder, or over the head;
but the best way is to make the backward movement over
the left shoulder, and the forward over the right shoulder,
the line thus describing an oval or parabola. By this
method the flies are not so apt to be whipped off, and it is,
withal, more graceful, more *en regle*.

The following diagram represents the arcs described by
the tip of the rod and the flies:

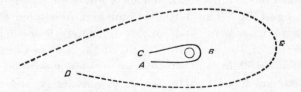

O is supposed to be the angler, and, as we are looking down upon him from above, it represents his hat. The dark line, *a b c,* is the curve described by the tip of the rod in the backward and forward movements of the cast— back over the left shoulder, and forward over the right; while the dotted curved line, *d e f,* is the approximate arc described by the tail-fly, leaving the water at *d,* and alighting, by a lengthened cast, at *f.*

By studying these diagrams in connection with the instructions given, the theory and mechanical principles will soon be mastered by the novice. He should then, by assiduous and patient endeavor, make a practical application of these principles, and become tolerably proficient in casting the fly, before he attempts to venture near the haunts of the Bass.

But various ways of casting come into play at certain times, and under peculiar circumstances; and the rod will be held more or less to one side or the other, or more vertically, as particular circumstances or emergencies demand. For the novice must remember that there are trees and bushes, and rocks and winds, to contend with in fly-fishing; and, moreover, as he becomes proficient, he will choose his own style of casting, for no two anglers cast the fly exactly alike.

However, all methods of overhead casting are but variations or modifications of the mode just described; and the particular circumstances calling for them will naturally suggest their necessity, use, or advantages to the angler as he becomes more expert, and gains in knowledge by practical experience. It is hardly necessary, therefore, or even advisable, to allude more particularly to other ways of overhead casting, as it would, in my opinion, tend more to confuse than to enlighten the beˑ ginner.

Then there is the sidewise cast, where the line is not thrown behind the angler at all, but to one side or the other. This style of casting is practiced with a short line, on very narrow waters, or where the banks of the stream are thickly clothed with tall grass or bushes, and where there is not sufficient clear space for throwing the line behind the angler.

In this mode of casting, the angler, instead of facing the stream, turns one side or the other toward the water, and casts by throwing the line landward, over the grass or bushes, to the right or left, as the case may be; and, when the line has unfolded in a straight line, to cast toward the water by an opposite sidewise cast. In all other respects, the management of the cast must approach, as nearly as possible, the regular overhead cast.

Another method of casting that occasionally comes into play is "switching." This mode is very useful where high banks, trees or bushes render the overhead and sidewise cast impracticable; though it admits of but a very short line being used, shorter than in the sidewise cast.

Switching is performed by raising the arm and rod to their fullest extent, vertically, thus drawing the flies close to, and in front of, the angler; then, by a quick, smart, circling motion of the rod, the flies are projected forward, or laterally, as the angler may wish. The forward motion is much like striking with a whip or switch, and is more easily imagined than described.

We will now presume that the tyro has perfected himself in casting a short line, and can throw his tail-fly into his hat nearly every time at a distance of fifteen feet; and right here let me say, beware of the angling brag who declares that he can cast his tail-fly into a glass of water at fifty feet every time! It can't be done. Also fight shy of the long-range fisher who insists that he can cast a hundred feet with ease! It can't be done. The longest cast, with a single-handed rod, I ever saw, without "loaded" flies, was eighty-one feet, and I believe the longest on record is Seth Green's eighty-six feet; while at the last (1880) tournament held by the New York State Sportsman's Association, seventy feet won the first prize. When the beginner can cast his fly into his hat, eight times out of ten, at forty feet, he is a fly-fisher; and, so far as casting is concerned, a good one.

But let us go back to our tyro, who has now become proficient with the short line, for it is time to lengthen his cast, which is done in this way: After casting and roving his flies on the surface by zigzag, jerky motions, to the left or right, and without provoking a rise, he pulls off from the reel with the left hand three or four feet of line; and, lifting his rod, slowly at first, by a gradually increasing motion, lifts the leader and flies, and throws them backward over the left shoulder, as before described. The resistance of the leader and flies, before they leave the water, takes the extra length of line from the rod, and it is unfolded behind the angler into a straight line, when he casts it forward over the right shoulder.

In this way the line is lengthened at every cast, if necessary, until the maximum or desired distance is reached. But the angler should never let his flies touch the ground behind him; but must so time the movement as to propel the line forward at exactly the right moment to prevent this.

Another caution: The angler should never attempt to cast his flies by main strength, for this will accomplish nothing but confusion; it takes but little force to retrieve or cast the flies with a well-made, springy and pliant rod. The rod, moreover, must never be carried back over the shoulder to a distance exceeding an angle of fifteen degrees off the perpendicular, for the backward throw is really accomplished by the time the rod is in a vertical position, and this might be said, also, to a certain extent, in regard to the forward movement or cast proper; for by the time the rod is fifteen degrees off the perpendicular in the other direction (in front), the main part of the cast is made, and the second part of the forward movement is only to follow the flies with the point of the rod, to ease their flight, as before mentioned; this latter part of the forward cast can no more aid or extend the flight of the flies than "pushing" on the reins can increase the speed of your horse.

I have now, in the fewest words possible, and in the simplest manner, endeavored to explain the "mystery" of casting the fly, and I trust the beginner will be able to understand it. It is almost impossible to describe the art clearly and satisfactorily by mere words. One hour with a good fly-fisher will teach the novice more than a hundred written pages. I have purposely omitted many little details of nicety and precision, which would only tend to magnify the supposed difficulties of casting, and create doubt, confusion, and a lack of confidence, in the mind of the beginner in the noble art of fly-fishing.

GENERAL INSTRUCTIONS.

It is useless to cast for Black Bass from high elevations near the water, as a bold bank, a projecting rock, a dam, etc., under ordinary circumstances; for the angler must remember that the most commanding situation for seeing the fish also furnishes the best facilities for being seen in return, and *vice versa*. In fishing from a boat, it must be kept in deep water, while long casts are made in-shore, toward the feeding grounds. We should never fish with the sun at our back, or in such a position as to throw the shadow of our rod or person upon the water.

From what has been said in the chapter on the " conditions governing the biting of fish," it will be apparent that it is absolutely necessary that there be a breeze sufficient to ruffle the surface of the water. It is perfect folly for the angler to cast his flies upon a smooth surface, if the water is clear enough for fishing. A gale is better than no wind at all, and it does not matter from what direction the wind blows, if the condition and temperature of water are right. A good breeze is the angler's best ally, for by rippling the water it breaks the line of sight, to a great extent, between him and the fish.

The angler should endeavor to cast his flies as lightly as possible, causing them to settle as quietly as thistle-down, and without a splash. After casting, the flies should be skipped or trailed along the surface in slightly curving lines, or by zigzag and tremulous movements, occasionally allowing them to become submerged for several inches near likely-looking spots. If the current is swift, allow the flies to float naturally with it, at times, when they can be skittered back again, or withdrawn for a new cast. Two or three times are enough to cast over any one spot, when a rise is not induced.

When Bass are biting eagerly and quickly, whipping the stream is to be practiced, that is, the casts are to be often

Fly-fishing—Landing the Bass.

and rapidly repeated, first to one side, then the other, allowing the flies to settle but a moment. In casting and manipulating the flies, the line must be ever taut; for often a Bass will thus hook himself, which he never does with a slack line.

STRIKING AND PLAYING.

The angler should strike by sight, or by touch; that is, he should strike the moment he sees the rise; for the Bass has either got the fly in his mouth, has missed it, or has already ejected it, when the rise is seen; it very seldom happens that the rise is seen before the fly is reached by the fish. The angler must also strike at the moment he feels the slightest touch or tug from the fish, for often the Bass takes the fly without any break at the surface, especially if the flies are beneath the surface.

Striking is simply a twist of the wrist, or half-turn of the rod, either upward or downward (upward with stiffish rods, and downward with very willowy ones), which is sufficient to set the hook if the rod and line maintain a proper state of tension; but when the careless angler has a slack line, and, consequently, a lifeless rod, he must necessarily strike by a long upward or side sweep of the rod, called "yanking;" and should he succeed in hooking the fish, the chances are that it will shake the hook out again before the slack can be reeled up.

The tip of the rod must always be held upward, so that the rod constantly maintains a curve with the line; and never, under any circumstances must the rod point in the direction of the flies after they reach the water, for this allows the direct strain of the fish to come upon the line

34

or leader. When a Bass is hooked, he must be killed on the rod; the rod must stand the brunt of the contest; the more pliable and springy the rod, the less likelihood of its breaking, for a stiff rod is more easily fractured than a flexible one. Give the Bass more line only when he takes it; make him fight for every inch, and take it back when you can; hold him by the spring of the rod, and do not hesitate to turn the butt toward him to keep him away from weeds, rocks, snags, or other dangerous places; this will bring him up with a round turn, and is called "giving the butt."

Do n't be in a hurry to land him; the longer he resists, the better for your sport; take your time and only land him when he is completely exhausted; for if he is well hooked, and the proper tension of rod and line maintained, he can not get away; on the other hand, if he is tenderly hooked, the more gingerly he is handled the better. Therefore, never be in a hurry, and never attempt to force matters; always keep a bent rod and taut line; if the Bass breaks water, the best plan is to lower the tip, so as to slack the line, and immediately raise the rod and tighten the line when he strikes the water again, for if he falls on the tightened line he is most sure to escape; this is one of his most wily tricks.

REMARKS, HINTS, AND ADVICE.

It has been doubted by some that the Black Bass will rise to the fly, or at best that they are uncertain in their modes and times of doing so, as compared with the Brook Trout. These doubts are mostly raised by those who angle for the Black Bass in precisely the same way as for the

Brook Trout, upon the supposition that the two fish are identical in habits and instincts. But while their habits of feeding are very similar—both feeding on the bottom, in midwater, or on the surface, on crustacea, larvæ, minnows, insects, etc.—they differ greatly in other habitual features and idiosyncrasies.

The Black Bass will rise to the fly as readily, under any and all conditions, as the Brook Trout, when fished for understandingly, and under proper precautions. There are times, seemingly favorable, when neither Bass nor Trout will rise to the fly.

One reason why the Bass is thought to be uncertain in rising to the fly is this: While he is fully as wary as the Trout he is not so timid. A Trout darts incontinently away at the first glimpse of the angler, and is seen no more; but the Bass will retire but a short distance, and as often will stand his ground, and on balanced fins will watch the angler vainly casting his "brown hackle" or "coachman" over him, perhaps laughing in his sleeve (shoulder girdle) at his discomfiture. The truth of the matter is, the Bass is not uncertain, but he is too knowing to be deceived by his flies, so long as the angler is in sight.

Fish are more suspicious regarding objects on the surface of the water than of those beneath. I have often demonstrated this, causing them to skurry away, by holding a long stick immediately over them, above the surface; while I could introduce the same stick underneath the water and even prod a fish with it, without alarming it much. This is why more caution is necessary in fly-fishing than in bait-fishing; the bait in one instance being on the surface, and in the other, beneath. If a Black Bass, in

rushing to the surface for the fly, sees the angler, he at
once stops in his course, and thenceforth the daintiest flies,
never so deftly thrown, will be cast in vain while the angler remains in view.

In a recent issue of the London *Field* appeared an article, written by the able editor of that valuable paper,
Francis Francis, Esq., on the frightening of Brook Trout
by the flashing and reflections of a varnished fly-rod,
when wildly waved by the angler in casting, and which, at
first sight, would seem to be plausible enough; but upon
mature consideration, and with all due deference to so eminent an authority as Mr. Francis, I am convinced that
there is not much in it, and that instead of proving the
matter he seems to be rather begging the question.

The theory of angling, like the theory of medicine, is
rather an uncertain subject, and opposite positions can be
taken and seemingly maintained upon almost any question
of either science, until the crucial test of practical experience proves their truth or falsity. The fact is, that fish
are not frightened by flashes of light or the reflections of
bright objects, but, on the contrary, are attracted by them;
any one who has ever fished by torchlight, or trolled with
a bright metal spoon, can testify to this, and there is a
method of fishing practiced by the Chinese, by means of a
board painted white and attached to a boat at such an angle as to reflect the light of the moon upon the water,
when the fish, attracted by this, jump upon the board as
the boat is moved along.

That fish are not much disturbed, if at all, by the flashing of a polished fly-rod *per se*, can be easily proven by
any one who, being securely hid behind a clump of bushes,
can wave his rod as "wildly" as necessary without alarm-

ing them to an extent to frighten them away or prevent their biting; indeed, the unnatural shaking or disturbance of a bush near the brink, by the careless angler, will alarm the denizens of the stream more than the most highly-varnished and brightly-mounted rod ever made, when waved over the stream by an angler who keeps himself hid from view; and herein lies, to my mind, the key to this whole matter.

It is the angler who scares the Trout, and not his rod; and this probably applies with more force to the comparatively narrow and open streams of Great Britain than to the more extensive waters of our own country; this view seems more probable in connection with the fact that Mr. Francis advises casting sideways instead of overhead, which method could only be practiced successfully on narrow streams, for sideway casts are necessarily short ones, and would not answer at all for most of our waters. There are situations, however, when the sideway cast can be used advantageously, and is used occasionally by all good fly-fishers.

The main rules to be observed in fly-fishing I conceive to be these : on narrow streams to keep entirely out of sight, and on open waters to make long casts; in either case, the fish, not seeing the angler, will not be alarmed at the flashing of the rod ; the finer the water the greater the caution that must be used on the one hand, and the longer must be the cast on the other.

Mr. Francis does not offer any remedy for the varnished rod, but merely suggests that it might answer to paint it sky-blue, or a dull, smoky tint, without polish; but this, I know, will not do. I have seen rods that had the varnish scraped off and were painted a delicate pea-green, to harmonize with the foliage of Trout streams, and I have seen the bark left on alder, elm, and tamarack poles when used in bait-fishing, but they were not more successful than the varnished rod.

Split bamboo and other jointed rods must of necessity be varnished to preserve their elasticity and beauty. Think of a delicate split bamboo tip coated with sky-blue paint! The very thought is heresy, and an offense against the eternal fitness of things that would make even the spots on a Brook Trout blush more deeply crimson. American split bamboo rods are the finest made rods in the world, and the numerous foreign orders received by the manufacturers fully attest this fact, and show, moreover, that they are duly appreciated abroad, as well as at home, highly varnished and flashing though they be.

There is one feature of this subject that is peculiarly gratifying to me, and I heartily thank Mr. Francis for the article in question. It concedes the fact that fish, having eyes, can see, and are not the near-sighted dupes that most writers would have us believe; this concession could not be put in a stronger light than by the assertion that they are frightened at the flashing of a varnished rod, and that a rod, therefore, should be rendered as nearly invisible as possible by painting it a sky-blue or cloud color. But if this were done, what a quantity of brash wood and poor workmanship, and what a multitude of sins of omission and commission would this sky-blue mantle, like charity, cover!

When fish are frightened at a fishing-rod at all, it is when its shadow is suddenly cast upon the water—which all prudent anglers are very careful to avoid doing, especially on small streams—and, viewed in this light, a sky-blue rod has not even a fancied advantage over the most highly-polished one.

The most important rule, then, to be observed, first, last, and all the time in fly-fishing, is: *Keep out of sight of the fish;* this is the first and great injunction; " and the second is like unto it:" *Keep as quiet and motionless as possible.* "On these two" laws depends all your success in fly-fishing. Let your necessary movements be deliberate and methodical, avoiding all quick, sudden, or energetic motions. Fish see and hear much better than we give them credit for. To keep out of the fish's sight we must be screened by such natural objects as bushes, trees, rocks, etc., or by keeping well back from the brink and making long casts. In wading the stream it is also necessary to make long casts. The latter is the best plan of fishing a stream, as the angler, being so near the water, is not so apt to be seen.

It is best, always, to fish down stream, even with the wind against one, for fish always lie with head up stream, and will be more apt to see your flies. The current will, moreover, take your flies down stream, and so keep your line taut. It is also easier to wade down, than up stream. Many other reasons might be given, but these will be sufficient. Cast just below ripples and rapids, over eddies and pools, along the edges of weed patches, under projecting banks and shelving rocks, near submerged trees or driftwood, off gravelly shoals, isolated rocks and long points or spurs of land ; it is useless to fish long, deep, still reaches of water.

The most favorable time for fly-fishing for Black Bass is during the last hours of the day, from sundown until dark, and also on bright moonlight evenings. On streams, an hour or two following sunrise, in warm weather, is quite favorable. On dark, cloudy, and cold days the middle hours are best. Bright sunny days, especially in hot weather, are not favorable to fly-fishing, except in quite cool, shâdy, and breezy situations. In short, the best conditions are a mellow or dusky light, a good breeze, and translucent water ; while the most unfavorable are a bright sun, a still atmosphere, and a smooth and glassy surface, with the water either very fine or very turbid.

And now, in concluding this portion of my subject, let me say a parting word to the beginner : Cast a straight line; keep it taut; strike upon sight, or touch; kill your fish on the rod ; take your time. It is better to cast a short line well, than a long one bunglingly. Should you cast your fly into a branch of a tree overhead, or into a bush behind you, or miss your fish in striking, or lose him when hooked, or crack off your tail-fly, or slip into a hole up to your armpits—keep your temper; above all things do n't swear, for he that swears will catch no fish. Remember, yours is the gentle art, and a fly-fisher should be a gentleman.

CHAPTER XXII.

CASTING THE MINNOW.

"And as to the rest that concerns this sort of angling, I shall wholly refer you to Mr. Walton's direction, who is undoubtedly the best angler with a minnow in England."—CHARLES COTTON.

NEXT to fly-fishing, casting the minnow is the most artistic mode of angling for the Black Bass. To obtain all of the pleasure and sport embodied in this style of fishing, none but the best and most approved tackle should be employed, which should approach, in its general features of elegance and lightness, the implements used in fly-fishing.

A faithful study of the conformation, habits, and idiosyncrasies of game fish should be the first consideration of the true angler; though the average angler usually contents himself with a superficial knowledge of the ways and means of capturing and killing the finny tribe, a big catch being the height of his piscatorial ambition. While good tackle is essential to success, a thorough knowledge of the habits of the fish is a *sine qua non*, without which no one can become an expert and successful angler.

Apropos of this might be mentioned the old and hackneyed story of the rustic youth with alder pole, twine string, and worm bait, and the *soi-disant* angler with split bamboo and well-filled fly-book, who indulged in a day's fishing on the same stream, with the result of a "big string" for

35   (409)

the boy, and one poor fingerling for the disgusted sportsman. The boy understood the "true inwardness" of the Trout, in which matter the discomfited citizen was lamentably ignorant, and relied entirely upon his splendid rig for success.

Where Black Bass are plentiful, as in the quiet ponds and lakes of Western New York, Northern Indiana, Michigan, Wisconsin, and Minnesota, at the Thousand Islands of the St. Lawrence, and in the extreme South, the merest tyro, who can throw his bait twenty feet from the boat, can, when the Bass are in a biting mood, show a big catch, though he may necessarily have failed to land two out of every three fish hooked. But on small rivers, where the angler casts to the right and left and across the stream from the banks, and while wading the shallows and bars, and the Bass are shy, educated, and fully up in a knowledge of the stream in its windings, eddies, pools, and rapids, the highest skill and a thorough knowledge of the habits of the fish are indispensable to a full creel; and this, at the same time, constitutes the pleasure and perfection of Black Bass angling.

But bear in mind, that sticking the butt of a long rod in the bank, and then, while reclining under the shade of some umbrageous tree, enjoying a pipe or the latest novel while waiting an hour for a bite, is not angling, but simply loafing, and attempting to obtain Bass under false pretenses.

Casting the minnow is quite an art, as much so as casting the fly; indeed, I think there are more good fly casters than good casters of the live minnow. Mediocrity in both methods of angling is readily acquired, but great excellence and perfect skill are rarely attained in either. The two methods are essentially and practically different, and require implements and tools commensurate with this difference.

While the fly-rod is willowy and long, the minnow-rod is short and comparatively stiff; the fly-line is rather heavy and of large caliber as compared with the minnow-line, which should be as fine and light as possible, consistent with strength. The artificial fly is cast by the weight of the fly-line and suppleness of the rod, while the weight of the bait, and swivel or sinker, give the necessary momentum for casting the minnow. The fly is usually cast overhead, directly in front of the angler, while the minnow can only be cast, for any great distance, to one side or the other, or obliquely, by underhand casting.

Minnow Tackle.

The Minnow Rod.—The rod for casting the live minnow should be shorter and stiffer than the fly-rod, but of about the same relative weight; for it, like the fly-rod, is a single-handed rod. It should be from eight to nine feet long. Eight and a quarter feet is the standard length that I have advocated for many years, though the manufacturers, in order to suit all tastes, now make this style of rod from eight to nine and a half feet long. It should weigh from eight to ten ounces, no less and no more. It should be well balanced, with a stiffish back, to insure good casting, but pliable enough to respond to the slightest movement of the fish. Most of the bend and play should be in the upper two-thirds of the rod, which bend should be a true arch, and not a horse-shoe curve, as is often seen in a poorly-constructed and weak-backed rod. The best material for a rod of this character is an ash butt and lancewood second and third pieces, the latter being usually known as the tip. The reel-seat should be from six to eight inches from the extreme butt, and no more, for this rod must be used with the hand alone, and should not extend under the elbow for support, like the old-fashioned long and heavy rods. It should have light standing guides instead of rings.

THE REEL.—The multiplying reel is the only one adapted to casting the minnow, and it should be the very best one made. It should run as rapidly and smoothly as possible, and multiply from two to four times. The best is the "Frankfort" reel — sometimes variously styled "Meek," "Milam," or "Kentucky" reel — though the very best of other good makers will answer well.

The improved Black Bass reels of Abbey & Imbrie, and Conroy, Bissett & Malleson, referred to in the chapter on reels, are excellent implements.

THE REEL LINE.—First and foremost among the suitable lines is the smallest size, G, or No. 5, plaited raw silk line. It should be braided hard and close, and tinted or parti-colored. Where the Bass are exceptionally large, size F, or No. 4, may be used, though the smaller or finer the line the better, for a gut leader can not be used in casting the minnow, and longer casts can be made with the finest lines. The proper length for a reel-line is fifty yards.

The boiled silk braided line is next best, but it is not so closely plaited, usually, as the raw silk-line, and consequently absorbs more water, which is detrimental to casting. When it is as hard braided as the raw silk-line it is about as good.

Next in order is the braided linen line ; the smallest size, G, or No, 5, is the only size to be used, and that is rather large.

The last, though with some not the least, in point of merit, is the relaid Japanese sea-grass (so-called) line, which is made of raw silk, and in some respects is a better line than any mentioned, being of smaller caliber, very hard twisted, and absorbing less water when new. But being a twisted line, it is apt to kink where much casting is practiced ; were it not for this detestable quality it would rank all other lines for bait fishing, as the smallest size, No. 1, is just the right caliber. I am trying to induce the manufacturers to braid a line of this same size, especially for Black Bass angling, and shall probably succeed.

Twisted silk, linen, or cotton lines should never be used in this mode of angling, as their kinking propensities will ruffle the temper of the mildest-mannered angler.

Hooks.—The hook beyond comparison, for Black Bass fishing, is the Sproat. It is a true, central-draught hook, and tempered just right. It has a short barb, with cutting edges, which will go right through any part of a fish's mouth. The next best, in the order named, are the O'Shaughnessy, Dublin Bend, Cork Shape, and round bend Carlisle (Aberdeen). These hooks are all numbered about alike, and the most suitable sizes are Nos. 1, 1-0, 2-0, and 3-0. Hooks should be tied on gut-snells, single or double, good single gut being best. Where pickerel abound, the gimp-snell may be used.

Swivels.—A brass box swivel of the smallest size should always be used, and often it will be heavy enough without an additional sinker.

Sinkers.—Ringed sinkers, or what is still better, the

patent adjustable sinker, with spiral wire rings for readily attaching and detaching to or from the line, are the only kinds to use, when they are found necessary.

FLOATS.—The float should never be used in casting the minnow if it can possibly be dispensed with. It is always in the way, and long casts can not be made when it is employed. In still fishing it may be used, and with advantage, especially where helgramites or crawfish are used as bait. The patent adjustable float with spiral rings, is an article of real merit, as it is well made and can be attached or removed in a moment.

RIGGING THE CAST.

In rigging the cast for the minnow, the reel must be placed underneath the rod, on a line with the guides. Many anglers use the reel on top, but this is essentially wrong. The weight of the reel naturally takes it under the rod, where it balances better and enables the rod to be held more steadily; the strain of the line also falls upon the guides, which insures a more perfect working of the rod. Both click and multiplying reels should always be used underneath; they are intended to be so used, and it will be found far the best way when one becomes accustomed to this plan.

The reel then being underneath, the line is rove through the guides and a box-swivel tied on the end; to the other ring of the swivel is looped the snell of the hook. The hook is then passed through the lower lip of a good-sized minnow—from three to four inches long—and out at the nostril; or if the minnow is smaller, out at the socket of the eye. If the minnow is carefully hooked, it will live a comparatively long time. If a sinker be required in addition to the swivel, it should be placed a foot above it.

MAKING THE CAST.

Now reel up the line until the sinker, or swivel, as the case may be, is at the tip of the rod, and we are ready to make a cast, which I will now endeavor to explain with the aid of the annexed diagram and cuts:

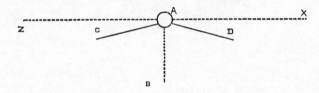

In the diagram, A represents the angler; we are supposed to be looking down upon him from above, so that only his hat and rod are visible. He is facing B. The angler now wishes to make a cast to the left, X being the objective point to which he desires to cast the minnow, some twenty yards distant. He grasps the rod immediately below the reel with the right hand, with the thumb resting lightly but firmly upon the spool, to control the rendering of the line; the right arm is extended downward, slightly bent, with the elbow near the body, and with the extreme butt of the rod nearly touching the right hip; the thumb and reel are upward, inclining slightly toward the left; the tip of the rod, or rather the minnow, just clears the ground or surface of the water; the position of the rod is now in the direction of the line A C, inclin-

Fig. 4.   Casting the Minnow to the Left.   Fig. 5.

ing toward the ground or water, making an angle of about 30 deg. with the line of the shoulders, X Z (the inclination of the rod is shown fully in figure 4); this is the situation at the beginning of the cast.

Now for the cast: The angler turns his face toward X, the objective point, without turning his body; he now inclines his body in the direction of C, advancing the right foot and bending the right knee slightly, and makes a sweeping cast from the right to the left, and from below upward, across the body diagonally, until the rod-hand is at the height of the left shoulder, and the arm and rod extended in the direction of A D, with the tip of the rod inclining upward, as shown in figure 5.

The movement of the right hand is almost in a straight line from a point near the right hip to a point near the left shoulder; the motion in casting is steady, increasing in swiftness toward the end of the cast, and ending with the "pitching" of the bait—instead of a violent jerk— somewhat similar to the straight underhand pitching of a base-ball.

In making the cast, the right elbow should touch the body, sweeping across it, and only leave it at the end of the cast, making the forearm do the work. At the end of the cast, the reel and thumb are upward, and the rod forms an angle of 30 deg. with the line of the shoulders X Z, and the minnow, instead of following the direction of the rod A D, as some might suppose, will, from the slight curve described by the rod during the cast, diverge toward the left, and drop at X, when the thumb should immediately stop the reel by an increased pressure.

Casting to the right is just the reverse of the above proceeding. The angler being in the same position,

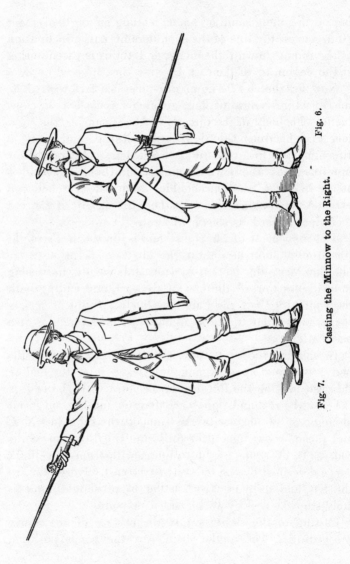

Fig. 6.

Fig. 7.   Casting the Minnow to the Right.

brings the right hand across, and touching the body, to a point in front of the left hip, the thumb and reel upward, but inclining toward the body, and the rod extending in the direction of the line A D, with the tip downward, as shown in figure 6 ; he now turns his face in the direction of the objective point Z, inclines his body and advances his left foot in the direction of D ; and makes a cast from left to right, from below upward, and ends the cast with the right arm and rod fully extended in the direction of the line A C, as shown in figure 7, while the minnow takes its flight toward Z.   This is a back-handed cast, and is somewhat analogous to the pitching of a quoit.

In making either cast the body should sway slightly and simultaneously with the rod arm, in the direction of the cast, to add force and steadiness; but on no account must the cast be made by " main strength," for it requires but slight muscular exertion to cast forty yards; and on no account must the rod be carried further toward the line X Z than an angle of thirty degrees, otherwise the bait will be thrown behind the angler.   Particular care must be taken to give the bait an *upward* impulse as it leaves the rod.

The first cast that the beginner makes will be likely to throw the bait behind him, for reasons just given.   He should, by all means, begin by making short casts, and lengthen them as he perfects himself by experience in managing the reel and controlling the cast.   While but a few yards of line can be cast directly in front of the beginner, he should practice casting at various angles with the line X Z, to the left and right.   He should avoid overhead casting, for that is the pot-fisher's method of *throwing* a bait, and is not only an awkward, but a very inefficient style of casting the minnow, and must not be practiced except where the reel is dispensed with, as in one mode of still-fishing.

At the beginning of the cast the thumb presses firmly upon the spool of the reel, until *just before* the tip of the rod gains its greatest extent or elevation, when the pressure is to be slightly relieved, so as to permit the release of the line, and allow the minnow to be projected in the direction of the cast. The exact time to lessen the pressure of the thumb and start the minnow on its flight, is almost a matter of intuition, which can hardly be explained; however, the proper time is soon learned by practice, in which event, the " wrinkle " comes to be performed by the angler automatically, or, as it were, unconsciously.

The entire cast must be made so steadily and so regularly, and the rod held so firmly at the end of the cast, as to prevent entirely any undue swaying or bending of the rod, in order that the line may follow the direction of the minnow in its flight, smoothly and evenly, and untrammeled and unretarded by any vibratory motions of the rod. I trust I make myself understood here, for this is the most essential, and, at the same time, the most difficult feature, or portion, of the cast to explain, or acquire.

The thumb must be thoroughly educated to control the rendering of the line during the cast, and this can only be accomplished by continual and *patient* practice, in training the thumb to apply just the requisite amount of uniform pressure, to prevent the overrunning of the line, or back-lashing of the spool.

The beginner should make up his mind, in the first place, to keep his temper, and to exhibit no impatience at the frequent slipping of his thumb, and the consequent snarling and tangling of his line. The more calmly and philosophically he views these annoyances and perplexities, the sooner will he overcome the difficulties and become *au fait* in the management of the reel. The best instruction I can give him is to make the pressure of the thumb gentle, but firm and *uniform*, during the flight of the minnow, and to stop the revolving spool the moment the bait alights on the water, by a stronger pressure.

These directions are as brief, plain and explicit, as it is possible to make them; they embody the main principles involved, and the novice, by a careful and practical application of them, can, by perseverance, soon become a good caster of the live minnow.

General Instructions.

If fishing from a boat, on a lake or large pond, the angler proceeds in his boat on the outside, or deep water side, of the fishing grounds, and casts *in* toward the feeding grounds, the oarsman rowing along rapidly or slowly, or holding the boat stationary, as circumstances demand. The boat being in deep water the fish are not so apt to see it, which is a great advantage. The angler can cast in any direction and to any distance, greater or lesser, within the length of his line, as he may desire. He can cast astern and proceed as in trolling, or cast to either side, or forward, and by reeling in the line keep the bait in motion. It can readily be imagined how expert casting has so great an advantage over any other method of bait-fishing, and that when once acquired it will never be relinquished for any other mode.

Bait-Fishing—Playing the Bass.

When a Bass is hooked the boatman should pull at once for deep water, for the better management of the fish, and to prevent its taking refuge among weeds, rocks, snags, etc. In deep water the fish has better play and more room, and the angler, having fewer difficulties to encounter, enjoys more thoroughly the ensuing contest and final capture and landing of his prey.

If fishing from the banks of a stream, the angler should keep as near the level of the water as possible, or, still better, he should wade the stream when practicable. He should cast below the riffles, near gravelly bars, submerged roots or snags, weed patches and projecting rocks in the bed of the stream, and under shelving rocks on the banks, etc. After striking a Bass, he should lead him into deeper water if possible, or, at all events, away from dangerous places.

After casting the minnow, and it alights at a favorable spot, it should be left for a longer or a shorter time, depending on the nature of the water fished, and upon the abundance, scarcity, and mood of the Bass. As the line slackens, it should be slowly reeled until the entire line is retrieved. Sometimes, when fish are plentiful and biting eagerly, it is best to make frequent casts, reeling in rapidly after each cast, especially in rather shallow water, so as to give a rapid swimming motion to the bait.

When the Bass takes the bait, the angler should let him have it from two to ten seconds, according to the mood of the fish. If he bites eagerly and wickedly, the angler may hook him at once; but if he seems shy, off his feed, and inclined to toy with the bait, let him have it a few seconds, and give him line as he takes it, keeping the thumb upon the spool as a drag, however, so as to feel

Bait-Fishing—Giving the Butt.

every motion of the fish. At the proper time the angler should check him by a stronger pressure of the thumb, when, if the Bass pulls strongly and steadily, and seems inclined to run away with the bait, he should be hooked at once by a slight " twist of the wrist," but not by a violent jerk, or by "yanking" the rod.

If, however, upon checking the Bass, he gives several tugs or a succession of slight jerks, it is better to let him run a few seconds longer, for he has the bait crosswise in his mouth and does not feel the steel; finally, when he pulls steadily, hook him as before described. The Bass should never be given time to gorge, or swallow the bait.

From the time a Bass first "bites" until he is in the landing-net, he should never be given an inch of slack line, under any circumstances. The rod must be held by the butt, with the thumb upon the reel, or, if the rod is held in the left hand, the line must be held against the rod, by the forefinger, which encircles it, and thus acts as a drag. The Bass is, of course, hooked by the right, or rod hand, and the rod is held in that hand so long so the Bass is inclined to pull steadily, or take line; but as soon as he shows a disposition to "let up," or turn toward the angler, the rod must be taken in the other hand, so as to leave the right hand free to use the reel. The Bass should be made to feel, constantly, the spring of the rod, which should always maintain a curve, by the tip being held in an elevated position. The Bass should fight for every inch of line, and the angler should take it again whenever possible. The fish must be killed on the rod.

Should the Bass break water, with a long line, merely let the rod straighten as he falls back, so as to slacken the line (but it should be recovered immediately when he

36

strikes the water), for if the Bass falls across a taut line he is almost sure to tear the hook out. If he breaks water with a short line, the rod may be elevated so as to keep the line above him, following him back as he falls into the water.

If there is danger of the Bass getting to the weeds, or to the protection of snags, roots, rocks, etc., he must be stopped at all hazards. If the rod is a good one, and pliable, the angler must not hesitate to give him the butt; this will bring him up standing, with no danger to a first-class rod; but if the rod is a stiff one, turning the butt to him will be most sure to break it; in this case it is best to keep the Bass away from dangerous places by main strength, and the natural bend of the rod. If fishing from a boat, great caution must be used to prevent the Bass from running under it, as he will be sure to do if he has the opportunity; and should he succeed, the rod must be quickly passed around the stern or bow, and the thumb at once released from the reel so as to allow the line to run out as rapidly as possible, otherwise a broken rod is the result.

When the fish is thoroughly exhausted, he should be landed, and not before. Most anglers attempt to land their fish too soon, thus curtailing their sport and endangering their tackle. The landing-net should be held several inches beneath the surface of the water, and held perfectly still, when the angler should bring the fish over it; then the net should be lifted quickly, and with one motion. The angler must never, himself, nor allow his assistant to, frighten the fish by lunging at it with the net, in attempting to secure it. More fish are lost in clumsy endeavors to land them, than in any other way.

The angler should never be in too great a hurry to land
his fish; for if he is well-hooked he can not get away,
while if he is hooked in a thin or weak part of the mouth,
there is a greater necessity that he should be gingerly
played and tenderly handled, until he is completely
"tuckered out," and turns up his belly to the sun. There
is never any thing gained by too great a hurry in Bass
fishing. On the contrary, "the more haste the less speed,"
is a maxim particularly applicable to this case.

In reeling in the line, whether playing a fish or retrieving the line, it should be guided on the spool of the
reel by the left middle finger, when the reel is underneath
the rod (as it always should be), or by the left thumb
when the reel is used on top; it should be reeled on regularly from left to right, and from right to left, like sewing-
cotton on a spool. This prevents that "bunching," or
piling, and the subsequent tangling and snarling of the
line, so common with beginners and careless anglers. It
is just as easy to reel the line correctly, and in regular
and uniform coils or turns, as to bunch it, if the novice
begins right; after the habit is once acquired, he does it
automatically or mechanically.

CHAPTER XXIII.

STILL-FISHING.

"And if you rove for a Perch with a minnow, then it is best to be alive, you sticking your hook through his back-fin; or a minnow with the hook in his upper lip, and letting him swim up and down, about mid-water or a little lower, and you still keeping him to about that depth by a cork." —Izaak Walton.

Still-fishing is the most universal mode of angling for the Black Bass. As the name implies, it consists in throwing in the baited hook, and waiting patiently for "a bite," the angler, meanwhile, keeping himself and rod as still as possible. Fly-fishing is surface fishing; casting the minnow is both surface and mid-water fishing; while still-fishing combines mid-water and bottom fishing. In fly-fishing and casting the minnow the bait is kept in pretty constant motion, while in still-fishing the bait is left to itself, or "still," for a longer or shorter time. Still-fishing on streams is best practiced from the banks, while on lakes or large ponds a boat is necessary.

TACKLE.

Still-fishing is often practiced without a reel, and sometimes without a rod, a hand-line, merely, being used. When no reel is employed, the rod should be quite long and light; the best being a cane pole, from twelve to fifteen feet in length. When the reel is used (as it always

(428)

ought to be) the rod recommended for casting the minnow is the best, though most still-fishers prefer a longer rod, say from ten to twelve feet, as they are not proficient in casting.

The length of the line for still-fishing depends upon the character of the rod. Where no reel is employed, it should be of about the same length as the rod; when the angler uses a reel, but is indifferent at casting, a line of twenty-five yards is sufficient; but when the regular minnow-rod is used by a good caster, fifty yards, as in casting the minnow, should be used. The line in each instance being the same as recommended for casting the minnow, except where no reel is used, when the smallest size twisted silk line, No. 1, is the best.

Still-fishers usually employ the float and sinker, and they may be used or not, according to circumstances; though one of the chiefest delights of the still-fisher is to watch the maneuvers of his float. Where the stream is shallow and full of snags, or the bottom covered with moss or grass, a float is necessary; and where the current is quite swift, or the water deep, a sinker must be used to keep the bait beneath the surface.

BAITS AND BAITING.

While a minnow is the best bait for casting, other baits, as the helgramite, crawfish, frog, cricket, grasshopper, etc., are as good, and sometimes better, for still-fishing. As a rule, the bait that is the most plentiful in the waters fished, will be found the most successful. The helgramite is a capital bait, either early or late in the season, when the Bass are on the ripples or in shallow water. It is a flat, dark, repulsive-looking worm, some two or three inches long, and a half-inch wide (the larva of the horned cory-dalis), and is found under bowlders, flat stones, decaying timbers, etc., in shallow streams. It is variously called helgramite, dobson, hellion, kill-devil, grampus, crawler, etc., and is best hooked by passing the hook under the cap covering the neck, from behind forward, bringing the hook out next to the head.

The crawfish, especially when casting its shell—when it is called "peeler" or "shedder"—is a good bait. In its usual state, it is best hooked through the tail; peelers can be hooked through the head or body. Grasshoppers, crickets, frogs, etc., are used with varying success in still-fishing, and sometimes the humble "wum."

General Instructions.

As the still-fisher never casts his bait very far, it is highly important that he keep as still and motionless as possible; and, if in a boat, must avoid striking the same with his feet, his rod, or the oars, as such sounds are heard very distinctly by the fish. He should fish toward the sun, so as to keep his shadow behind him. He should keep his line as taut as possible, with his thumb always upon the spool of the reel (if he uses one), and as the line becomes slack, should reel it in.

In fishing a lake or pond, the still-fisher anchors his boat in a favorable spot, which should be in rather deep water, just off a shoal or bar, ledge of rocks, or point of land, or near beds of rushes or lily-pads, so as to fish between the boat and the feeding-grounds, that is, be-tween deep and shallow water, and near enough to cast his bait quite up to the haunts of the Bass, above-mentioned, whenever necessary.

If his minnows are lively and strong, and carefully hooked, it is advisable not to make frequent casts, but rather to suffer the bait to remain, so long as it keeps in motion, for a lively minnow will attract a Bass anywhere within thirty feet, in tolerably clear water. If helgramites or crawfish are used for bait, they must be kept gently moving, at times, by the rod.

The management of hooking, playing, and landing a Bass is just the same as described in the preceding chapter, except where a reel is not used, in which case the Bass should be killed on the rod, all the same, though the angler must use a great deal of judgment in managing his rod, to thoroughly enjoy the sport, which is considerable where the rod is long, slender, and light.

He should lead his fish, at once, into deep water, where he must be held until tired out. He should be kept in mid-water, not suffered to go to the bottom, nor encouraged to approach the surface. He should lead him to and fro, to the left and right, whenever possible, for by keeping the fish in constant motion it soon tires him out, and subserves, to some extent, the purposes and uses of a reel.

In still-fishing a stream, the angler should stand, or sit, as near the level of the water as possible, never fishing from a bold bank or other elevation, unless well screened from the observation of the fish. He should keep quiet and still, when he may possibly be mistaken for a stump or other inanimate object. He should leave his bait in the water as long as possible, only moving it occasionally, by slow, cautious and gentle manipulations, and in every

other respect remember that he is "still-fishing," and
govern himself accordingly; for too much caution can not
be exercised in this mode of angling.

The noisy "fishing party," which indulges in loud talk-
ing, shouting, and laughter, and has a "good time" generally, no doubt thoroughly enjoys itself in its own way,
but will take but few fish; it is the "lone fisherman" who
is always successful, for obvious reasons.

CHAPTER XXIV

TROLLING.

" And then you are to know that your minnow must be so put on your hook that it must turn round when 'tis drawn against the stream.—Izaak Walton.

TROLLING WITH THE ROD.

TROLLING with the rod, and with the artificial fly, the live minnow, or the spoon for bait, is capital sport; and is a very popular style of angling in the lakes and lakelets of the North-west. It is more *en regle* than still-fishing, and is, besides, more exciting sport, possessing advantages over the latter method in several respects.

The angler can fish with a long line, even though he be indifferent at casting; for, as the boat moves along, the line can be pulled off from the reel, yard by yard, with the hand, while the resistance of the bait, or leader, in the water, takes it from the rod. The bait, being in constant motion, is more likely to be seen and taken by the fish than in still-fishing; while the great length of line takes the bait so far from the boat as to remove or quiet any suspicions or apprehensions of danger on the part of the wily Bass.

Then the boat, not being anchored, as in still-fishing, the boatman can favor the angler in many ways when playing or landing his fish. Then, again, in moving over so much and so great a variety of ground, the angler is

37

more apt to find where the Bass are feeding, and thus to know just the character of the ground and depth of water to try successfully on each particular occasion. And, lastly, it secures a constant change of location, and adds enough of the spice of variety to satisfy the most impatient angler.

The minnow casting-rod, previously described, is the one best adapted to this or any other mode of bait-fishing, though any light and pliable rod, not exceeding ten or eleven feet in length, will answer, and even the fly-rod can be utilized here. A stiff and unyielding rod should not be used, for the sudden and violent "bite" of the Bass, in this method of angling, with the rod ever bent, and taut line, would be very likely to break it, unless the rod were of the hoop-pole pattern.

The only lines admissible here are the braided raw or boiled silk-line, and the braided linen-line; twisted lines can not be used at all on account of their kinking. The caliber should be a size larger than recommended for casting the minnow, which, in silk-lines, would be sizes E, or No. 3, and F, or No. 4: and, in linen lines, F, or No. 4, and G, or No. 5. The length should be from fifty to seventy-five yards.

It is best to use a leader from six to nine feet long, with either flies, the minnow, or spoon. The float should not be used. One or two swivels are necessary; but, usually, no sinker is required.

If artificial flies are used for the troll, a gut-leader, nine feet in length, and three flies, may be employed; or, a twelve-feet leader, and four flies, as preferred by some. The flies should be placed about three feet apart on the leader. An attractive combination of varieties in the flies should be observed.

A very good assortment would be a "General Hooker" for the tail-fly, a "Coachman" for the first dropper, a "Grizzly King" next, and, lastly, if four are used, an "Abbey." Another good troll would be a "Professor" for tail-fly, a "Montreal" next, the third a "Brown Hackle," and, last, a "Ferguson." But, of course, other flies will be used by the angler, as found more attractive and killing; for different waters often require different flies, in trolling, as well as in fly-fishing.

Three split shot, No. 1, should be placed at equal distances along the leader, so as to keep the flies submerged from one to three feet below the surface. The boat should be propelled quite slowly in trolling with flies, so as to permit their sinking to the proper depth, and, likewise, to enable them to be easily seen by the fish.

If the first Bass hooked takes an upper fly, by playing him judiciously and cautiously, one, or even two, additional Bass may often be induced to take the lower flies, though I do not advise this plan with a light rod; one at a time will afford better sport, and last much longer.

If a spoon-bait is to be the lure, only the smallest sizes, as fly-spoons, or trout-spoons, should be employed. Usually no sinker will be needed; but one or two swivels should always be used—one next to the spoon, and the other several feet above it. In trolling with the spoon, the boat should move at a sufficient rate of speed to cause the spoon to revolve rapidly a foot or two beneath the surface of the water.

In trolling with the live minnow, but one hook should be used. Give a wide berth to the English abominations known as spinning-tackle, gangs, traces, etc., consisting of from three to a dozen hooks arranged in groups of three, with single hooks for impaling the minnow; these contrivances are intended for Pike-fishing, and should never be used for the Black Bass. A single hook is sufficient for all purposes. The minnow may be hooked through the lips; or, perhaps, the best way for trolling, is to pass the hook through the mouth and out at the gill-opening, then carry it back and insert it just behind the dorsal fin—a needle, armed with a strong thread, is then passed through the lips of the minnow, and tightly tied to the snell, this obviates the use of the lip-hook; a minnow will spin as well hooked in this way, as with the most approved spinning-tackle.

The angler, with his boatman, in trolling with the rod, proceeds in a boat over the fishing-grounds, with from thirty to fifty yards of line out. The rod must be held with the tip elevated, so as to keep the rod constantly curved, and the thumb should be applied to the spool of the reel, so as to be ready at any moment for the violent rush of the Bass, for he bites very wickedly at the moving bait. The fish must be hooked at once, though he often fastens himself. If the angler has a long line out, he must reel in his fish as soon as possible, until he has him within proper bounds, when he can kill him at his leisure. The manipulation of the Bass after he is hooked is just the same as described in the chapter on casting the minnow, to which the reader is referred.

It is useless to troll in deep water, far from shore; it should only be practiced in water from three to ten feet deep, following the trend of the shore, as far as possible, where the proper conditions exist, which are given in a previous chapter.

TROLLING WITH THE HAND-LINE.

Trolling with the hand-line is a very tame and simple mode of angling; in fact, is the most simple method practiced, there being no skill, whatever, required in luring or in manipulating the Bass after he is hooked. It is a very questionable style of sport, at best; and, considered in this light, is exceedingly flat, and savors strongly of pot-fishing. It is indulged in on lakes, ponds and broad rivers, mostly by boys, and those unfortunates who can not, or will not, learn to handle the rod.

With a good breeze and a fast-sailing boat, trolling for Blue Fish, Sea Trout, Spanish Mackerel, and other marine fishes, with hand-line and squid, is fine sport; but, on the bosom of a quiet lake, trolling for Black Bass, with hand-line and spoon, is a cruel pastime, and a wanton destruction of a noble fish. It is only excusable when in camping out, without suitable tackle, and when, like the boy digging at the tenantless woodchuck hole, one is "out of meat," which, in Southern parlance, constitutes "a groundhog case," in which event, perhaps, the end justifies the means.

The necessary tackle for this mode of angling consists of a strong hand-line of linen or cotton, from fifty to seventy-five yards long; braided lines are to be preferred, as they do not kink. The line should be large enough to prevent cutting the hands, and, at the same time, to withstand the dead strain of a lively fish. Sizes C, or No. 2, and D, or No. 3, are the best and most suitable.

Any of the numerous revolving spoon-baits, or spinners, will answer with or without the so-called "fly," or tuft of feathers, or braid; for the bright metal spoon is what lures the Bass, and it can not be made more attractive for hand-trolling by the addition of feathers, braid, etc.

Abbey & Imbrie's New Fluted Spoon, No. 4; J. H. Mann's Perfect Revolving, No. 20, Oval, No. 16, Kidney, No. $6\frac{1}{2}$, and Egg, No. $3\frac{1}{2}$; and L. S. Hill's Improved Spoon, Nos. $1\frac{1}{2}$ and 2, are all excellent trolling-baits for hand-lines.

The ordinary original tin or brass spoon, with single hook soldered on, is about as good as any of the later inventions. A single hook is certainly preferable to the groups of two or three, usually attached to spoon-baits; the latter often being crushed or broken by the jaws of a large fish.

Small spoons are more successful than large ones, for Black Bass. In the absence of a spoon-bait, the floor of the mouth of the Pickerel, cut into the semblance of a fish, is tough, white and glistening, and is a good substitute; a similar strip, cut from the belly of the Dog Fish, also answers a good purpose. One or two swivels should always be used with trolling-bait; a sinker is seldom necessary.

With this simple outfit, early in the season, before the aquatic weeds and grasses are fully grown, this mode of fishing is quite successful. The method of procedure is as follows:

The angler sits in the stern of the boat, and, while the oarsman rows at a moderate rate of speed along and over the feeding-ground, he runs off forty to sixty yards of line; the spoon, revolving gracefully beneath the surface, proves an effective lure. A violent jerk on the line announces the fact that an unfortunate Bass has "hooked himself;" often he will leap into the air, vainly endeavoring to shake the glittering deception from his jaws, but his efforts usually only serve to fix the several hooks more firmly in his mouth, and, provided he does not crush them, or tear them out and escape, he is "hauled in," hand over hand, by muscle and main strength, without a single chance for his life—dragged to an ignoble death by a hand-line and spoon. This may do for the Pickerel; but, oh, gentle reader, an' you love me, spare the Bass this indignity!

CHAPTER XXV.

SKITTERING AND BOBBING.

"Then, if you get a grasshopper, put it on your hook, with your line about two yards long; standing behind a bush or tree, where his hole is, and make your bait stir up and down on the top of the water."—IZAAK WALTON.

SKITTERING.

"SKITTERING" is best practiced with a long and light natural cane-rod, from twelve to fifteen feet long, and a strong line of nearly the same length. No reel is used, for, like "bobbing," this mode of fishing is only successful in grassy and weedy situations, where the water is comparatively shallow, notably, in the lagoons and bayous of the extreme South, and where the fish must be landed as soon as possible after being hooked. To the end of the line is attached a small trout-spoon, or the skittering-spoon, which is still smaller, being the smallest revolving spoon made.

The *modus operandi* is as follows: The angler stands in the bow of the boat, which is paddled or poled by the boatman as noiselessly as possible, just outside of or along the channels of clear water, among the patches of rushes, lily-pads or bonnets. The angler, by means of the long rod and short line, skitters or skips the spoon along the surface of the water with a jerky or vibratory motion, causing it to spin and glance close up to the edges of the weeds, where it is viciously seized by the Bass, who has been lying in wait among the water lettuce, or under the broad pads of the water-lily, for just such an opportunity.

The angler has now no time to loose, but must rapidly draw the Bass along the surface of the water to the boat, into which he must be lifted at once, for he is as good as gone if he gets below the surface, among the weeds; nor must the Bass be allowed to leap into the air with so short a line, but he must be dragged quickly along the surface, with his head above the the water, until the line can be taken hold of close to the hook, or the finger hooked in the gill-opening, and the fish dextrously lifted over the side of the boat.

In such situations, skittering is exciting sport, and is not without its attractions. The bright glancing spoon, the expert and skillful management of the rod, the mighty rush and splash of the Bass as he snaps up the shining bauble, and his subsequent lashing and floundering as he is irresistibly drawn toward the boat, vainly endeavoring to get either in or out of the water, and the final adroit manner of landing him, go far toward making this a legitimate sport, as it undoubtedly is, in the localities mentioned, inasmuch as reel-fishing can not be practiced for reasons before given.

BOBBING.

"Bobbing" is another style of angling peculiar to the section of country just mentioned, and though it can not be regarded as so artistic or legitimate, it is far more killing than skittering. It is a mode of fishing especially adapted to the waters of the Gulf States, where it is much practiced. The implements for bobbing are few and simple, consisting merely of a strong rod from ten to twenty feet in length, two or three feet of stout line, and the "bob," heretofore described in Chapter XVII.

I can not describe this method of angling better than to quote from Bartram, who wrote of the "Trout" (Black Bass) of Florida and the way of taking them with the bob, in 1764, as follows:—

"They are taken with a hook and line, but without any bait. Two people are in a little canoe, one sitting in the stern to steer, and the other near the bow, having a rod ten or twelve feet in length, to one end of which is tied a string line, about twenty inches in length, to which is fastened three large hooks, back to back. These are fixed very securely, and tied with the white hair of a deer's tail, shreds of a red garter, and some parti-colored feathers, all which form a tuft or tassel nearly as large as one's fist, and entirely cover and conceal the hooks; that is called a "bob." The steersman paddles softly, and proceeds slowly along shore; he now ingeniously swings the bob backwards and forwards, just above the surface and sometimes tips the water with it, when the unfortunate cheated Trout instantly springs from under the reeds and seizes the exposed prey."

I have many times seen the bob used in Florida just as described by Bartram more than a century ago, and it is just as effective to-day as it was then. If there is any thing in the notion of certain angling authorities, that fish after a time become educated or accustomed to certain artificial baits, as flies, etc.—becoming first suspicious, and

finally refusing them altogether, then the Black Bass of
Florida must be very dull of comprehension, must have
sadly neglected their educational privileges and opportunities, or else the said "theory," like many another from
"across the herring pond," originated in the fertile brain
of some unfortunate angler to account for an empty
creel.

CHAPTER XXVI.

CONCLUDING REMARKS.

THERE is a right way, and, *per contra*, a wrong way, to do every thing. I have endeavored in the preceding pages to point out the right way of doing things pertaining to angling, but I feel that my duty would be but half accomplished, did I not give some advice relative to the proper use and care of fishing tackle, before taking leave of my reader. I am the more impelled to do this from the fact that I have seen so many fine and elegant rods, reels, and lines improvidently ruined, through sheer carelessness, in most instances, and through ignorance in others.

Every angler should, himself, look after the welfare of his tackle, and not trust it to the care of guides, boatmen, or servants. Every true angler should do this, *con amore*, as every true sportsman should, himself, clean his gun and feed his dogs at the close of a day's shooting, or every true sailor, himself, snug and stow his boat when the anchor is dropped. As a good workman is known by his jealous care and skillful use of his tools, so is a good angler known by the way he uses and handles his tackle, a good sportsman by the way he uses and handles his gun and dogs, and a good sailor by the way he uses and handles his boat. It is, therefore, essential that the new hand should know the right way, to avoid the wrong way; not only on the

(444)

score of the fitness of things, but on the score of economy, for more tackle is hopelessly ruined by a lack of proper care, than by the most severe, though judicious, use.

CARE OF THE ROD.

The *right* way to "joint up," or put a rod together, is to take the joints, or pieces, from the case, remove the plugs, or stoppers, and put them in the pocket; then attach the reel to the butt, and see that it fits firmly and securely, and will not be likely to work loose; next wipe the male, or inside ferrules of the joints, to insure their being dry, clean, and bright; then the tip and second piece are to be put together first, and the butt last. Be particular in "jointing up," to place the standing guides, or rings, on a straight line with the reel (there are usually small marks or punctures on the male and female ferrules as a guide), and in fitting the joints, do so by inserting the smaller, or male ferrule into the larger, or female ferrule, and push home firmly, but gently, and be very careful to avoid a twisting, or screwing motion, especially with split bamboo rods, for this is not only liable to warp the ferrules, but also to separate the strips of such a rod. After the rod is properly jointed up, place the butt end carefully on the ground, reeve the line through the guides, or rings, and bring it down and tie it to one of the bars of the reel by a single bow-knot, until ready to attach the cast of flies, or the swivel and hook.

The *wrong* way to joint up a rod, and I will describe it as I have seen it done, many times, is to put the butt and second piece together first; then drop the butt end on the ground and shove it to one side, or behind you, and then put the tip on—the rod swaying and bending, in the meantime, rendering this somewhat difficult to do, but which is finally accomplished by twisting or screwing it on, the butt boring a hole in the ground, the while—and in case no one has stepped on your rod (which I have seen done more than once), hold the rod perpendicularly, and settle the joints by tamping the butt-end on a stone, or piece of wood. The reel is yet to be adjusted ; to do which you may either rest the tip on the ground in front (using it as a boring instrument in this instance), or hold the rod horizontally with the butt against the pit of the stomach, to the great danger of some one stumbling over your rod, or of your striking it against a tree or rock while endeavoring to ship your reel ; and yet—" tell it not in Gath "— I have seen this very scene played over and over again by those who called themselves anglers ; and so they were, in the aggregate, or on the whole, but not in detail. To hold the rod across the body, sitting or standing, or perpendicularly, while adjusting the reel, is just as awkward and unsafe.

Remember, then, to remove the plugs and put them in the pocket—you will have them then whenever you unjoint your rod, for the separated joints should never be left a moment without the plugs in the female ferrules ; in this way you will preserve the proper shape of the ferrules, and your rod will always go together and come apart easily, provided you keep them clean and smooth. Then, ship the reel ; then put the smaller joints together first, and the butt piece last.

The right way to " unjoint," or take apart, the rod (I will spare the reader the infliction of a description of the wrong way) is first to remove the leader, or swivel and hook, reel the line on the spool slowly—I say slowly, for I have seen the tip of a rod snapped off while the wet line was being reeled rapidly, or in a hurry, by its catching in one of the rings, or clinging in a coil around the tip. The reel is next to be unshipped, and the rod wiped perfectly dry; all sand, dirt, or fish-scales must be carefully rubbed off, and especially must the ferrules be rendered clean and bright, to prevent any foreign substance getting into them when the rod is being unjointed, for the smallest particle of grit or sand may spoil the fitting of the rod. The rod must now be taken apart in the reverse order in which it was put together; the butt first, and the smaller joints last; in unjointing, pull the joints apart by using gentle and steady force, in a straight line, with the hands close to the ferrules, when they will separate readily. Be particular about this, for I have seen an angler with the joint against his breast, his hands widely separated, pulling on the two pieces in a curved line, as if he would bend the rod around his body, which proceeding had a greater tendency to strain and warp the ferrules than to separate them.

Having separated the joints of the rod, the plugs are next to be inserted, and the reel unshipped. Examine each joint, or piece, and if bent, or warped, straighten it carefully, and place them in the case, large end down; in tying the case, tie it loosely, otherwise you may bend the small joints. Never put your rod away in a damp case; should it be wet, dry it thoroughly after reaching home.

When the rod is put together, never stand it in a corner, or lean it with the tip resting against any thing; better lay it down flat. In putting a rod away after the season, it should be laid on a shelf, or in a flat box. It should be kept in a cool room, of uniform temperature, and never in a room heated by a furnace or a stove. A dry atmosphere will cause the joints to shrink, and the ferrules to become loose, while a damp, or constantly changing atmosphere will cause them to twist and warp. The wrappings of the guides, rings, or hand-piece should be frequently looked to, when in use, and the rod should be varnished once or twice during the season. Coach varnish is good, but the best, perhaps, is a saturated solution of shellac in alcohol; it should be put on quite thin and evenly, and one or two coats applied as may be needed, using a soft rag or sponge; it soon dries and is perfectly waterproof. In Izaak Walton's day rods were painted, and he gives minute directions for preparing the sizing, the paint, and the manner of applying them. Wood, to preserve its elasticity, must be protected from the changes of the atmosphere.

CARE OF THE REEL.

A fine reel should receive as much care as a watch, so far as this can be done, consistently, with its use. It should never be laid on the sand or bare ground, or exposed in any way to favor the introduction of sand or grit into the working parts. When not in use it should be kept in a box, or in a buckskin or chamois bag. At the beginning and end of each season it should be carefully taken apart, cleaned and oiled. After use, it should be always wiped clean, and rubbed with an oiled rag or chamois skin.

A first-class reel will last an angler his life-time, with proper care. Especially is a multiplying reel to·be well cared for, as it is more complicated, and has more gearing than a click reel. The screw that holds the movable handle to the crank should be frequently noticed, to see that it is firmly screwed in, otherwise it may come out in casting, and both screw and handle be lost. On this account, this screw should never be oiled. The drag, alarm, click—or by whatever name the "brake" of a multiplying reel may be known—should be used only when really necessary, and as seldom as possible, for its frequent use wears out the gearing of the reel.

See that the reel fits your rod perfectly and tightly, so there will be no shaking, wabbling or coming loose during a severe strain. If the reel-plate fits the rod too loosely, place strips of parchment or card-board between the plate of the reel and the groove of the rod, until the reel-band will just slip over the plate and hold it firmly. If the reel-plate is too long, or too thick for the reel-seat of the rod, one or the other, or both, must be cut to fit; at all events, see that your reel fits its seat firmly and securely.

Always, if you can, use the reel "underneath," with the handle to the right side, when reeling the line; and always turn the crank, in reeling, "away" from you, or in the direction that the hands of a watch move. It may seem unnecessary to mention this latter precaution, but I have known it to be used the contrary way. When angling, and the fly or bait is in the water, never, for a moment, lay the rod down with a turn of the line around the crank of the reel to serve as a drag, for I have several times seen both rod and reel jerked overboard, and irretrievably lost, by just such inexcusable carelessness and stupidity, and the savage "bite" of a big fish.

38

CARE OF THE LINE.

The line should be thoroughly dried, *always*, after use. This injunction is of the highest importance to the angler. The entire line—not merely the portion that may have been used—should be stretched between two trees, or around pegs or nails driven up for the purpose, and exposed to the sun and air; or, if at night, or if the day be damp, it should be coiled around the back of a chair, and placed near the fire. I can not impress the necessity of this care too strongly on the beginner, for he will see so many bad examples in those who ought to know better, but who habitually put away the reel and wet line, to the everlasting injury of both, because it is "too much trouble," or they are "too tired," to perform their bounden duty of drying their lines; such men are "pot-fishers," and will stand their rods, jointed, up in a corner all night. They are on a par with the "pot-hunter" who, after a hard day's tramp, permits his dogs to go supperless to bed, and his gun to remain foul until morning.

Silk-lines are especially liable to mildew and rot if put away damp or wet. Even waterproof lines should have a good airing after use, or they will retain more or less dampness, which, in the end, will work their destruction. After drying a line, it should be rubbed, or reeled through a woolen cloth, to remove any sand, grit or mildew. The economy of this whole matter is one thing, and its expediency another; the value of a line may be a small affair, but the breaking away of a good fish through a defective line is a serious event. I once knew a good fellow, but a poor angler, who, after a day's fishing, carefully dried a fifty-cent handkerchief for fear it would mildew, while he left a three-dollar line, wet, on a twenty-dollar reel and a thirty-dollar rod, standing in the corner all night, because he was "going a-fishing again in the morning."

The line should be thoroughly tested at the beginning of the season, during its whole length; and, if not found fully up to the standard, should be discarded. It should also be tested, occasionally, during the season; in fact, the better way is to test it always before using it. A line that will sustain a dead weight of two pounds is strong enough, if used with a pliant rod, and no other should be used for Black Bass angling. By examining and testing the line, *always*, before using it, it may save much mortification, and many a fish. Though you can not loose a fish by the breaking of the line—for, as Father Izaak says, "no man can lose what he never had"—you can lose your temper under such trying circumstances, which is worse.

It would be useless to give any directions for waterproofing lines, for it is a very difficult thing to do well; and, moreover, prepared lines are now so cheaply and well made, that it will pay the angler to buy them, if he wants waterproof lines. If a line loses its color or tint, it can be soaked in strong green tea, or a weak solution of indigo, to be afterward well dried. To take the kink—so far as it can be done—out of laid or twisted lines, let them out their full length, and draw them loosely through the water, without hook or sinker, from the stern of a boat as it is rowed along; to be then stretched and dried. Never use a reel-line with a knot in it; better, by far, make some boy happy by giving it to him to catch Perch and "Sunnies."

CARE OF OTHER TACKLE.

Artificial flies should be closely looked after, summer
and winter, to preserve them from their worst enemy—the
moth. When put away for the winter, see that the fly-
book, or other receptacle, is perfectly clean; dust out the
leaves and pockets before putting the flies in. See that
the flies are perfect in feather and snell; reject all that
are much worn or seem moth-eaten, and those which have
worn, frayed or otherwise imperfect snells. Place patch-
ouly, or gum camphor, wrapped in paper, in the pockets
and between the leaves, and inclose the whole, securely, in
cotton cloth.

Leaders should be carefully looked to, and only those
that are perfect retained. Imperfect ones may be utilized
for snells. Hooks should be kept sharpened, and free
from rust; it is a good plan to wipe them, after use, with
an oiled rag; those that are rusted should be thrown
away. All tackle, in short, should be kept neat and
clean. It is a great pleasure to the angler to overhaul
his tools and tackle several times during the winter, to
see that every thing is all right. A little attention to
these details, and a following of the advice given in this
chapter, will more than pay the angler for the price of
this book, and may inculcate habits of order and economy in the novice, which will certainly promote his pleasure and happiness, and may save him many a dollar, if
applied to other walks in life.

PARTING WORDS.

And now, in taking leave of the angler—or he who

has mentally resolved to become an angler, and who has
followed me through the pages of this book—I do so with
regret; for it has been to me a labor of love to describe,
in my way, the methods and the delights of angling. It
has revived the memory of many happy hours, spread over
many years of checkered sunshine and shadow. The
bright pages in the book of memory stand out like the
flashing stream in the bright sunlight, while the sorrows
are hid in the deep shadows of its thickly-wooded glens.

"With thee conversing I forget all time." I live,
again, in scenes forever past, but never to be forgotten;
with rod and reel, again I wander along the upland streams,
among the cedars and chinkapins, and on the tide-waters
and salt-marshes of "My Maryland;" on Long Island's
sea-girt shore; on the broad bosom of the St. Lawrence,
with its clusters of emerald isles, and on the charming
lakes of the Empire State; among the low green hills of
"the valley," the broom-sedge of the "Piedmont" section,
and on the broad bays of the "Old Dominion;" in the
coves and bights of the stormy Huron, the treacherous
Michigan, and the great inland sea, Superior, with its
crystal waters and great hills, crowned by the scarlet
banners of the mountain ash ; by the pine-clad rivers of
the "Old North State;" along the rocky streams of Kentucky and Tennessee, flecked with the roseate tassels and
snowy disks of the redbud and dogwood; among the
moss-covered rocks of the highland rapids, and under the
fragrant magnolia and feathery cypress of the silent estu-
aries of the "Palmetto State " and Georgia; on the clear,
sparkling lakelets of Wisconsin, glinting and dancing
amid fields of golden grain and broad green pastures, or
hiding in sheltered nooks, among the tamaracks and black

birches; on the broad Susquehanna, the blue Juniata, and among the hemlocks and maples of the Pennsylvania hills; under the moss-draped live-oak and stately palm, amid the orange-groves and myrtles, the mangrove and sea-grape, on the sluggish streams, the broad lagoons, and among the coral-reefs and sunny keys of Florida; under the cool beeches and broad sycamore, the graceful elms and lofty cottonwood, of the quiet streams of Ohio, Indiana, Illinois and Missouri; in the cold, crystal streams, gliding among the everlasting hills, clothed with tangled forests of balsam and pine, in Michigan. It has taken me back even to the days of lang syne, when, with a bit of cock's hackle, tied on a pin-hook, and a willow wand for a rod, I first essayed the angler's art, and made sad havoc among the minnows, chubs and "gudgeons."

I can only hope that the reader will experience as much pleasure in perusing the foregoing pages, as I have done in penning them; and he will please remember, that, though he may differ with me on each and every page, I will not quarrel with him; but, should we ever meet, as brothers of the angle, in some sequestered spot on lake or stream, we will, while smoking the pipe of peace, talk the matter over cooly, calmly and dispassionately. But he may rest assured, that, though all roads lead to Rome, and though there are many ways of catching a Bass—I have traveled some of the roads, and tried most of the ways—if he faithfully follows in my footsteps, he will never regret it, and never have cause to wish he had tried the other way.

And now I leave you, with this injunction; and, though I have mentioned it before, I do so at parting, that it may be the more impressive:

ALWAYS KILL YOUR FISH AS SOON AS TAKEN FROM
THE WATER; AND EVER BE SATISFIED WITH A MODER-
ATE CREEL.

By so doing, your angling days will be happy, and your
sleep undisturbed; and you, and I, and the fish we may
catch, can say, with the sweet singer of Israel:

"The lines are fallen to me in pleasant places."

THE END.

INDEX

— TO —

SCIENTIFIC HISTORY OF THE BLACK BASS.

39   (457)

INDEX TO LIFE HISTORY AND ANGLING.

(460)

CONROY, BISSETT & MALLESON,

MANUFACTURERS OF

FINE FISHING TACKLE,

65 Fulton Street, N. Y.   **Factory, Brooklyn, E. D.**

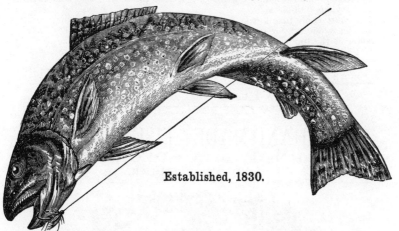

Established, 1830.

SEND FOR NEW ILLUSTRATED CATALOGUE. Price 15c.

THE CELEBRATED HENSHALL BLACK BASS ROD.

Ash and Lance-wood, 2 tips and tip-case; 8¼ to 9 ft. long; Weight,
9 to 10 oz.; German silver mountings.................................. $15 00

Brass mountings.. 12 00

The same as the above of Six-Strip Hexagonal Split Bamboo,
Waterproof, German silver ferrules.............................. 25 00

Or with our New Bronze mountings................................... 18 00

See Catalogue for other Black Bass Rods.

THE CELEBRATED KENTUCKY REEL, No. 3, $14.00; No. 4, $15.00.

Our new nickeled 4-ply Black Bass Reel, adjustable click and drag—
a good substitute for the Ky. Reel. No. 3½, $9.00; No. 4, $7.50; No. 5, $6.00.

See Catalogue for other Special Black Bass Reels.

[See next page.]

[1]

CINCINNATI, *October*, 28, 1880.

Messrs. CONROY, BISSETT & MALLESON,
                    New York City.

GENTLEMEN:

Your favor of the 26th and the "Rod" came to hand to-day. The Rod is about perfect in length, proportion, and weight—the great essentials—for a Black Bass Minnow Rod. I am more than pleased with it. Its action, I am sure, will be in harmony and keeping with its other good qualities, and I will soon give it a practical test. The finish and style is first-class. . . . .

I must compliment you upon the production of so handsome and serviceable a rod, for serviceable it must prove, from the excellent character of the timber and mountings.

I will write you further in a few weeks, after trying it. . . . .

Yours very truly,

J. A. HENSHALL.

[2]

HANOVER
ON
The Law of Horses.

A Practical Treatise on the Law of Horses: embracing the Law of Bargain, Sale, and Warranty of Horses and other Live Stock; the Rule as to Unsoundness and Vice, and the Responsibility of the Proprietors of Livery, Auction, and Sale Stables, Innkeepers, Veterinary Surgeons, and Farriers, Carriers, etc. Second edition, revised and greatly enlarged. By M. D. HANOVER.

8vo. Law Sheep. $4.00.

In this work the author has chiefly sought to investigate the principles which constitute the Law of Warranty in the sale of horses, and to present them in a clear and concise form.

Contracts, Frauds, Carriers, Negligences, and other branches of the law have also been treated of, so far as they relate to horses and other live stock. The rule as to unsoundness and vice in horses, and the responsibility of innkeepers, livery-stable keepers, and others having the care of horses, have been carefully presented.

The aim of the author has been to afford assistance to the lawyer, and at the same time to enable the unprofessional reader to gain a general acquaintance with the law on the subject. He has also given full notes of the decisions of the American and English courts.

"This is a little book that will prove useful to that large class of persons, lawyers and others, interested in horses. The arrangement is good, and the law well and clearly stated."—*Albany Law Journal.*

"It is invaluable to those interested in the subject of which it treats. It should take its place as an authority in every law library."—*Legal Gazette.*

"Such a work as this, in which the law relating to live stock is carefully collated and arranged, and presented in a popular form which non-professional readers could understand, has long been needed, and we believe this work will be generally sought after by all who deal in this description of property."—*National Live Stock Journal.*

"Very many of the little lawsuits in county courts arise from fraud or imposition in selling or swapping horses. In this book we have a perfect encyclopedia of the law and custom on these questions."—*Rural New Yorker.*

ROBERT CLARKE & CO
Law Publishers, Booksellers, Importers,
[4]   CINCINNATI

HISTORICAL AND MISCELLANEOUS

PUBLICATIONS OF

ROBERT CLARKE & CO.

CINCINNATI, O.

ALZOG (John, D. D.) A Manual of Universal Church History. Translated by Rev. T. J. Pabisch and Rev. T. S. Byrne. 3 vols. 8vo. 15 00

ANDERSON (E. L.) Six Weeks in Norway. 18mo· 1 00

ANDRE (Major) The Cow Chace; an Heroick Poem. 8vo. Paper. 75

ANTRIM (J.) The History of Champaign and Logan Counties, Ohio, from their First Settlement. 12mo. 1 50

BALLARD (Julia P.) Insect Lives; or, Born in Prison. Illustrated. Sq. 12mo. 1 00

BELL (Thomas J.) History of the Cincinnati Water Works. Plates. 8vo. 75

BENNER (S.) Prophecies of Future Ups and Downs in Prices: what years to make Money in Pig Iron, Hogs, Corn, and Provisions. 2d ed. 24mo. 1 00

BIBLE IN THE PUBLIC SCHOOLS. Records, Arguments, etc., in the Case of Minor *vs.* Board of Education of Cincinnati. 8vo. 2 00

Arguments in Favor of the Use of the Bible. Separate. Paper. 50

Arguments Against the Use of the Bible. Separate. Paper. 50

BIDDLE (Horace P.) Elements of Knowledge. 12mo. 1 00

BIDDLE (Horace P.) Prose Miscellanies. 12mo. 1 00

BINKERD (A. D.) The Mammoth Cave of Kentucky. Paper. 8vo. 50

BOUQUET (H.) The Expedition of, against the Ohio Indians in 1764, etc. With Preface by Francis Parkman, Jr. 8vo. $3 00. Large Paper. 6 00

BOYLAND (G. H., M. D.) Six Months Under the Red Cross with the French Army in the Franco-Prussian War. 12mo. 1 50

BRUNNER (A. A.)   Elementary and Pronouncing French Reader.
18mo.   60

BRUNNER (A. A.)   The Gender of French Verbs Simplified.
18mo.   25

BURT (Rev. N. C., D. D.) The Far East; or, Letters from Egypt,
Palestine, etc. 12mo.   1 75

BUTTERFIELD (C. W.) The Washington-Crawford Letters; being
the Correspondence between George Washington and William
Crawford, concerning Western Lands. 8vo.   1 00

BUTTERFIELD (C. W.) The Discovery of the Northwest in 1634,
by John Nicolet, with a Sketch of his Life. 12mo.   1 00

CLARK (Col. George Rogers) Sketches of his Campaign in the
Illinois in 1778–9. With an Introduction by Hon. Henry
Pirtle, and an Appendix. 8vo. $2 00. Large paper.   4 00

COFFIN (Levi) The Reminiscences of Levi Coffin, the Reputed
President of the Underground Railroad. A Brief History of
the Labors of a Lifetime in behalf of the Slave. With Stories
of Fugitive Slaves, etc., etc. 12mo.   2 00

CONSTITUTION OF THE UNITED STATES, ETC. The Declaration of
Independence, July 4, 1776; the Articles of Confederation,
July 9, 1778; the Constitution of the United States, September 17, 1787; the Fifteen Amendments to the Constitution,
and Index; Washington's Farewell Address, September 7,
1796. 8vo. Paper.   25

CRAIG (N. B.) The Olden Time. A Monthly Publication, devoted
to the Preservation of Documents of Early History, etc.
Originally Published at Pittsburg, in 1846–47. 2 vols.
8vo.   10 00

DRAKE (D.) Pioneer Life in Kentucky. Edited, with Notes
and a Biographical Sketch, by his Son, Hon. Chas. D. Drake.
8vo. $3 00. Large paper.   6 00

DuBREUIL (A.) Vineyard Culture Improved and Cheapened.
Edited by Dr. J. A. Warder. 12mo.   2 00

ELLARD (Virginia G.) Grandma's Christmas Day. Illus. Sq.
12mo.   1 00

FAMILY EXPENSE BOOK. A Printed Account Book, with appropriate Columns and Headings, for keeping a Complete Record
of Family Expenses. 12mo.   50

FINLEY (I. J.) and PUTNAM (R.) Pioneer Record and Reminiscences of the Early Settlers and Settlement of Ross County,
Ohio. 8vo.   2 50

FLETCHER (WM. B., M. D.) Cholera: its Characteristics, History,
Treatment, etc. 8vo. Paper.   1 00

FORCE (M. F.) Essays : Pre-Historic Man—Darwinism and Deity
—The Mound Builders. 8vo. Paper.   75

FORCE (M. F.) Some Early Notices of the Indians of Ohio. To What Race did the Mound Builders belong. 8vo. Paper. 50

FREEMAN (Ellen.) Manual of the French Verb, to accompany every French Course. 16mo. Paper. 25

GALLAGHER (Wm. D.) Miami Woods, A Golden Wedding, and other Poems. 12mo. 2 00

GIAUQUE (F.) The Election Laws of the United States: with Notes of Decisions, etc. 8vo. Paper, 75c.; cloth, 1 00

GRIMKE (F.) Considerations on the Nature and Tendency of Free Institutions. 8vo. 2 50

GRISWOLD (W.) Kansas: her Resources and Developments; or, the Kansas Pilot. 8vo. Paper. 50

GROESBECK (W. S.) Gold and Silver. Address delivered before the American Bankers' Association, in New York, September 13, 1878. 8vo. Paper. 25

HALL (James.) Legends of the West. Sketches illustrative of the Habits, Occupations, Privations, Adventures, and Sports of the Pioneers of the West. 12mo. 2 00

HALL (James.) Romance of Western History; or, Sketches of History, Life, and Manners in the West. 12mo. 2 00

HANOVER (M. D.) A Practical Treatise on the Law of Horses, embracing the Law of Bargain, Sale, and Warranty of Horses and other Live Stock; the Rule as to Unsoundness and Vice, and the Responsibility of the Proprietors of Livery, Auction, and Sale Stables, Inn-Keepers, Veterinary Surgeons, and Farriers, Carriers, etc. 8vo. 4 00

HART (J. M.) A Syllabus of Anglo-Saxon Literature. 8vo. Paper. 50

HASSAUREK (F.) The Secret of the Andes. A Romance. 12mo. 1 50

THE SAME, in German. 8vo. Paper, 50c.; cloth. 1 00

HASSAUREK (F.) Four Years Among Spanish Americans. Third Edition. 12mo. 1 50

HATCH (Col. W. S.) A Chapter in the History of the War of 1812, in the Northwest, embracing the Surrender of the Northwestern Army and Fort, at Detroit, August 16, 1813, etc. 18mo. 1 25

HAYES (Rutherford B.) The Life, Public Services, and Select Speeches of. Edited by J. Q. Howard. 12mo. Paper, 75c.; cloth, 1 25

HAZEN (Gen. W. B.) Our Barren Lands. The Interior of the United States, West of the One-Hundredth Meridian, and East of the Sierra Nevada. 8vo. Paper. 50

HENSHALL (Dr. James A.)   Book of the Black Bass: comprising its complete Scientific and Life History, together with a Practical Treatise on Agling and Fly Fishing, and a full description of Tools, Tackle, and Implements.   Illustrated.   12mo.   3 00

HORTON (S. Dana.)   Silver and Gold, and their Relation to the Problem of Resumption.   8vo.   1 50

HORTON (S. Dana.)   The Monetary Situation.   8vo.   Paper.   50

HOUSEKEEPING IN THE BLUE GRASS.   A New and Practical Cook Book.   By Ladies of the Presbyterian Church, Paris, Ky.   12mo.   12th thousand.   1 50

HOWE (H.)   Historical Collections of Ohio.   Containing a Collection of the most Interesting Facts, Traditions, Biographical Sketches, Anecdotes, etc., relating to its Local and General History.   8vo.   6 00

HUNT (W. E.)   Historical Collections of Coshocton County, Ohio.   8vo.   3 00

HUSTON (R. G.)   Journey in Honduras, and Jottings by the Way.   Inter-Oceanic Railway.   8vo.   Paper.   50

JACKSON (John D., M. D.)   The Black Arts in Medicine, with an Anniversary Address.   Edited by Dr. L. S. McMurtry.   12mo.   1 00

JASPER (T.)   The Birds of North America.   Colored Plates, drawn from Nature, with Descriptive and Scientific Letterpress.   In 40 parts, $1 00 each; or, 2 vols. Royal 4to.   Half morocco, $50 00; Full morocco,   60 00

JORDAN (D. M.)   Rosemary Leaves.   A Collection of Poems.   18mo.   1 50

KELLER (M. J.)   Elementary Perspective, explained and applied to Familiar Objects.   Illustrated.   12mo.   1 00

KING (John.)   A Commentary on the Law and True Construction of the Federal Constitution.   8vo.   2 50

KING (M.)   Pocket-Book of Cincinnati.   24mo.   15

KLIPPART (J. H.)   The Principles and Practice of Land Drainage.   Illustrated.   12mo.   1 75

LAW (J.)   Colonial History of Vincennes, Indiana, under the French, British, and American Governments.   12mo.   1 00

LLOYD (J. U.)   The Chemistry of Medicines.   Illus. 12mo.   Cloth, $2 75; sheep,   3 25

LONGWORTH (N.)   Electra.   Translated from the Greek of Sophocles.   12mo.   1 50

McBRIDE (J.)   Pioneer Biography: Sketches of the Lives of some of the Early Settlers of Butler County, Ohio.   2 vols.   8vo. $6 50.   Large paper.   Imp. 8vo.   13 00

McLaughlin (M. Louise.) China Painting. A Practical Manual for the Use of Amateurs in the Decoration of Hard Porcelain. Sq. 12mo. Boards. 75

McLaughlin (M. Louise.) Pottery Decoration: being a Practical Manual of Underglaze Painting, including Complete Detail of the author's Mode of Painting Enameled Faience. Sq. 12mo. Bds. 1 00

MacLean (J. P.) The Mound Builders, and an Investigation into the Archæology of Butler County, Ohio. Illus. 12mo. 1 50

MacLean (J. P.) A Manual of the Antiquity of Man. Illustrated. 12mo. 1 00

MacLean (J. P.) Mastodon, Mammoth, and Man. Illustrated. 12mo. 60

Mansfield (E. D.) Personal Memories, Social, Political, and Literary. 1803–43. 12mo. 2 00

Manypenny (G. W.) Our Indian Wards: A History and Discussion of the Indian Question. 8vo. 3 00

Matthews (Stanley.) A Summary of the Law of Partnership. For the Use of Business Men. 12mo. 1 25

May (Col. J.) Journal and Letters of, relative to Two Journeys to the Ohio Country, 1788 and 1779. 8vo. 2 00

Mettenheimer (H. J.) Safety Book-keeping; being a Complete Exposition of Book-keepers' Frauds. 12mo. 1 00

Minor (T. C., M. D.) Child-Bed Fever. Erysipelas and Puerperal Fever, with a Short Account of both Diseases. 8vo. 2 00

Minor (T. C., M. D.) Scarlatina Statistics of the United States. 8vo. Paper. 50

Montana Historical Society. Contributions. Vol. I. 8vo. 3 00

Morgan (Appleton.) The Shakspearean Myth; or, William Shakspeare and Circumstantial Evidence. 12mo. 2 00

Name and Address Book. A Blank Book, with printed Headings and Alphabetical Marginal Index, for Recording the Names and Addresses of Professional, Commercial, and Family Correspondents. 8vo. 1 00

Nash (Simeon.) Crime and the Family. 12mo. 1 25

Nerinckx (Rev. Charles.) Life of, with Early Catholic Missions in Kentucky; the Society of Jesus; the Sisterhood of Loretto, etc. By Rev. C. P. Maes. 8vo. 2 50

Nichols (G. W.) The Cincinnati Organ; with a Brief Description of the Cincinnati Music Hall. 12mo. Paper. 25

Ohio Valley Historical Miscellanies. I. Memorandums of a Tour Made by Josiah Espy, in the States of Ohio and Kentucky, and Indiana Territory, in 1805. II. Two Western Campaigns in the War of 1812–13: 1. Expedition of Capt. H. Brush, with Supplies for General Hull. 2. Expedition of Gov. Meigs, for the relief of Fort Meigs. By Samuel Williams. III. The Leatherwood God: an account of the Appearance and Pretensions of J. C. Dylks in Eastern Ohio, in 1828. By R. H. Taneyhill. 1 vol. 8vo. $2 50. Large paper,   5 00

ONCE A YEAR; or, The Doctor's Puzzle. By E. B. S. 16mo. 1 00

PHISTERER (Captain Frederick.) The National Guardsman: on Guard and Kindred Duties. 24mo. Leather.   75

PHYSICIAN'S POCKET CASE RECORD PRESCRIPTION BOOK.   35

PHYSICIAN'S GENERAL LEDGER. Half Russia.   4 00

PIATT (John J.) Penciled Fly-Leaves. A Book of Essays in Town and Country. Sq. 16mo.   1 00

POOLE (W. F.) Anti-Slavery Opinions before 1800. An Essay. 8vo. Paper, 75c.; cloth,   1 25

PRACTICAL RECEIPTS OF EXPERIENCED HOUSE-KEEPERS. By the ladies of the Seventh Presbyterian Church, Cin. 12mo.   1 25

PRENTICE (Geo. D.) Poems of, collected and edited, with Biographical Sketch, by John J. Piatt. 12mo.   2 00

QUICK (R. H.) Essays on Educational Reformers. 12mo. 1 50

RANCK (G. W.) History of Lexington, Kentucky. Its Early Annals and Recent Progress, etc. 8vo.   4 00

REEMELIN (C.) The Wine-Maker's Manual. A Plain, Practical Guide to all the Operations for the Manufacture of Still and Sparkling Wines. 12mo.   1 25

REEMELIN (C.) A Treatise on Politics as a Science. 8vo. 1 50

REEMELIN (C.) A Critical Review of American Politics. 8vo. *In Press.*

RIVES (E., M. D.) A Chart of the Physiological Arrangement of Cranial Nerves. Printed in large type, on a sheet 28x15 inches. Folded, in cloth case.   50

ROBERT (Karl). Charcoal Drawing with out a Master. A Complete Treatise in Landscape Drawing in Charcoal, with Lessons and Studies after Allonge. Translated by E. H. Appleton. Illustrated. 8vo   1 00

ROY (George). Generalship; or, How I Managed my Husband. A tale. 18mo. Paper, 50c.; cloth,   1 00

ROY (George). The Art of Pleasing. A Lecture. 12mo. Paper.   25

ROY (George). The Old, Old Story. A Lecture. 12mo. Paper. 25

RUSSELL (A. P.). Thomas Corwin. A Sketch. 16mo.   1 00

RUSSELL (Wm.) Scientific Horseshoeing for the Different Diseases of the Feet. Illustrated. 8vo.   1 00

SAYLER (J. A.) American Form Book. A Collection of Legal and Business Forms, embracing Deeds, Mortgages, Leases, Bonds, Wills, Contracts, Bills of Exchange, Promissory Notes, Checks, Bills of Sale, Receipts, and other Legal Instruments, prepared in accordance with the Laws of the several States; with Instructions for drawing and executing the same. For Professional and Business Men. 8vo.   2 00

SHEETS (Mary R.) My Three Angels: Faith, Hope, and Love. With full-page illustrations by E. D. Grafton. 4to.   Cloth. Gilt.   5 00

SKINNER (J. R.) The Source of Measures. A Key to the Hebrew-Egyptian Mystery in the Source of Measures, etc. 8vo.   5 00

SMITH (Col. JAMES). A Reprint of an Account of the Remarkable Occurrences in his Life and Travels, during his Captivity with the Indians in the years 1755, '56, '57, '58, and '59, etc. 8vo. $2 50.   Large paper,   5 00

STANTON (H.) Jacob Brown and other Poems. 12mo.   1 50

ST.CLAIR PAPERS. A Collection of the Correspondence and other papers of General Arthur St.Clair, Governor of the Northwest Territory. Edited, with a Sketch of his Life and Public Services, by William Henry Smith. 2 vols. 8vo.   6 00

STRAUCH (A.) Spring Grove Cemetery, Cincinnati: its History and improvements, with Observations on Ancient and modern Places of Sepulture. The text beautifully printed with ornamental, colored borders, and photographic illustrations. 4to. Cloth. Gilt.   15 00

An 8vo edition, without border and illustrations.   2 00

STUDER (J. H.) Columbus, Ohio: its History, Resources, and Progress, from its Settlement to the Present Time. 12mo.   2 00

TANEYHILL (R. H.) The Leatherwood God: an account of the Appearance and Pretensions of Joseph C. Dylks in Eastern Ohio, in 1826. 12mo. Paper.   30

TEN BROOK (A.) American State Universities. Their Origin and Progress. A History of the Congressional University Land Grants. A particular account of the Rise and Development of the University of Michigan, and Hints toward the future of the American University System. 8vo.   2 00

TILDEN (Louise W.) Karl and Gretchen's Christmas. Illustrated. Square 12mo.   75

TILDEN (Louise W.) Poem, Hymn, and Mission Band Exercises. Written and arranged for the use of Foreign Missionary Societies and Mission Bands. Square 12mo. Paper.   25

TRENT (Capt. Wm) Journal of, from Logstown to Pickawillany, in 1752. Edited by A. T. Goodman. 8vo.   2 50

8 *Historical and Miscellaneous Publications.*

TRIPLER (C. S., M.D.) and BLACKMAN (G. C., M.D.) Handbook for the Military Surgeon. 12mo. 1 00

TYLER DAVIDSON FOUNTAIN. History and Description of the Tyler Davidson Fountain, Donated to the City of Cincinnati, by Henry Probasco. 18mo. Paper. 25

VAGO (A. L.) Instructions in the art of Modeling in Clay. With an Appendix on Modeling in Foliage, etc., for Pottery and Architectural Decorations, by Benn Pitman, of Cincinnati School of Design. Illustrated. Square 12mo. 1 00

VAN HORNE (T. B.) The History of the Army of the Cumberland; its Organization, Campaigns, and Battles. *Library Edition.* 2 vols. With Atlas of 22 maps, compiled by Edward Ruger. 8vo.Cloth, $8 00; Sheep, $10 00; Half Morocco, $12 00. *Popular Edition.* Containing the same Text as the Library Edition, but only one map. 2 vols. 8vo. Cloth. 5 00

VENABLE (W. H.) June on the Miami, and other Poems. Second edition. 18mo. 1 50

VOORHEES (D. W.) Speeches of, embracing his most prominent Forensic, Political, Occasional, and Literary Addresses. Compiled by his son, C. S. Voorhees, with a Biographical Sketch and Portrait. 8vo. 5 00

WALKER (C. M.) History of Athens County, Ohio, and incidentally of the Ohio Land Company, and the First Settlement of the State at Marietta, etc. 8vo. $6 00. Large Paper. 2 vols. $12 00. Popular Edition. 4 00

WALTON (G. E.) Hygiene and Education of Infants; or, How to take care of Babies. 24mo. Paper. 25

WARD (Durbin). American Coinage and Currency. An Essay read before the Social Science Congress, at Cincinnati, May 22, 1878. 8vo. Paper. 10

WEBB (F.) and JOHNSTON (M. C.) An Improved Tally-Book, for the use of Lumber Dealers. 18mo. 50

WHITTAKER (J. T., M. D.) Physiology; Preliminary Lectures. Illustrated. 12mo. 1 75

WILLIAMS (A. D., M. D.) Diseases of the Ear, including Necessary Anatomy of the Organ. 8vo. 3 50

YOUNG (A.) History of Wayne County, Indiana, from its First Settlement to the Present Time. 8vo. 2 00